Christmas with Ho

"If you need some inspiration to get into the Christmas spirit this year, look no further than the beautifully written stories and poems in *Christmas with Hot Apple Cider*. Highlighting talented Canadian writers, this collection is the perfect treat to enjoy by the fire with—what else— a hot cup of apple cider! I highly recommend both the book and the experience."

Cheryl Weber, Co-host and Senior Executive Producer,
100 Huntley Street

"It doesn't take long to scratch beneath the surface when you ask, 'What story do you remember most about Christmas?' Smiles or frowns line the face as they recall, with fondness or sorrow, memories of Christmas. The 'big' days of the year have a way of crystallizing in memory places, people, events, and circumstances. *Christmas with Hot Apple Cider* is ideal to revive our good memories, reminding us of family and friends whose lives have added to ours. A perfect Christmas gift. This book will be treasured as something special and fill hearts and minds with why we make this day special. A wonderful offering. A present that has multiple lives beyond this one day of the year."

Brian C. Stiller, Global Ambassador, The World Evangelical Alliance

"Enchanting, tender, exhilarating... An exquisitely colourful twinkling palette of blessings!"

Claire de Burbure, MD, PhD, Medical & Environmental Teacher

"These lyrical words remind us that courage and faith are the rocks we stand on when meeting life's toughest challenges. In a world that at times seems drifting, divided, and uncertain, the reader will find solace and inspiration in these pages."

Paul Torrie, President, Global Resolutions Inc.

"Christmas is a time for family, friends, miracles, gifts and nostalgia... and of course hot apple cider! With a variety of themes spanning nonfiction, fiction, and even poetry, *Christmas with Hot Apple Cider* will touch your heart and warm your soul. The offerings in this collection are sometimes humorous, sometimes heartbreaking, but always tender. A great book to help you remember the Reason for the holiday season and to remind you that Christmas miracles are closer than you may realize."

Carrie Schmidt, ReadingIsMySuperPower.org

"If you adore all things Christmas, you'll love this wonderful collection of holiday offerings! *Christmas with Hot Apple Cider* has something for everyone—fiction, poetry, real life reflections—all written with a touch of faith and humour to uplift the soul. You'll definitely want to add this to your Christmas list!"

> **Susan Anne Mason**, award-winning author of *Irish Meadows* and the Courage to Dream Series, Bethany House Publishers

"This book has the gentle feel of a special family quilt, much like the log cabin quilt featured in one of the stories. All the parts fit together beautifully, yet each one tells a unique story. Snuggle up with this book, and let its warmth and rich diversity take you on a journey of smiles, tears, and remarkable memories."

> **Marguerite Cummings**, Editor, contributor to multiple volumes in the Hot Apple Cider Books Series

"You don't know Canada until you know these stories from authors who understand and can express the values that have always endeared Christmas to our families."

> **Lorna Dueck**, CEO, Crossroads Global Media Group, YES TV, 100 Huntley Street, Context with Lorna Dueck, Tricord Media

"A delightful potpourri of heart-warming stories set in our favourite season."

> **Gerry Bowler**, Historian and author of *Christmas in the Crosshairs*

Praise for Previous Hot Apple Cider Books

"A collection of short stories, poetry, and wisdom seeking to heal and mend the soul after difficult and stressful situations.... Highly recommended."

> *Midwest Book Review*

"Be sure to buy more than one, for you will probably have the urge to share this gem of a collection with others."

> *Faith Today*

"This comforting and encouraging book should be in every home, library, church, and school."

> **Pauline Christian**, President, Black Business and Professional Association

Christmas with
Hot Apple Cider

STORIES *from the* SEASON
of GIVING *and* RECEIVING

Edited by

N. J. LINDQUIST

That's Life! Communications

Markham, Ontario

Christmas with Hot Apple Cider

That's Life! Communications
Box 77001, Markham, ON L3P 0C8, Canada
905-471-1447
thatslifecommunications.com
comments@thatslifecommunications.com

ISBN Print Book: 978-1-927692-41-7
ISBN Digital Book: 978-1-927692-42-4

All scripture quotations, unless otherwise indicated, are taken from the HOLY BIBLE, NEW INTERNATIONAL VERSION®. NIV®. Copyright © 1973, 1978, 1984, 2011 by Biblica, Inc.™ Used by permission of Zondervan. All rights reserved. www.zondervan.com The "NIV" and "New International Version" are trademarks registered in the United States Patent and Trademark Office by Biblica, Inc.™

Cover design and interior layout by N. J. Lindquist.
Cover apple photo ©Tanguta from depositphotos.com.
Cover gift tree photo ©Krisdog from depositphotos.com.
Photo on page 219 taken by a patient who gave it to Grace Wulff.
All other interior photos were purchased from depositphotos.com with a few from dreamstime.com, istockphoto.com, and shutterstock.com.

Library and Archives Canada Cataloguing in Publication

Christmas with hot apple cider : stories from the season of giving and receiving / edited by N.J. Lindquist.

Short stories and poems.

Issued in print and electronic formats.

ISBN 978-1-927692-41-7 (softcover).--ISBN 978-1-927692-42-4 (ebook)

1. Christmas--Literary collections. 2. Canadian literature (English)--21st century. I. Lindquist, N. J. (Nancy J.), author, editor

PS8237.C57C59 2017   C810.8'0334   C2017-904899-6   C2017-904900-3

Christmas can be the best of times or the hardest of times.
We dedicate this book to those whose longings
and memories are magnified in this season.
We hope that our stories of hope, faith, courage, and love
will bring light and comfort to all who read them.

Table of Contents

Foreword

Linda Hall

When I was a little girl, as every Christmas Day came to a close, I would retreat to my room, hide under my bed covers, and cry. No, I wasn't sad that I hadn't received the gifts of my choice. (I usually did!) I wasn't sad that Christmas hadn't been all that I had wished it to be. (It usually was!) I would cry because it was all over. All that excitement was over, all that anticipation, all that FUN! I knew that the lights, now unplugged, would soon be pulled off and boxed up. The tree (always a real one, so carefully put up and decorated by my parents on Christmas Eve, well after we kids had gone to bed) would soon be bare and thrown out, the ornate ornaments carefully repacked in tissue. I was sad beyond measure to let it all go.

I was fascinated by nativity scenes back then. After the nativity scene was set up each Christmas in our church foyer, I would regularly get my hands slapped for "playing" with the figures. I think that as we grow into adulthood, it's easy to forget the wonder, the celebration, and the awe of the Christmas story. This newest collection, *Christmas with Hot Apple Cider: Stories from the Season of Giving and Receiving,* took me back—back to where my Christmas memories began.

This anthology includes Christmas reflections—some sad, some tragic, some happy, some funny—but all hopeful. There are stories of Christmases down on Canadian farms, Christmases far from home, Christmases of loss… The stories have different moods—lonely ones, stormy ones, happy ones.

I am also pleased that this collection has some very fine fiction (always a favourite of mine) and some gorgeous poetry. There is even one drama.

Long after the nativity scenes have been put away for another year, the trees shorn of their decorations and left waiting at the curb like so much trash, and January has descended like a cold monster upon our country, the message of these stories will still resonate.

Jesus came as a baby for me. Jesus died for me. When I was a child I didn't fully understand what that meant. I still don't. Not entirely. It remains part of the Mystery of my Faith. But the one thing I do know is that it all begins with Christmas.

So grab yourself an oversized cup of hot apple cider; find a comfy chair; wrap yourself up with a Christmas afghan; and enjoy this wonderful assortment of short stories, memories, and poems! I'm sure you'll find something in these pages to bring back the child in you, the child who loved Christmas so much that you were sad when it was over.

Linda Hall doesn't remember a time when she wasn't either writing something or reading. Even now, there is always a book in her hand.

An award-winning author, Linda has written more than 25 novels of mystery and suspense, plus many short stories.

Her most recent book, *The Bitter End*, is the second in the highly acclaimed Em Ridge Mystery Series, which began with *Night Watch*. The third book, *The Devil to Pay*, will be out later this fall. The adventures continue for widowed boat captain, Em Ridge!

Like Em, Linda enjoys being on the water. When she's not writing or reading, she will often be out sailing or kayaking, using the time on the water to come up with story ideas.

Besides writing, Linda reviews books twice a month on her blog, "I Like It!"

Website: writerhall.com
Blog: lrhallbooks.blogspot.com

Introduction

We all have Christmas memories—stories that have affected us because of their significance. Joy, anticipation, disappointment, gratitude. These feelings come from our experiences.

When we put out the call for submissions for this anthology, we didn't have a specific theme beyond their having something to do with Christmas. Of course, we hoped for some stories that would cause readers to think about their own Christmas experiences and traditions.

As we read the submissions, we were struck by how many of them featured gifts—both gifts received and gifts given—often in creative ways. Perhaps that shouldn't be surprising since, at its core, Christmas is a celebration of the great gift of salvation given to us in the person of Jesus Christ. So N. J. decided that the subtitle should be "Stories from the Season of Giving and Receiving."

It's been a pleasure helping N. J. work through the final process of selecting the pieces—fiction, nonfiction, poetry—that showed different aspects of Christmas. It was clear to me that every story and poem was meaningful to the writer, which made it even more difficult to choose which ones to include in the book. I've been impressed by people's willingness to share these stories—to let others into their lives to see their insights and feelings, both positive and negative.

One of my hopes for the book is that readers will be challenged to capture their own or their family members' stories—perhaps not for publication, but at least for their own families and future generations.

I especially enjoyed reading the stories about unique ways that people have commemorated this central point in our Christian heritage. Rather than focusing on materialistic pursuits, many families have discovered new ways to make the meaning of Christmas real to them and their loved ones.

For those to whom this series is new, the idea for the first Hot Apple Cider anthology burst forth exactly 10 years ago. We saw it as a way to give more Canadian writers who are Christian an opportunity to have their voices heard. We published the first book less than six months later.

This is the fifth book in the series, and at present 123 writers have shared one or more of their stories or poems. For some, being included in one of our anthologies was their first time being published, and we're proud to have given them that opportunity.

One of the reasons for choosing "Hot Apple Cider" as the title for the anthologies is that hot apple cider is generally regarded as a comfort food (especially to those of us who have enjoyed outings in cold weather). All the books include stories that will comfort readers. But there are also stories that will challenge, encourage, and inspire.

Three of these books have been used in bulk by ministries to say "Thank you" to their audiences. Through these programs, along with sales directly to customers, more than 100,000 paperback books as well as many ebooks are in circulation—which means that many, many people have been touched by these books. We trust that you will also be blessed by this book and will share your blessing with others.

Les Lindquist

Partner at That's Life! Communications

P.S. Since the publishers are from Canada, we've used Canadian spelling. So "color" is "colour" and "labeled" is "labelled," etc. Also, we measure our temperature in Celsius: 0°C is 32°F.

A Manger, Some Straw, and a Toddler

Nonfiction

Ann Brent

I gasped and yelled, "Jacob, stop!" Our one-year-old grandson was tearing across the kitchen floor as fast as his little legs could carry him, heading toward the four stairs that led down to our family room.

I dropped the dirty salad bowl I was holding and dashed across the kitchen. "Wait!" I tried, hoping to get his attention before the inevitable tumble.

My husband, George, who was in the kitchen helping me load the dishwasher, was a bit quicker than me this time. He snatched the adventurous boy up into his arms seconds before Jacob launched headlong down the stairs.

I slid to a stop beside them and exhaled. The baby gate wasn't in place because I didn't know Jacob had been released from his highchair in the dining room, where we had left the rest of the family to chat over their empty dessert plates. Our children lived in different cities and didn't get to see each other often enough. Lingering around the table following Christmas dinner was a treat.

Jacob and his parents lived in a bungalow, so he hadn't yet mastered the art of going down stairs. At the same time, he was fearless and determined to try everything—especially those things you tried to keep him away from.

After George showed Jacob how to sit down and turn around in order to go down the stairs safely backward, he and I seized the opportunity to spend a few moments alone with our first grandchild down in the family room.

Jacob headed for the rustic nativity scene on the small table by George's recliner. Once there, he peered inside, looking at each figure in turn. The straw on the stable floor and in the manger seemed to fascinate him, and his tiny fingers poked at the yellow pieces. Then he touched a donkey and a shepherd before grasping a tiny white lamb with his chubby fingers.

While he was engaged with the scene, I decided to introduce this tender-hearted boy to one of our family traditions.

Thirty years earlier, when our children, Karen and Jason, were preschoolers, George and I recognized the challenge of balancing the "I wants" of the season with the real meaning of Christmas. In the hope of nurturing a spirit of giving, we created a game. At the end of November, when we set out our nativity scene, I removed baby Jesus from the manger, leaving his bed empty. Throughout the four weeks leading up to Christmas Eve, as we anticipated the arrival of baby Jesus, each member of the family was to look for good deeds to perform for other people. The tricky (and exciting) part was that you had to do something thoughtful without being seen doing it.

For each kind deed we completed, we secretly earned a small piece of yellow straw from a little basket I'd placed on a low shelf in the kitchen. When no one was watching, we discreetly added our bits of straw to Jesus' tiny bed to make a soft, warm cradle for his arrival. And each year, by Christmas Eve, a nice fluffy bed was ready to welcome the newborn babe.

The exciting weeks leading up to Christmas were filled with kind surprises—a bed made, toys picked up, clothes put away, dishes cleared from the table—all done mysteriously.

Even as young children, Karen and Jason thought of creative ways to earn pieces of straw. And because they were personally invested, after a month of preparing the cradle, they looked forward eagerly to Christmas Eve.

When the children were ready for bed, we sat on the carpet around the nativity scene. As the Christmas tree lights twinkled, we read the biblical account of Jesus' birth. Then one of the children would have the privilege of placing the baby Jesus carefully into his manger bed. I faithfully recorded which child had this special honour each year in order to keep things fair.

Now I embraced Jacob and crouched beside him so we could both look into the simple wooden stable. "Christmas is all about how much God loves us," I said. "He loves us so much that He sent Jesus, His Son, to be born on earth. And Christmas is when we celebrate Jesus' birthday."

I pointed out Mary and Joseph and said, "There was no room for his parents to stay inside the inn, so they stayed with the animals. And that night, baby Jesus was born in the stable."

It was a very short description of the Christmas story, but I was pleased that Jacob was clearly attentive and focusing on my words. As I touched Mary, Joseph, and the other key figures, he watched carefully, his eyes moving with my finger as I told the story. This rarely still toddler was captivated.

"That night, God placed a bright, new star in the sky to show where Jesus had been born." I touched the origami star Karen had made long ago. As always, it perched on the arched roof of the stable.

"And He sent angels to tell the shepherds in the fields this wonderful news." I pointed to the crocheted angel who stood guard over our nativity scene, and Jacob reached out to touch its pure white halo.

"Every Christmas Eve when your daddy and Auntie Karen were little, we read the Christmas story and they took turns placing baby Jesus in his manger bed."

Jacob had watched with rapt attention throughout the story, seemingly taking in every detail. Now I held baby Jesus out toward Jacob on the palm of my hand. "This year it's your turn. Can you put baby Jesus into his bed?"

I was touched that Jacob had followed my every action, and hung on every word. It was clear to this Nana that he had understood the whole story. My heart was warmed as I took in this important moment. What a privilege to be able to share this powerful story with my precious grandson! I felt as if I were passing a torch, carrying on a beloved family tradition. My heart was filled with incredible joy.

Jacob didn't pause for a moment; he reached out and very carefully took the tiny baby figure from my hand.

I helped him lean a little closer to the nativity scene so he could easily reach inside. Then he popped baby Jesus into his mouth.

I managed to rescue the baby before he was swallowed, and George and I enjoyed a great laugh together. Apparently, Jacob had not grasped quite as much of the story as I'd thought.

But it was a beginning—the first of many times I'd be able to share the wonderful Christmas story with Jacob and, later on, the other cherished grandchildren who joined our family.

One of the joys of the season is sharing long-held traditions and recounting stories of Christmases past. This year, we'll get out the nativity scene, remove baby Jesus, add straw to the manger, share the Christmas story from Luke, and chuckle together as we remember the year Jacob tried to eat baby Jesus.

  Christmas with Hot Apple Cider

This Is Christmas Eve

 ## Donna Bonnett Tanchez

Snow drifts,
Sparkling with the promise of secret diamonds
When the sun caresses them,
Sit in the streetlight like cool dollops of
Whipped cream.

Cars drive up,
Passengers jump out.
Boots crunch the snow underfoot
As we scurry down the path
And up the steps.

"Welcome! Welcome!"
Voices cut through quiet,
Frigid air meets warm breath.
Shoulders are slapped and embraced,
Coats come off, hair is checked,
White candles are pressed into hands.

Shuffle, sit,
Lights turn off,
Candles are lit,
With silver tin holding them, protecting them.

All rise and sing.
The flames from our candles waver slightly
But do not falter.

Heads bow,
Fingers overlap fingers,
Quiet whispers join other hushed voices.

Christmas with Hot Apple Cider

Legs move,
Costumes go on,
Small bodies huddle together,
Waiting for the cue.

Swallow hard,
Wet palms wiped on sleeves,
Shaky breaths,
Here we come!

Lines delivered,
Resounding applause follows.
Relief, pride, and happiness fill the place
Nerves once occupied.

One last prayer before
Candles are blown out,
Friendly smiles and cheerful laughter follow.
Coats are shrugged on.
Warm hearts greet cold air and merrily move on.

Cars carry us
Home, to where a tree stands,
Patiently waiting for shiny packages.

Then to bed, where memories of
Snow, songs, candles, and friendship
Feature in dreams, and in later years, will
Warm our memories.

This is Christmas Eve.

  Christmas with Hot Apple Cider

Christmas, 1940

Nonfiction

Ray Wiseman

Two days before Christmas

I stood at the kitchen window with my older brother, Junior, watching the wind drive the snow horizontally across the yard. There was so much snow that it sporadically obscured the barn, even though it was no more than a snowball's throw away. It was fascinating to watch as gusts of white seemed to dip and rise, slashing at fence posts, gates, and clothesline as if bent on total destruction.

Our old house trembled, and the windows shook and rattled.

"I'm not going out there," I whined.

"Lucky you, 'fraidy pants. Mom asked me to check the chickens for you when I feed the pig." Junior thumbed his nose at me as he spoke.

I didn't dare challenge my big brother for using that rude gesture, so I changed the topic. "Do you think Dad will come home for Christmas?"

"Not a chance. You know that he never gets out of that crazy house unless he's really well—and he can't be well because Mom hasn't had a letter in weeks."

I gave him the dirtiest look I could muster. "You mustn't call it that. It's a mental hospital."

Junior assumed a pose that reminded me of my Grade 1 teacher and said, "Even if he came home, Dad would have no money. And Mom has no money. And the neighbours won't even come by during this storm. So, little brother, there goes Christmas!"

I was trying to think of an argument when the house shuddered and the window glass began to vibrate. I reached out to steady it, but backed off when Junior yelled, "Don't touch it—it's going to break!"

Outside, we could see the barn gate, which was made of four ten-inch boards, flapping back and forth. The window didn't break, but the gate did—each board snapping in turn.

I foolishly said, "It's a good thing we didn't leave Captain in the yard; horses like open gates, and he might have run away."

"Captain is safe in the barn." Mom spoke behind us. "The barn is solid and won't blow down, but this house might." We hadn't heard Mom approach. She held our two-year-old sister Shirley by the hand, and with her other hand pointed toward the cellar door. "Run into the cellar if the house starts to go." She said it as casually as if she were directing us to a pew in church.

Her fearlessness should have calmed me, but I glanced at the cellar door, felt fear, and began to shake like the barn gate had before it broke. *Can a body break in two?* I wondered.

One day before Christmas

The storm had eased somewhat. The house hadn't fallen in. We hadn't needed to escape into the cellar. And my body hadn't broken in two.

Junior and I did our chores, visiting the barn and chicken house to feed the critters and clean up where necessary. The pig and chickens had all survived, as had Captain, our horse.

The weather remained bad enough to discourage playing outside, so Junior and I dug up some old magazines. We sat on the floor, comparing photos of warplanes, farm machinery, dairy cows, and people.

In one magazine, Santa Claus scowled at us from the page as though someone had stolen his reindeer. We didn't read the text to see what had distressed him, but I said, "Maybe Santa will smile now the worst of the storm has passed."

Junior placed his hand on Santa's face. "There's no such person as Santa," he said. Now he reminded me of his Grade 3 teacher.

"Is, too!" I yelled.

"Is, not!"

"Is, too!" I jumped up. "I'll ask Mom. She knows."

But Mother conveniently entered the room just then, possibly to learn the reason for all the yelling.

"Mom," I demanded, "Junior says there's no Santa. Tell him there is."

"I'm afraid we told you about Santa when you were little. In fact, Santa doesn't exist. It's just a story," Mother said. She turned to go, glanced over her shoulder, and said, "At your age, you should know the truth."

That awful news made me cry and run for my room.

Junior yelled after me, his voice following me right into our bedroom. "If Santa doesn't exist, then Jesus doesn't exist either. That's just another story adults tell to keep us kids in line."

I spent the rest of the day trying to put my shattered life back together.

I knew Christmas couldn't come with Dad in the hospital and Mom without any money. And besides, the storm had blocked the roads so no one could get through. Now we had no Santa to fly from farm to farm. And why celebrate Christmas anyway if the story of Jesus is just a lie?

Christmas Day

Junior and I awakened on Christmas morning in our second-floor bedroom. We pushed our heads from under the covers of the big double bed for what promised to be the worst Christmas ever. But our eyes grew large as we focused on the foot of the bed where two stockings bulged with toys and goodies.

For a moment, our heads protruded from the covers like gophers peeking from their holes. For a long moment we didn't move. Our breath froze in the ill-heated room. Then we grinned at each other and bounced up, racing toward the two stockings.

We then retreated under the covers to examine the loot, our cries filtering through the layers of blankets and patchwork quilts:

"A cap gun—I got a gun!"

"I got one, too!"

"A candy and an orange!"

"Look, nuts!"

"I got crayons!"

Moments later, I emerged from the bed, landed on my knees on the floor, and pulled a chamber pot from beneath the bed, thankful that Mom didn't insist we use the outhouse during nasty weather.

Then Junior threw back the covers and, with Christmas stocking under his arm and toy pistol in hand, said, "Let's go see what Shirley got."

"Wait for me!" I yelled.

Although the rule was "Wash before coming down in the morning," neither of us wasted time breaking the ice in the wash basin.

And what do you think? There were parcels under the tree, too! Wind-up trains for Junior and me, and a doll for Shirley.

When we cast wondering looks at Mother, she said, "This is a wonderful Christmas because Aunt Elsie sent a big box with things for each of us. I've had them hidden since they arrived two months ago. The toy guns and trains belonged to your cousins. Without Aunt Elsie's help, it would have been a bleak Christmas."

Christmas nearly 80 years later

Memories become the daily adventures of older folks. Whether traumatic or joyful, they live in the nooks and crannies of our minds the way old family pictures and keepsakes occupy various corners of our homes. I revisit the memory of that ancient Christmas often, and I cherish the lessons learned so long ago— some of them social and some theological.

Simply put:

- I learned that you can't believe everything your big brother says—and sometimes not even the things your mother tells you.

- I learned that Santa Claus does exist, even when he changes his name to Aunt Elsie.

- And I learned that God truly lives, for He protected us from that vicious storm and many more like it. Plus, who else could have prompted Aunt Elsie to send those gifts halfway across Canada so they'd arrive before the storm and be there exactly when we needed them?

  Christmas with Hot Apple Cider

Seven Silver Dollars

Nonfiction[1]

Valentina Gal

Larysa shivered in the biting wind and thought that the sky looked like brittle, pale blue ice. Even her poor eyesight allowed her to see the shallow rays of the winter sun as they slanted across the corner of Barton Street and reflected off the store windows, but she couldn't see any details.

It was a December morning in Hamilton, in 1959, and seven-year-old Larysa was waiting with her family for the bus that would take them to the Essex Packers' Christmas party. The annual party was given by Papa's boss as his "thank you" for another year's worth of hard work.

Papa said that he would have preferred a raise to at least a dollar an hour instead of the 85 cents he currently got for doing the hard and dirty job of butchering the pigs at the meat packing plant. But Mama reminded him that the party was for the children so he should stop complaining and find his Christmas spirit. So they'd put on their Sunday best and here they all were, waiting for a bus and wondering if it would ever come.

"I see it!" shouted Simon, Larysa's older brother.

Larysa could hear the electric whine of the trolley as it approached. Before the doors could swing completely open, the children were clamouring aboard. "Stop dragging," complained Simon. Since Larysa couldn't clearly see where she was going, Papa always told Simon to help her whenever the family went for an outing.

Larysa heard the nickels drop as Simon put both their fares into the coin slot. George and Anna could ride free because they weren't six years old yet.

Mama and Papa herded the children toward the back of the bus, and Simon showed Larysa to a seat. They all settled down for the ride to St. Nicholas Church in the east end of the city.

Barton Street was so long that it went across the whole of Hamilton. It was lined on both sides with every kind of small business necessary for the well-being of the area's immigrants and working poor. Larysa could tell when the bus rolled past the toy store with its dazzling Christmas window. Simon had excitedly described it to her when she'd come home for the holidays from the boarding school for the blind. Larysa hoped that St. Nicholas would bring her the Chatty Cathy doll in the window display.

She didn't have to see what stores the bus was passing because they were all familiar. She'd often accompanied Mama or Papa on weekly shopping trips. They passed Henry's, where the family bought their shoes, Wilson's Drug store, the Chinese take-out restaurant, the Dairy Queen, and the German butcher shop. Then the bus stopped for passengers from the large IGA on the corner, where Mama got their groceries.

"Papa, there's Mr. Fagan's appliance store," said George. "We got our stove and fridge there, didn't we?"

Larysa said, "I wish we could stop there now. Mr. Fagan always gives us candy."

"You moron!" Simon said. "We're going to get a big box of candy from the party."

"I know," Larysa said. "But Mr. Fagan is always so nice to us."

The smell of the Italian bakery teased their noses as it sneaked out of the boxes of pastries carried by a group of patrons who boarded the bus at its next stop.

"Don't forget to cross yourselves," Mama said as they passed St. Vladimir's Ukrainian Orthodox church. "Remember, God lives there. It is a holy place."

No one mentioned the Ukrainian lawyer's office, which Larysa knew was right next door.

When the bus turned down Parkdale Avenue and came to a stop, the children could hardly contain their anticipation. They pushed through the back door of the bus and ran ahead of Mama and Papa, Simon dragging Larysa as he went.

Larysa could hear the party before the church doors opened and she was hustled into the merriment. A clown stopped twisting a balloon into the likeness of an animal and helped the family out of their coats and hats. Larysa was glad of that because she didn't like the sound of the balloon squeaking as it was formed into its new shape. A second, bigger and more jovial clown ushered them to a row of chairs and gave each child a candy cane.

The basement hall below St. Nicholas Church was filled with rows of wooden chairs on which sat the workers of Essex Packers meat factory along with their families. People greeted them warmly.

"My goodness," Catherine Kolkin said to Mama, "your sons have really grown since last year!"

Catherine's mother, who was called Babushka, was sitting next to her daughter. Babushka crossed herself and mumbled a half silent prayer in Larysa's direction. Larysa knew that she crossed herself, because Mama had told her that every time Orthodox people pray, they must cross themselves three times.

"And look at Anna! What a beautiful baby!" Catherine continued.

Larysa hated this part of any community gathering to which she was taken. While her brothers and sister were acknowledged and proudly introduced, most of her parents' friends politely ignored her, and Papa never introduced her unless the person with whom he was speaking showed interest.

"Will there ever be anyone who likes me?" she thought as she sat quietly waiting for the party to begin.

The sound of happy voices swirled around her. Simon had found some friends from school, and George was already wrestling with another little boy whom Larysa didn't know. Since she couldn't make eye contact, she may as well have come alone.

She tried to separate the voices out of the dull roar of the crowd to see if she could find one that was familiar, but she failed. Then someone with red and yellow clothing spoke to her. "What, little girl? No smile today?"

One of the clowns, she thought. Larysa dutifully pasted a smile on her face.

"Don't worry," the clown said. "St. Nicholas will soon be here. 'Till then, maybe this will help." He gave her a large handful of candy canes.

At the front of the room was a raised stage. Larysa could hear the feet of the other children running across its wooden floor. Other children pretended to be St. Nicholas, climbing onto a large, decorated chair at one corner of the stage and shouting "Ho! Ho! Ho!" Beyond the chair towered a huge Christmas tree whose pungent branches Larysa could smell from where she sat.

Someone tinkled the keys of a piano. She'd have liked to go close to it, but Larysa knew she had to stay with Mama so she wouldn't get hurt.

She stared at the bright patches of sunlight that were coming through the windows at the top of the wall and shining on something with lots of colours that blurred together. "What's that thing with all of the colours, Mama?" she asked.

"Those are the piles of presents for all the good boys and girls," Mama replied. "Have you been a good girl?" Mama turned back to her conversation with Babushka.

A microphone began to crackle and thump as someone handled it. "Welcome to our annual Christmas party," a man's voice said, first in English, then in Ukrainian, Polish, and Russian. "We invite you and your families to help yourselves to lunch."

People began lining up at the table for hotdogs, hamburgers, small containers of milk, both white and chocolate, and Larysa's favourite, Dixie Cup ice cream. She knew she could eat as much as she wanted because the meat factory provided as much food as its workers could consume. After all, they had produced the meat, so there was no need to show restraint.

While they waited in line, Simon and his friends challenged each other to a hotdog-eating contest.

Mama didn't lecture when Larysa asked for a second Dixie Cup, although she would only let her have vanilla. That was so it wouldn't stain her new white dress should Larysa drop some of it.

"May I have your attention?" boomed the man's voice through the microphone. "It looks like the line is almost done, so Mamas and Papas, get yourselves a coffee and get ready to sing some Christmas carols! Maybe St. Nicholas will hear you singing and come sooner."

Everyone settled into their seats.

14   *Christmas with Hot Apple Cider*

Larysa could hear the piano. Mrs. Klementowich, who had been a piano teacher in Poland before the war, must have offered her services again this year.

Gradually, the voices of the workers joined in. Everyone laughed as they muddled through "Deck the Halls." Larysa was pleased with herself because she knew all of the words. She had learned them at school.

When Mrs. Klementowich played "The First Noel," the French workers sang it in French while others tried their broken English. As each carol was played, those who knew the original words sang them in their mother tongue while the rest did the best they could. However, when Mrs. Klementowich played "Silent Night," the whole hall hushed. In one reverent tone, all of the workers sang together. Though their words came from many languages, their hearts praised the Holy Child with one harmonic voice.

Larysa shivered. When the singing stopped, she didn't move. She wanted this magic feeling to last forever.

The sound of ringing sleigh bells shattered the celestial moment. St. Nicholas had arrived! Mrs. Klementowich played "Jingle Bells," and mothers and fathers joined in with their broken English. The little children jumped up and down excitedly while the older ones resumed the activities in which they were engaged before the singing started.

Larysa could hear the bells jingling on St. Nicholas's wrists as he shook hands and patted as many heads as he could reach from the aisle while making his way to the stage. When the merry gentleman finally settled into his chair, the host's voice roared into the microphone again. "Welcome, St. Nicholas. Would you like to say a few words to all of these children?"

"Thank you, President Melnik. Thank you for inviting me and thank you for providing such a beautiful party for the children of your workers."

The room erupted in appreciative applause. The burden of their hard existence was laid aside for these few hours and Mr. Melnik was, for a short time, their gracious benefactor. St. Nicholas went on with the usual "Who was good?" remarks, and then the line for distribution of gifts began.

Each age was called out in turn. First, baby girls under a year of age were brought to St. Nicholas by their parents, followed by baby boys and their families. So it went, through all the age groups.

By the time the announcer called the seven-year-old girls, Larysa was restless and bored. Mama told Simon to stand with her in line. He was resentful because this chore took him away from his friends. "Why do I always have to be the one to take her?" he asked.

There was a moment of silence. Larysa knew that Mama was giving Simon her "Do it or you're dead" look. Once, Simon had told Larysa she was lucky she couldn't see it.

After they were in line, Simon moved sulkily toward St. Nicholas and his helpers without saying a word. When they were near the Christmas tree, Larysa stopped to feel its decorations. She loved its smell, its prickly needles, and its brightly coloured lights. She resisted the temptation to poke her fingers through the holes of the glass Christmas balls the way she did at home.

Suddenly she felt as if someone was watching her.

"Hello, little girl," said President Melnik in English. In Ukrainian, he said to someone, "You know, this is Gregory's little blind girl."

"I'M NOT LITTLE! My name is Larysa," she snapped in Ukrainian.

"I guess not," President Melnik said. "Little girls can't speak Ukrainian so well, can they?" He chuckled a deep chuckle.

"Mama says that you shouldn't talk about somebody in another language while they are standing there."

"Mama is right, of course. So, is there anything else a smart girl like you can do well?"

Larysa smiled. "I can sing."

"Show-off!" interjected Simon.

"Can you sing for us?" Mr. Melnik asked.

"Only if I have a microphone," she replied.

Simon muttered something else, but she didn't hear.

"Okay," Mr. Melnik said. "You won't be scared?"

"Ukrainian girls are never scared," Larysa said in her best Ukrainian. She stuck her chin out.

"Yeah, right!" Simon whispered.

Mr. Melnik laughed and took Larysa's hand to help her onto the stage. Simon trailed behind them.

Mr. Melnik took the microphone off its stand. Into it, he said, "Today, we have a little Ukrainian girl with a special treat for us. Some of you may know that this is Gregory and Barbara's blind daughter, Larysa. She wants to sing for St. Nicholas."

Mr. Melnik replaced the microphone and adjusted it for Larysa's height.

"Okay, Larysa. Show us what you can do."

Larysa stood up straight. She pushed her shoulders back and fingered the red velvet flowers that were embroidered diagonally across the bodice of her white nylon dress. She cleared her throat and said, "Thank you for letting me sing. I will try 'What Child is this?'"

The happy din in the hall subsided as Larysa became lost in the music of the old "Greensleeves" tune that she had recently learned in school.

> What Child is this who, laid to rest
> On Mary's lap, is sleeping?
> Whom angels greet with anthems sweet,
> While shepherds watch are keeping...?[2]

Her voice squeaked a little on the chorus, but she didn't stop. Her heart was beating fast as she finished the refrain. She went on to sing the second verse with more confidence, and her voice didn't squeak at all on the second refrain.

When she stopped, the hall roared with applause.

"You were right," Mr. Melnik said. "You can sing very well. How old are you, Larysa?"

"Seven."

"Seven years old and you can sing like that!"

"Thank you, sir."

"Now I have a surprise for you. Hold out your hand."

Larysa obeyed.

"Count to seven."

Larysa counted out loud. "One, two, three..."

Seven silver dollars clinked as Mr. Melnik dropped them into her hand.

Simon's exhalation of surprise whistled through his teeth.

"One for every year of your life," Mr. Melnik said. "May you have many more years, and may they be filled with music. Whatever you do, Larysa, never stop singing." He bent down and kissed her on her forehead.

"Thank you again, sir."

Papa came to get her and Simon from the stage. He said nothing to Larysa. But when they were seated, he turned to Mama and said, "Imagine! He gave her more than one day's pay." To his friends, he said, "Well, you know, we are a musical family."

Larysa knew that, at least for today, Papa was proud of her.

Mrs. Kolkin observed that she hadn't known Larysa could sing so well. Simon's friends wanted to look at her seven silver dollars. The clown gave her more candy canes. Babushka said a prayer of thanks for Larysa's gift of music. Larysa wasn't alone at the party anymore.

After Simon finally received his present from St. Nicholas, they stood in line to collect the box of candy that was given to each child to take home. Then they struggled into their boots and heavy winter coats. When Papa finally donned his Russian fur hat, they were ready to go out into the cold December night.

On the long bus ride back down Barton Street, Papa took the seven silver dollars from Larysa for safekeeping. When they got home, he put them into the blue music box that no longer played the song from Swan Lake.

1. This is a true story from the author's childhood. Names have been changed.

2. "What Child is This?" William C. Dix, 1865 (Public Domain)

  Christmas with Hot Apple Cider

Santa Visits Lakeview Farm

Nonfiction

Sharon Espeseth

After supper that Christmas Eve, the year I was five years old and my sister Joan was seven, we heard sleigh bells ringing. At first, they were in the distance, and then they got closer and closer to our little wooden house. Finally the bells jangled loudly right outside the kitchen door.

We watched from across the small room as Mom opened the door and a cold draft blew in. Mom threw her hands in the air and laughed at the white-whiskered, brown-suited man standing there. Joan and I didn't see what was so funny. In fact, we were nervous about this strange man Mom was inviting into our house.

And we couldn't understand why Mom was laughing so hard. Our normally quiet and sensible mother laughed so hard she had tears in her eyes. Holding her big, jiggling tummy—she was going to have a baby any day—she kept laughing and laughing.

Puzzled, we crept from the living room door farther into the kitchen. Keeping an eye on this chubby-looking fellow wearing brown snow pants and a hooded brown woolly sweater, we inched closer to our jovial mother.

"Look who's here, girls!" Mom said. "Can you say 'Merry Christmas' to Santa?"

We looked from Mom to the man whose white whiskers didn't look at all like whiskers. They looked more like the white cotton Mom dabbed on our scraped knees after we'd taken a tumble.

Santa crouched down and put his arms out.

"Aren't you going to give Santa a hug?" Mom prompted, holding back another giggle.

Joan and I looked at each other. We'd seen pictures of Santa in Eaton's Christmas catalogue. That Santa looked like the one in our book, *'Twas the Night Before Christmas*. Santa, or St. Nicholas, was dressed in red, not brown, and he didn't look like this man at all.

This brown-suited Santa wasn't plump like St. Nicholas, either. In fact, without the big, lumpy tummy, he'd be about the size of our dad.

With Mom watching, we gave the man the hug we felt we were expected to give.

His brown sweater was scratchy and he smelled a lot like Dad did when he came in from the barn. Maybe this was what Santa smelled like after feeding his reindeer.

Standing up, Santa said, "I see two young girls live here, and it looks like another baby is on the way." He rudely sized up our mother's belly. "Let's see what I have in my bag."

He pulled two presents out of a not-very-clean potato sack. The presents looked like wrapped shoeboxes. Strange Santa read the names on the parcels.

"Joan. Are you Joan?" he asked my sister.

She nodded and walked slowly toward him to take the gift he was holding out.

"You must be Sharon," he said to me.

I nodded and tiptoed toward him. Quickly, I grabbed my present and returned to Mom.

"What about your manners, girls? Did you say 'Thank you' to Santa?"

We both turned toward him and Joan said, "Thank you." I opened my mouth, but the words stuck in my throat.

Mom bent down and read the cards on the presents. "It says, 'Not to be opened until December 25th.' That's tomorrow. Why don't you put your gifts under the tree so you can open them in the morning?"

We carefully carried our treasures to the living room and put them under the spruce tree Dad had set up two days earlier. Mom had helped Joan and me make paper garlands and angels to hang on the tree, and we were proud of how it looked.

As we placed the parcels under the tree, I accidentally jostled mine. It made a sound—the same sound we'd heard when Joan and I bumped a box on the lake the day before.

  Christmas with Hot Apple Cider

Yesterday, in the afternoon, Dad had cleaned the snow off our patch of ice so Joan and I could skate on the small lake down the hill from our house.

We sat on a log while Dad strapped our bob skates to our winter boots. Then he helped us onto the ice and got us started skating. Once he was sure we were okay, he went to the nearby woods to cut spruce trunks into logs for the stove.

We hadn't skated long before Joan noticed a big cardboard box half hidden in the cattails—or bulrushes as we called them (from the story of Moses). Curious, we had to look.

We skated, or rather waddled, toward the reeds. Once there, we walked on our skates to get to the box.

Since I wasn't very good on my skates, I tripped and fell onto the box. We immediately heard a noise that sounded like a baby crying. It startled us, and we were a bit worried, but we decided this couldn't be a real baby.

That's when we remembered the dolls we'd seen in the Christmas section of the Eaton's catalogue.

Joan had read the description to me. These dolls could open and shut their eyes. They also had baby bottles and diapers, and they could make a crying sound when they were turned over.

What if this was a doll? Maybe even two dolls? If so, what were they doing here in a box on the lake? Were they our Christmas presents? We both had rag dolls, but to have a doll like the one in the catalogue would be so wonderful. Was it possible?

"Maybe the dolls are meant to be a surprise," Joan explained. "If we say anything before Christmas, we'll spoil the surprise."

We still had lots of unanswered questions. Were these dolls from Mom and Dad? Could they be our gifts from Santa? But, if they were from Santa, why would he bring the dolls to our home before Christmas? And why leave them *here*?

"Santa drives his reindeer and he has the gifts in his sleigh," I said. "And it isn't nighttime."

Joan got this funny look on her face. "I don't know how it works, but I don't think we should say anything to Mom and Dad. This will be our secret."

I had never been good at keeping secrets, but I said I would try.

"Pinky promise?" she asked. So we took our mitts off and crooked our pinky fingers together.

Before getting out of bed on Christmas morning, Joan said, "Remember to act surprised if our presents are dolls."

I nodded.

We got up, and pattered off in our slippers to waken our parents and coax them into the living room so we could open our gifts.

Joan could have saved her words about acting. When we opened our presents and saw those beautiful dolls that were our very own, we were both overwhelmed with joy and love and thankfulness and all the good feelings that come to children when they know they're loved and it's Christmas.

  Christmas with Hot Apple Cider

Through the Eyes of a Child

Brian C. Austin

Listening for sleigh bells,
squirming in the bed.
When will Mommy and Daddy get up?

Endless night.
Brightly wrapped packages
pull…
call…
beg…

The alarm by Mommy's bed…
She said it wouldn't be set.
Or—is it sleigh bells?

Coffee pot bubbling.
Why do grownups drink
such awful stuff?

Blankets on the floor.
One slipper on,
the other?
Somewhere…

Pounding down the stairs,
one foot louder
than the other.

Daddy's grumpy voice
pretending,
laughing inside.

Christmas!

Scary Saint Nick

Nonfiction

Jeannette Altwegg

Walking through any mall in December, one soon realizes that there isn't much mystery left in the season. Seriously, there's nothing magical about watching hordes of people, like an army of ants, rushing from store to store just so they can strike another name off that Christmas shopping list.

And what about those poor kids being dragged in front of a bearded grisly old man in a red suit just so the parents can have a picture of their two-year-old sitting on Santa's lap? Have you ever wondered why those children are crying? It's because they know what I know: Mr. Claus is one scary dude.

Growing up in Switzerland, I used to be terrified of Santa Claus. Of course, I didn't have that grandfatherly image of the chubby, white-bearded, jolly old elf bringing presents at Christmas. My Santa was lean, mean, and scary.

While the real presents were those we received on Christmas Eve, the Swiss tradition I grew up with taught that on December 6, Santa Claus visits the homes of children, bribing them with mandarin oranges, nuts, and chocolates. Naughty children, however, were threatened into being good boys and girls by the terrifying prospect of getting stuffed inside Santa's sack by his helper *Schmutzli* and carried off to his cottage in the forest. That warning alone frightened the living daylights out of me. It was so bad that whenever I spent any time in the woods I worried that perhaps this was the very forest where "he" lived.

Every year, I dreaded the day *Samichlaus*, as he is called in Swiss-German, would stomp into our living room, his arrival heralded by ringing bells and the clomp of heavy boots. Let me tell you, that booming "Ho! Ho! Ho!" takes on a whole new meaning when you're nervously trying to remember whether or not your good deeds have outweighed your bad during the past year. And

  Christmas with Hot Apple Cider

Santa is not kidding when he says he knows if you've been bad or good, because he has "The List," which he reads out loud for all to hear. No, not even the promise of chocolate could stop my jitters on *Samichlaus Abend* (Santa Night). Because, before we even got a glimpse of any goodies, we were required to recite something for Santa.

For some reason, the only poem I could ever recall under duress was a crude ditty calling Santa a name and demanding he give me nuts and pears before I'd come out of my hiding place behind the oven. Not the greatest way to make a good impression. Even now, 30 years later, I can still recite the rhyme word for word in Swiss.

> *Sami, Niggi Näggi*
> *Hinder em Ofe stek I.*
> *Gib mer Nüss und Bire,*
> *De chumen I wider füre.*[1]

In retrospect, the ordeal might not have been quite as distressing if there hadn't been that story of my dad being thrown into Santa's sack one year. As I recall the tale, his twin sister wailed so loudly that Santa let my dad out of the bag when they got to the corner of the house.

Supposedly, it never did him any real harm, but did anyone ever consider the possibility that such a yarn might permanently damage young and impressionable minds like mine?

I was almost 13 when we moved to Canada and I was introduced to a whole new Santa. I quickly learned that Mr. Claus is not feared, but rather revered, on this side of the ocean.

He doesn't come through the front door on December 6 to scare kids into behaving, but instead he leaves gifts in stockings hung by the chimney for girls and boys to open on Christmas morning. There are various parades with Mr. and Mrs. Claus—wait, he got married? And even though he apparently now lives at the North Pole, he makes appearances at the various local malls during the month of December. Toys for girls and boys are prepared by elves who, although they may look like children, with their green curly-toed hats and shoes have more in common with leprechauns.

Even the delivery of the presents is a bizarre affair, which includes a sled pulled by reindeer and a slide down the chimney in the middle of the night.

And what about the so-called Christmas music? I mean, seriously. There are only so many times one can handle listening to "Santa Baby" before going completely bonkers.

Not only that, but one of the more popular songs people blithely sing at Christmastime is "Santa Claus is Coming to Town." It's in the lyrics of that song that I realized that the Santa in North America isn't that different from the one I grew up with after all. Oh, the melody is quite jaunty and fun to tap your toes to, but if you actually listen to the words, you soon realize that Santa is one scary fellow. For starters, the man hates temper tantrums. Which, I realize, aren't on anyone's list of favourite things. However, from the first stanza, the song makes it clear that Santa is not someone you might be able to persuade with tears.

Then there's the bearded man's obsessive fixation on keeping records. I mean, Christmas is supposed to be the season for giving and forgiving, but for some unfathomable reason, this man's agenda is not only to find, but also to document, reasons to hold a grudge.

And what about those alarming hobbies of his? Not only does Santa have a problem with breaking and entering homes in the most unconventional way possible, but he's also portrayed as a clairvoyant with voyeuristic tendencies, apparently omniscient, and not above scare tactics to get youngsters to behave! Definitely a shady character who should give any parent pause.

So why are grownups so eager to make little children believe Santa is real?

My actual Christmas experience was a little different: the focus was on the original Christmas story and the Christ Child.

We always had a real tree, freshly cut by my dad on the morning of Christmas Eve and lovingly decorated by my mom during the afternoon. As children, we weren't allowed into the living room until after supper, but oh, how our excitement grew as the sun went to sleep! When my parents opened that door to reveal the glittering evergreen, lit with real candles, their warm glowing lights shimmering off dozens of gleaming red and silver ornaments, it truly became a magical time. And the nightmarish encounters with *Samichlaus* earlier that month became but a distant memory.

Every year, three generations of my family gathered in our living room on that one hallowed night, all sitting in eager anticipation. First, our little choir sang many Christmas hymns. One of my favourites has always been *"Stille Nacht."* There is something about the music and words of "Silent Night" that quiets the mind and fills the heart with solemn wonder, no matter which language it's sung in.

After the carols, my grandfather would read the story of Jesus' birth, followed by a prayer. I remember there was an atmosphere of reverence for the Christ Child who had come into our world. Vulnerable as an infant, His birth was a gift to the world. Our own giving and receiving of presents that night became an extension of our joy at His birth, and an overflowing of thanksgiving for all the blessings we'd enjoyed in the past year.

To this day, our tradition to gather as a family remains. Christmas isn't Christmas without the singing, the nativity story, and each one of us giving thanks for our loved ones in prayer before even one present is opened

That's why I have never been able to accept Santa Claus as part of the Christmas experience. The fable parents tell their children of some stranger dropping their gifts off by sneaking in through a chimney in the middle of the night is not only preposterous, it takes so much away from the true miracle of Christmas—Christ leaving His home and becoming vulnerable as a human being, an infant.

Maybe I see it this way because I grew up in a time and place where Santa was never really part of the Christmas story. Christmas is, after all, Christ's birthday, which has nothing to do with scary bearded men in red suits. Rather than trying to earn gifts with good behaviour and scare tactics, isn't it more appealing to share our time and presence at Christmas with each other while recalling the miraculous gift of God come to earth?

1. Walter Käslin, *"Samiglais Niggi Näggi"*

An Immigrant Christmas

Nonfiction

Angelina Fast

On August 19, 1948, my family and I arrived in Quebec City on the *Kota Inten*, a ship filled with immigrants from Holland.

Later that day, we boarded a train to take us from Quebec City to our destination—a farm just inside the Ontario border on the way to Ottawa. The farmer was to be our sponsor.

My family consisted of my father, my mother, my brother Henk (who at 14 was as tall as my father), me (12-year-old Angelina), my sister Anne (age seven), and my brother John (age three).

Since we had no idea how long the journey would be, we peered through the windows to watch for signs.

After several hours, Henk exclaimed, "Here it is! I saw the sign. It said 'Vankleek Hill.'"

We gathered our things and stepped down onto a platform, where Dad showed the station master a piece of paper with our sponsor's name and address on it.

At that time, Canada accepted only farmers as immigrants, and each one was matched with a sponsor, meaning someone who would guarantee the immigrant a job and a place to live. This was shortly after World War II ended.

When peace had finally come, many people in Holland began to talk of emigrating. The common refrain was, "There is no future for the children in our war-torn country."

My mom and dad had also become convinced that moving to a better country was the best thing to do. "Canada" had become a familiar word around our supper table until finally the decision was made. After that, our household was packed up, medical exams were completed, and a sponsor was found.

Now we stood on the platform in Vankleek Hill, staring at each other, wondering what would happen next.

The station master said, "I'll make a phone call for you."

After some time, a dusty red truck pulled up. The driver helped us load our suitcases into the back of the truck and instructed us children to sit on them while Mom and Dad sat in the front.

After a short drive, we arrived at a house on a dark country road. It was a long house with a veranda across the front and an overhanging roof.

A middle-aged man who looked rather scruffy, with messed up hair, came to the door. He was our sponsor. "Oh, here you are," he said. "Come on in." Then he continued, "You can go upstairs. There are some rooms and beds. Just help yourself. My wife has given birth to twins and she's staying at her mother's."

We carried our suitcases upstairs and found several small rooms. My parents shared the room with the double bed, Henk and John had one with a single bed and a cot, and Anne and I got the one with two single beds.

During the next two weeks, Dad and Henk worked long hours in unaccustomed heat, gathering the last of the summer wheat harvest. But the heat wasn't the worst part. Dad, a sensitive animal lover, was grieved to tears to see that the farmer beat his animals.

Mom did the best she could finding food to cook for us. There was a large box of corn flakes on top of the fridge, and we were fascinated to find out how good they tasted with milk.

The farmer didn't show up for meals. We assumed he went to his wife and newborn twins to eat and sleep.

We were a kilometre or so from a crossroads, where there was a small country store. One day, Mom sent me there by myself to buy cookies. My English consisted of only a few words, so I objected, telling her I wouldn't know what to say. She said, "Say 'baby cookies.'" It worked, and I came home with a package of arrowroot biscuits.

Other memories I have from that time include having sponge baths in a bowl of water on the back porch, using an outhouse that was close to the house, and finding an Eaton's catalogue. My sister Anne and I spent hours admiring pictures of clothing and household items we'd never seen, let alone owned, in war-torn Holland.

Since my parents had been told we'd have our own house in Canada, Mom kept asking the farmer, "House? Where is our house?"

At the end of the first week, he finally said, "Come with me."

We walked past a field to a somewhat dilapidated wooden cabin. The farmer opened the door, and we stared at a dirt floor partly covered with boards.

Mom, so very anxious to have a place of our own, said, "Beautiful, beautiful."

I knew her comment was an effort to be polite. I held my nose because the musty smell was overwhelming,

That night, Mom took a walk down the country road, crying. A neighbouring farmer spotted her. He came out of his house and introduced himself. He asked if she'd like to have some cobs of corn. Mom didn't know what he'd said so she replied with a hesitant, "Yes." Mom carried the cobs home in her apron, opened the door, and, seeing us huddled together in the living room, began to wail. "And now we have to eat chicken feed!" The only corn we were acquainted with in Holland was, indeed, chicken feed.

When Mom had composed herself, she told us about the neighbour who had given her the corn. "His name is Wesley," she said. And he told me, "I have another place for you. I will take you there a week from Monday, on Labour Day." Then she added, "So he must know that we're not in a good place."

We spent the Sunday before our departure with the only other Dutch immigrant family we had met in the district. They fed us and bedded us down for the night.

The next morning, Wesley came with his truck. He was young and tall, with dark hair and eyes. For a moment, I wondered whether he was one of the Canadian soldiers who had rolled into our village in huge tanks in April of '45 to liberate us from the oppressive Nazi regime. On our way out, he stopped at the railway station. There, on the platform, stood three huge crates with our last name stamped on them in big black letters!

Mom was delighted. "Oh, our furniture has arrived!"

Just about everything we had in our house in Holland was in those three crates, including her organ!

Wesley said, "I thought you'd like to see this." Then he added, "I'll arrange for the railway to transport your crates, and we'll make sure you get everything."

  Christmas with Hot Apple Cider

We stopped for lunch at a restaurant and sat together at a table by a window.

Wesley said, "Would you like a hamburger?"

Not knowing what that word meant, we all thought it was best to nod a "Yes." While we ate, Mom and Dad asked Wesley about our new employer.

"Her name is Mrs. Williamson," he replied. "She has a hobby farm and riding horses and she's looking for someone to help care for her animals. And she has a house for you to live in!"

"That's amazing," Mom said.

"I love horses," Dad added. "We had two in Holland. "But what about our sponsor?"

"I discussed your move with him," Wesley replied. "He seemed rather relieved because the house he had for you is far from adequate for our Canadian winters."

"Does it get cold here?" Mom asked with concern in her voice.

"Yes, it can be quite cold, and sometimes we have a lot of snow," Wesley replied.

I saw Mom hug herself and shiver.

Wesley then turned to us children and asked, "Would you like Jello for dessert?"

Not knowing what that could be, we all nodded again. When it arrived, we were fascinated with the bowls of shiny red dessert. Henk took a spoonful and exclaimed, "Look! It moves! It's alive!" The rest of us followed suit and we couldn't help but giggle as we watched the Jello wiggle, much to Wesley's delight.

We drove on and after a few hours crossed a bridge spanning a wide expanse of water. Wesley turned off the highway into the village of Sainte-Anne-de-Bellevue. He stopped beside the St. Lawrence River so we could see the water raging over rapids under the high bridge.

"Wow! We've never seen water like this!" Henk exclaimed.

Wesley took St. Marie Road out of the village, and after a few kilometres veered into Mrs. Williamson's place—a beautiful mansion-like house at the end of a tree-lined driveway. She came out of a side door and greeted us all warmly. She looked a bit older than Mom, with curly, greying hair and blue eyes.

"Come in, come in," she said, and invited us into her very large sunroom. It had windows all around. She gave us something to eat and later brought us bedding and showed us there was room for us all to have a good night's sleep.

I didn't go to sleep right away. It was so amazing to lie on a soft sofa in such a luxurious room with the light of a crescent moon shining in through one of the many windows. Wesley had called Mrs. Williamson a "millionaire." I thought of her as an angel. A rich angel.

When we woke in the morning, she invited us to have breakfast in her kitchen. As we enjoyed hot cereal and toast, she said to Mom, "I'll show you your house today. You can move in when your furniture arrives. In the meantime, you will eat and sleep at my place."

"You are so kind," Mom answered.

Mrs. Williamson continued, "It's a two-bedroom Cape Cod cottage, but I have plans to enlarge it. I think we'll add a big kitchen, two more bedrooms, and another bathroom." She stood up, moved to the bay window, and said, "You can see the house from here, although it's hidden somewhat by the trees."

Mom got up, looked, and replied, "Beautiful, beautiful." I could tell that this time she meant the words.

Mrs. Williamson said, "But first, let's see the children off to school. I'll drive them today, and after that they'll be able to take the school bus."

Moving to the counter, she smiled at me and asked, "Do you like peanut butter and jam?"

I didn't know what peanut butter was, so I just nodded.

When the three lunches were made, we all climbed into Mrs. Williamson's big blue car. After we reached the village of Sainte-Anne-de-Bellevue, she drove into a park-like space with circling roads and beautiful large red brick buildings.

"This is Macdonald College," she announced. "It's an English college in a predominantly French town." As she drove up to the smallest building set apart from the large ones she said, "And this is your school—Macdonald High School. It has Kindergarten to Grade 11."

  Christmas with Hot Apple Cider

She escorted us inside and spoke to the principal, Mr. Davies. He called three other teachers to come, and with many smiles and gestures, they warmly welcomed us and placed us in grades: Anne in Grade 3, Henk in Grade 9, and me in Grade 7.

A few days after we arrived, the French teacher, Miss Revel, told us to come to the Grade 11 classroom at 12:30.

When we arrived, she gave us each a notebook and instructed us to draw two lines down a page, creating three columns. She gave us an English word and the corresponding French word to be written in the first and second columns. Henk, who'd had a year of English and French in High School in Holland, was to come up with the Dutch word for the third column. We had an English/Dutch dictionary to help us.

Each day, we were to memorize the new words, which were soon put into phrases and later into sentences.

At home, Mom and Dad joined us in the evening to memorize the words. Some were tongue twisters for them. One evening, we were to practise, "I put the clothes in the clothes closet." Mom tried and tried. Finally, in exasperation, she stood up, raised her hands, and blurted out, "I put de klodders in de klodderkast." We all laughed. But as I look back, I realize that Miss Revel gave up a year of noon hours to teach three immigrant children their new language.

By December 18, a week before Christmas, we had settled into our new home and were starting to feel comfortable in our new land.

It was snowing that day, and Anne had her nose pressed against the window in the living room, watching thick flakes gently swirl down. Suddenly she exclaimed, "A car is coming! Mom, a car is coming!"

I walked over to stand beside her and saw a grey car inching toward our house.

Mom walked in from the kitchen and stood behind us. "I wonder who that could be," she said. "Who do we know that would come to visit us on a snowy Saturday morning? Maybe they're meaning to go to the Cole family next door."

The three of us watched as the car continued to move slowly toward us. Our long laneway stretched from our house to St. Marie Road. It was covered with snow, and with empty fields on each side, the snow blew across it. We saw the grey car swerve a bit, but it stayed on the laneway.

John squeezed in between Mom and me as the car turned into our yard and stopped. The doors opened.

"Oh, it's Rev. and Mrs. Doxsee!" Mom exclaimed.

"And Cynthia also!" my sister added as she saw her red-haired school friend hop out of the car.

Rev. Doxsee was the minister of the United Church in Sainte-Anne-de-Bellevue, where we, upon invitation, had attended some services.

He opened the backseat door and leaned in to grasp a cardboard box and carry it toward the house.

Mom hurried to open the front door for him.

Mrs. Doxsee and Cynthia also reached into the back and emerged, each holding two smaller parcels wrapped in brown paper. The three climbed the veranda steps and took off their boots in our front entry.

"We came to visit you!" Cynthia squealed, eyes dancing above her freckled nose.

Anne smiled a silent response. She was still hesitant to speak English words, but Cynthia had been her friend and interpreter ever since the first day of school, when Cynthia had run home for lunch crying, "Mom! Mom! We have a girl in our class who can't talk!" After that, when Anne needed to use the washroom, she would nudge Cynthia, who sat beside her, point her finger down, and Cynthia would raise her hand and ask the teacher if Anne could be excused.

Now Cynthia and her parents brought the gifts inside and set the big box on the kitchen table, the other packages in the living room. "These are for Christmas!" Cynthia declared. "You can open them on Christmas Day! Big surprise for you!" she added, giggling.

Rev. Doxsee put on his boots again, went back to the car, and pulled out two very long boards and two equally long sticks. He brought them inside.

  Christmas with Hot Apple Cider

"Skis and poles," he said as he placed the items against the front entry wall. "Here are some skis for you. Have fun with them, okay?"

"Okay," I said obediently, wondering how we were going to manage to slide on these thin narrow planks. Holland is flat with virtually no hills or mountains and no great amounts of snow, so skis were foreign objects to us. With the many canals there, skating is the winter sport.

"Would you like a cup of coffee?" Mom asked our guests. Her English was now quite adequate for simple conversation. In Holland, Mom and Dad had biked into a nearby city once a week to take English lessons. Mom's motto was, "We're going to a new country, and we will learn their language."

As the coffee was percolating, the back door opened and Dad and Henk entered. "I could smell the coffee in the barn!" Dad said jokingly. He warmly greeted our guests.

Rev. Doxsee now encouraged Mom to open the cardboard box. We strained to see the contents: sugar, flour, oatmeal, corn flakes, oranges, a bag of peanuts, and six chocolate bars!

We profusely thanked our guests.

Rev. Doxsee said, "All the gifts are from the people at church."

"Oh, please, thank them for us," Mom said. "This is so kind of them. I feel a bit overwhelmed."

"You're so welcome," the Reverend replied. "We're all glad you've come to join our community."

When they left, we waved to them from the living room window, and Mom said, "Wasn't that a beautiful surprise!"

"Yes, but why do we have to wait a whole week before we can open the packages?" I asked.

"Well, that's what they said," Mom replied. "That must be the custom here, so we'll do as they say."

After the Doxsees left and Mom said we couldn't open the gifts, Henk piped up, "But we have one gift that is open!"

He took the skis, placed them on the floor, and figured out how to fasten his shoes into the metal clasps.

"See? All ready to go!" he exclaimed. So on Thursday, when the Christmas holidays began, Henk and I walked to the St. Marie

Road hill, each carrying a ski and a pole. We attempted to go down the snow-covered field beside the road, but continually fell. It was frustrating that we couldn't seem to slide gracefully from side to side. We gave up and trudged back home.

When we reached the end of our laneway, we saw Colin Cole from next door. He was 16 and always friendly and helpful, as were his mom and dad and younger sister, Elizabeth.

Colin walked over to us and said, "So you went skiing, did you?"

"Well, we tried," Henk answered.

"Where did you go? And where did you get the skis?"

"They were a Christmas gift from the people at church," Henk replied. "And we tried to go down the St. Marie Road hill."

Colin took a look at our skis and said, "These are cross-country skis, and not meant to use going downhill. Downhill skis have boots attached to them so that your feet are steady. You use these skis to slide across a field."

"Oh, no wonder we had such difficulty," Henk said, laughing.

When we entered the house, we again eyed the gifts on the living room floor—brown paper packages tied up with string.

In Holland, we received gifts on St. Nicholas Day—December 5. I had received a pencil the year before and treasured it. On Christmas Day, there was no custom of gift exchange. Rather, we all went to church to celebrate the birth of Jesus. That night, we'd have a Sunday school program, where all the children received a little book.

Each Christmas, a tall evergreen tree decorated with real burning candles had stood in the centuries-old Dutch church. Pails of water had sat around the bottom of the tree—just in case. Dad, the Sunday school teacher, would stand between the tree and the ornate pulpit to tell a story. The whole church would be very still as Dad dramatized the story with his deep voice.

Suddenly, I remembered something that had happened at Christmas four years before, when I was eight. That was the winter of 1944, also referred to as the "hunger winter." The enemy had cut off food supplies, and more than 20,000 people died of starvation. It was also very cold that winter.

  Christmas with Hot Apple Cider

Mom and Dad had taken in a woman from Rotterdam, who had a boy and a little girl. We lived in the north of Holland, and, with Dad's fruit and vegetable farm, we at least had potatoes and vegetables to eat.

The five-year-old girl had a beautiful voice, and Dad asked her to sing at our church's Christmas program. She stood—a tiny figure in front of a towering tree, with candlelight dancing on her white-blond curls—and her voice filled the church as she sang a haunting melody that left an indelible impression on me. "I bring a gift for Jesus and place it under the tree."

A gift for Jesus? That was a new idea to me. Children received gifts, but to *bring* a gift—?

But now we were in Canada, and we had lots of gifts to open—in just a few more days.

Finally, Christmas morning arrived! Anne and John were the first ones up and gleefully shouted from the living room, "It's Christmas—we can open the gifts!"

And so the grand opening began. One parcel contained a book for each of us: mine was a Nancy Drew story. The next parcel had socks and mittens for us kids. Then a big box of chocolates! The last parcel had four separately-wrapped gifts with our names on them. I received a ceramic angel ornament, Anne a comb and some pretty hair barrettes, John a toy truck, and Henk a small flashlight. We were all ecstatic!

After breakfast, Dad said, "I'm off to the stables to feed the horses."

Henk and I asked if we could go along.

"Yes, sure," Dad replied.

We took the path to the stables and when Dad opened the door a warm aroma met us. I went to the four occupied stalls and gently rubbed the noses of the beautiful animals.

Mr. Demers entered the stable. He was French and looked after the cows and chickens in the other barn. He was always smiling or laughing, and now he boisterously greeted us with, "Joyeux Noël! Merry Christmas!"

After a short while, Mrs. Williamson also appeared. She greeted us warmly with, "Good morning, everyone, and Merry Christmas!"

She had some instructions for the men, and they moved close to understand her words and gestures. Suddenly, all three burst out laughing. Three languages bound together by laughter. I thought of the three columns in our notebooks and Miss Revel's smiling, encouraging face.

We spent the day relishing our new gifts. I got acquainted with Nancy Drew, a character my classmates had talked about. John drove his little truck all over the place. Anne fussed with her hair. We watched Henk ski/slide across the field in front of our house. And we ate chocolates!

In the late afternoon, I helped Mom set the table for supper. She lit a few candles and turned down the lights. It looked so cozy.

After supper, it was time for the story. We had a large book called *The Children's Bible,* and each night Dad read us a story. Often, we begged him to read one more. Sometimes he agreed.

Tonight, it was the Christmas story. We knew it by heart, yet we were still captivated. Joseph and Mary had to travel all the way to Bethlehem, and once there, they found no place to sleep. Finally someone said they could stay in a stable. During the night their baby was born.

"Imagine having a baby in a barn with a dirt floor," Mom commented. I thought of the farmer's cabin with the dirt floor. So Mary and Joseph were sort of like immigrants?

I knew what happened later on. The young family had to move all the way to Egypt to escape a murderous king. There, they were immigrants indeed—strangers in a strange land. I hoped there were kind people who looked out for them. People like Wesley and Mrs. Williamson and the Doxsees and Miss Revel and the Cole family.

And now I wondered about giving gifts. All these people had given us such generous gifts of friendship, food, shelter, and even clothes.

One time, Dad had read us a story that Jesus had told his followers. It was about the end times and dividing people into two groups. One group was made up of those who had not been kind to others. The other group comprised those who had helped people. He said, "I was hungry and you gave me something to eat, I was thirsty and you gave me something to drink, I was a stranger and you invited me in, I needed clothes and you clothed me, I was sick and you looked after me, I was in prison and you came to visit me." And then He said, "Whatever you did for one of the least of these, you did for me."[1]

I thought again of the line in the little girl's song, "I bring my gift."

And I wondered, "So—what do I bring?"

Years later, I would hear "The Little Drummer Boy" ask the same question. He decided to bring his best.

And I have strived to follow his example. Not only at Christmas but all year round.

My siblings and I enjoyed the excellent instruction at Macdonald High School for four years. In April of 1952 my family moved to the Niagara Peninsula in Ontario. Mom and Mrs. Doxsee decided it was best for me to finish Grade 10 at Macdonald High, so Mrs. Doxsee invited me to stay at their place until the end of June. After exams, she took me to the train station for my journey home.

Some 15 years later, I had the privilege of visiting with the Doxsees once more. They were retiring and busy packing up their belongings. Mrs. Doxsee gave me a beautiful blue and gold ceramic vase.

She said, "I'd like for you to have this as a keepsake."

I still have the vase and treasure it along with the memory of this dear couple. After Rev. Doxsee passed, Mrs. Doxsee moved to a seniors' residence in Niagara. We enjoyed visiting and reminiscing about those early immigrant days. And I had the opportunity to continue to express my gratitude.

1. Matthew 25:35–36, 40

No Presents

Gloria Raynor

Coming out of sweet, sweet sleep
to a beautiful Christmas morning
with sunshine pouring through my window,
I hurry out of bed without washing my face
Nor even brushing my teeth—
just simply dashing downstairs
to look under the Christmas tree
And see what's there for me.
In dismay, finding nothing.
No! She said there was no money, but—?
No! It isn't possible!
Heartbroken, shattered in pieces,
mind blown within from disbelief—
A Christmas without presents?

Rushing frantically up the stairs,
tears streaming down my face, shouting,
"Mama, Mama, the tree stands bare downstairs.
How can this be? What did I not do right?
No gifts under the tree for me?
Mama, Mama, where is my Christmas?"

Mama stands there staring out the window
speaking in her sweet, gentle
voice with a beautiful smile on her face
saying, "No money for Christmas, my child.
You know I have worked very hard this year
but the bills keep coming in,
and things, my child, have changed
since your papa passed away.
Not even paper to wrap the Christ
of Christmas, my child," says Mama.

"So let us take Him in our hearts and unfold Him at the table,
then relish the delightful sweet aroma of the meal He has provided,
giving thanks once again for having good health
for yet another precious year.
And asking Him for great strength to carry us through
this beautiful day and the coming year."

Mama then embraces me so tightly,
with lots of love and kisses,
I feel an overwhelming joy—
a filling of inner peace.
The disappointment of no gifts under the tree
diminishes as Mama's love reveals to me
the true meaning of Christmas,
which is the love of Jesus Christ,
even without presents under the tree.
Yes, the love of Jesus Christ,
without presents under the tree,
wraps up my heart with contentment.

The Umbrella Christmas Tree

Nonfiction

Margo Prentice

I was only five years old and very excited that Christmas Day wasn't far away, which, of course, meant that Santa would soon visit. I remember my brother, Armand, who was three years old, jumping up and down as he, too, looked forward to Christmas with excitement and anticipation.

It was 1942, and my beloved daddy had been gone nearly three years because of a far-away war. I remembered that he was tall and handsome and that he carried me around in his big arms. I also remembered the day my mother cried a lot because she got a letter from the government saying her husband was "missing in action." I was too young to understand what those words meant, but I wasn't worried. I knew my daddy would come home to me and my brother.

After Daddy had left, Mother moved us from the city of Winnipeg to the outskirts of a small prairie town about 50 miles away. A family friend let us live rent-free in a small cottage.

In the Canadian prairies, winters are cold, with temperatures dropping to –20°C (–4°F) for months. But I knew in my heart that Santa would come no matter what the weather. Santa had magic powers and visited all the children in the world.

Armand and I spent the days before Christmas playing indoors because it was too cold to play outside. We liked to look out the window to see the snow falling in a blizzard, swirling against the glass. Beautiful magical crystals formed on the windows in front of our eyes.

My mother had explained that the baby Jesus was born on Christmas Day and that was why we celebrated. She said He was born in a barn and there were angels and animals around him. I don't know how much I understood, but I could hardly wait until Christmas Day finally arrived.

  Christmas with Hot Apple Cider

During World War II, food was rationed. This meant that our mother could get only a small amount of things like milk, eggs, butter, flour, and sugar. I remember that there weren't many special things in the house. Yet I knew in my heart that on this special day of the year I would feel joy and happiness.

We didn't have a Christmas tree or gifts, but I knew Santa would bring presents and we would have a tree. Santa was magical; he could do anything!

On Christmas Eve, Mother heated water on the stove and filled a tub big enough for me and Armand to have a bath in front of the stove in the kitchen. Shivering, we were dried and put into warm nightgowns, sweaters, toques, and socks to keep us warm during the night. We had a special supper of pancakes with jam and a cup of tea. Once we were snuggled in bed together, Mother came into the room and we said our prayers. Cozy and warm, we went to sleep, dreaming of the next day.

On Christmas morning, it was so cold in the house that we could see our breath. Mother put our clothes under the blankets so we could get dressed without having to get up. She told us to wait until she lit the stove and not come out of the bed until the house was warm. "If you wait," she said, "there'll be a wonderful surprise from Santa for you in the living room."

Armand and I waited until we could no longer see our breath, then jumped out of bed and ran to the living room.

I couldn't believe my eyes!

On top of Mother's sewing machine table was the most beautiful Christmas tree I had ever seen. No, it wasn't actually a tree. It was an umbrella standing in a pot and halfway opened so it had the shape of a Christmas tree. The umbrella was decorated with Christmas balls hanging from the tips of the ribs, and it had garlands of buttons and lace draped all around it. An angel perched on the very top. The umbrella tree was so beautiful it took my breath away.

Beside the tree was my old dolly. But she didn't look the same. She was wearing a new Christmas dress made of red and green velvet. Even her hair had been fixed. I thought Santa was truly a magical person!

Armand's old wooden truck was there too, but it had been repaired and painted, and there was a small teddy bear sitting in the back.

Santa had also put an orange and some candy into one of Armand's socks, and into one of mine. They were both hanging from the sewing machine.

We sat down to a breakfast of warm milk, tea, and pieces of bread with sugar! Later, it became warm enough that Mother suggested we all go outside and play in the snow, which we did. We built a snowman and made snow angels, and we laughed and had an amazing time.

For lunch, we ate a piece of bread with jam and had our oranges for dessert. The rest of the day, I played with my newly dressed doll.

When it got dark, we had a nice supper of porridge with milk and brown sugar. Then Mother took us to the glassed-in veranda, where we all looked out the window at the stars and sang "Silent Night" and "Away in the Manger" over and over again.

I remember this as my best Christmas ever. I never forgot my umbrella Christmas tree and how much my mother loved us!

Now as I observe my children and all they do for my grandchildren at Christmas time, I realize why Christmas is so special. It's all about love. Just as God loves and protects us, so my mother loved and protected us. And this love is passed on through the generations.

Author's Note:

My father was found a year later. He had been wounded somewhere in Belgium and was found lying in a field nearly dead, with nothing to identify him. He was taken to a convent, where nuns looked after him until he regained consciousness a few months later. He eventually returned home, a weary warrior happy to be back with his family.

Christmas Behind Barbed-Wire Fences

Nonfiction

Tina Michele Weidelich
from the stories of
Andrzej Urbanowicz

My 17-year-old granddaughter and I chat up a storm as we wait for my daughter, Tina, to bring my old, beat-up, leatherette suitcase—the one I used in 1957 when I crossed the Atlantic by ship from Europe to Canada. After Tina drags it into the living room, slides open the metal latches, and props it open, I peer inside. I'm looking through the Christmas decorations for the big, bright star. When I find it, I hold it carefully in my 90-year-old, wrinkled hands.

Out of nowhere, a wave of sadness comes over me. My throat tightens, and I can hardly breathe. I take a deep breath to gather my composure, but my thoughts have gone back to Christmas of 1944, when I was the same age my granddaughter is now.

That long ago Christmas Day I was an orphan being held behind barbed-wire fences at a prisoner-of-war camp in Austria. I was confused and in shock, reliving the days of horror, death, and destruction while I'd been fighting in the Polish Warsaw Uprising, our revolt against German occupation.

I counted six times when I could have been killed. And I wondered why I'd been spared. As far as I knew, all of my loved ones were dead. Why not me?

Not that I wasn't used to difficulty.

I was born in Poznań, Poland, in 1927, just as my parents were on the brink of separation. For that reason, I wasn't welcome. When

I was three, my parents divorced, and my mother, my five-year-old sister, and I moved into my grandparents' home in Warsaw.

My mother worked full time to support the family while my grandparents kept an eye on us kids. But, eventually, looking after us became too much for my grandparents, and they pressured my mother to come up with a solution. She decided to send my sister and me away to boarding schools.

When I was ten, my sister was sent to a school run by nuns, and I was sent to a Catholic boys' residential school in the same town. By train, it took more than five hours one way to travel the 300 kilometres from Warsaw to the school, which meant I visited my family only at Christmas and during summer vacations. Many weekends, while other boys went home, I had to stay at the school.

The first two years at boarding school were awful. At home, I was used to having my own way and running wild around our neighbourhood with little supervision. Boarding school felt like an army setting, with so many rules and regulations. I wrote many desperate letters to my mother, begging her to take me back home to live with her.

She didn't. Instead, she came once or twice each year to visit me. I resented her for sending me away, and my relationship with her became quite cold. Every night I cried quietly in my bed, hiding my tears. I felt lonely, unloved, and forgotten.

One blessing during that time was that each day a Catholic brother, who was in his 40s, would take a group of about 20 of us students for a walk and we would all talk together. I loved the conversations about God the Father and how we can trust in Him. Because of these regular walks and church services, I learned about God and fell in love with Him. In time, I decided to put my hope in God, and He replaced the father I couldn't remember.

Most nights after that, I talked to my Heavenly Father—sometimes in tears—and slept peacefully.

Speaking of fathers, after my parents divorced, I saw my earthly father only once—in 1939, when I was 12. I was home for summer vacation and there were only a few more days before I had to go back to my dreaded school. I was outside, playing with my friends, and when I came home for lunch my grandmother quickly whisked me into the house and told me, "Your father is here."

Immediately I felt anger and resentment. I could barely remember the last time I'd seen him.

When I entered the family room, I noticed my sister sitting on our father's knee, giggling and giving him big hugs.

My father saw me, said, "Hello," and reached out his hand for me to come.

In spite of the regret I think I spotted in his eyes, I didn't move.

He sighed, retracted his hand, and explained to us that he had been called to active duty in the Polish army. He had come to say goodbye.

The entire time he was there, I stood as if I were an observer. When he got up to leave, I said good-bye—but only after my grandmother insisted. I looked out the window and watched his figure disappear in the distance as he walked out of my life.

A few days after I saw him, World War II began.

I didn't find out until many, many years later that he was killed the following year as part of the mass murder in Russia when the Russian communists, under Stalin, executed more than 20,000 Polish war prisoners, including about 8,000 officers, in the Katyń forest.

When I was 15, after school ended for the summer, my sister and I stayed with my mother and grandmother in my mother's newly rented apartment near Warsaw. Our grandfather had died, and my mother was suffering from cancer. My heart broke each day as I watched her battle the extreme pain. Because of the war, she wasn't able to get painkillers.

One night, I finally broke down and asked her to forgive me for not trusting and loving her. She told me that she forgave me.

A few nights later, I sat in her room and watched her die in agony.

My sister and I were now orphans. We were both in shock, and we felt out of control. Our grandfather had died and our grandmother was old and frail and unable to support us financially. We had no idea who would pay for our schooling and look after us. In my despair, I prayed, "God, what is going to become of me? Help!"

My prayer was answered when, unexpectedly, we received money for our schooling from my father's brother. We were both astounded! I was thrilled to go back to school, and, that December, with the war still raging, I felt convicted to join the Polish Resistance army. Despite the danger, joining the resistance was a declaration of my refusal to be a slave and my desire for freedom.

I recruited my sister, and it became a terrific morale booster for both of us. Training and implementing assignments took us out of our depression and mourning and gave us a reason to press on.

My sister received her orders first. She immediately gathered her essentials and we quickly said good-bye, neither of us suspecting it would be the last time we'd see each other on this earth.

The next day, August 1, 1944, at the age of 17, I reported for duty to fight in the Warsaw Uprising.

The uprising was led by the Polish Resistance Home Army and was timed to coincide with the Soviet Union's Red Army's approach from the east. The goal was for the Polish army to help the Russian troops liberate Warsaw from the Germans without major damage to the city. The battle was expected to last only a couple of days. However, the Soviet army stopped short, and the Germans regrouped. In the end, the battle, which resulted in the destruction of Warsaw, lasted nine long weeks.

We had few resources with which to fight. All I was given was a three-inch, small-calibre pistol and two bullets—which might seem like a joke. But I was one of the fortunate ones: only about 25 per cent of the soldiers had any sort of weapon.

During those long weeks, I counted six times that I came close to death. The most memorable was when I was standing guard inside a building deemed essential because it was in a strategic location for fighting the Germans. All I had was my small pistol.

  Christmas with Hot Apple Cider

Overhead, planes were dropping bombs, and three of them hit the building I was in. Miraculously, I escaped from the rubble without injury, though I was covered in a thick layer of dust and was without my helmet and gun. My hair was so matted and tangled that I later had to have my head shaved.

I kept thanking God for saving me, but at the same time, as throughout the entire uprising and after, I felt guilty for not dying with my comrades in arms.

Some weeks later, my commander gave me a rifle and more ammunition, which had been taken from a fallen German soldier.

As the Russians held back, the Germans took over one section of Warsaw at a time. They bombed, sent in tanks, and then brought in their infantry. We suffered heavy casualties.

I kept very busy rotating between jobs: standing on guard, checking people's passports, building barricades, carrying the wounded on stretchers to the hospital, and transporting water and supplies.

Near the end of September, I was on the front line awaiting a Nazi armoured tank attack. It was the eighth week of the Warsaw Uprising. The buildings all around us had been previously air-bombed and I was lying in the rubble, covered in dust, with my rifle and eyes pointed into the distance at the German army. The tanks were just sitting there waiting. It was their move.

I watched, all alone with my blanket, rifle, and a handful of bullets. It smelled like the city was on fire. It was.

Occasionally a woman would risk her life to bring me soup or bread for nourishment. The civilians helped us a great deal, and every day I was fed. However, I fully expected to die before long.

As I waited, I thought how this was the stupidest thing I'd ever done in my life. We were surrounded by Germans, and there was no way out of Warsaw. There was nowhere to hide, nowhere to run. I was a sitting duck. I prayed continually.

We sat and slept on guard there for one week. I was exhausted from having had only five hours sleep per night for the previous two months. I'm sure I nodded off from time to time during that week of just waiting. For me, the waiting was worse than being killed on the spot—although I didn't want to die.

On October 2, the fighting ceased. My corporal came over and told me that we had surrendered and that our duty to protect the command centre of the Warsaw Uprising was ending. A few days later, I obeyed another command to march out in formation with my fellow freedom fighters, put down my weapon, and surrender to the German army.

At the time, I felt defeated and would rather have died. I still can't believe God rescued me from that terrible mess. Out of the 100 men in my unit, only 10 of us came through the Warsaw Uprising.

The German army arrested us and took us out of Poland as prisoners of war. They moved us randomly to different camps every six weeks, so I often found myself among strangers.

At one point, I was at a base camp in the Austrian Alps close to the city of Salzburg. After days of hanging around, starving and freezing, I volunteered to work. I didn't know what type of job or where it would be, but I thought keeping busy would distract me from my misery.

I ended up working in Salzburg on sewers the Allies had bombed. While we dug, the guards kept warm by a fire. Occasionally they allowed us to join them so we could warm ourselves up from the bitter winter cold. I tried my best to dig through the frozen clay, but it was a mission impossible. None of us got very deep.

On Christmas Eve, after digging all day, I returned, exhausted, to the 50-foot-long barrack. There was no Christmas tree and no extra food. The only heat for the one-room structure was provided by two stoves in the central passage.

With five other men, I moved as close as I could to a stove. On that bleak night, we spoke about our families and how we might never see them again.

We were students, young professionals, actors, and artists. Good company. We spoke about our dreams of finishing university and finding jobs. Then a young fighter from Wola started singing the Polish rendition of "O Holy Night"—a song I knew from boarding school. We all joined in.

When the singing died down, we continued chatting. We debated whether we should go back to Poland or to the West once we were freed. We wondered how we could make a living or complete our studies.

When it got late, we prepared for bed. Passing by a window, I paused and looked out. In the mountains, I saw the sky laden with thousands of stars. I spotted one big, bright star and remembered the star of Bethlehem that led the wise men to the birthplace of Jesus. I immediately felt hope. That star seemed to promise me that God would lead me to a better future.

We went to bed. My neighbours and I lay close together and each placed our single blanket on top of us to form a three-layered blanket. This was the only way we could keep warm in the frigid atmosphere.

That Christmas morning, I fell asleep peacefully, knowing that I was in good hands—my Heavenly Father's hands.

God did give me a better future. Despite a few more close calls and tough times, He provided me with an education and jobs. When I was 30, He brought me to Canada—the land of opportunity. He blessed me with a wife, children, and grandchildren. He gave me a heart of love and gratitude.

At 90 years old, I'm celebrating my 60th Christmas in Canada in the warmth of my family's home.

After I hand the Christmas star to my 17-year-old granddaughter, she climbs the stepladder and places it on top of the Christmas tree. I can't help but smile. Despite the sadness of my lost childhood and my difficult teen years, I praise God for the better future I prayed for and He provided.

And I thank Him that not only have my children and grandchildren had a far better life than I did at their ages, but that I can trust Him to care for them as He cared for me.

A Christmas Prayer

Maureen E. Kowal

In the dark of night,
With a cold snap in the air,
The church's open door beckons him.
Inside, the choir sings softly
In the glow of candlelight.
Glancing at the holly berries and poinsettias,
He eases his old body down on a pew
And bows his weary head in prayer.
A small hand clasps his—
Warm hand against cold one.
"Grandpa," says a young voice,
"Don't sleep through Christmas."
Lifting her onto his knees, he whispers softly,
"Not sleeping. Talking to Jesus."
She touches his face with her hand,
And asks, "Grandpa, can I pray with you?"
"Yes, sweetheart," he whispers softly,
"Together we'll pray a Christmas prayer."

My Forever Home, 1948

Nonfiction

Carol Ford

I wiggle down under my bed covers, where I feel warm and safe. The room is dark, and the sweet smell of cookies is still in the air. My new mommy and I baked all day yesterday and filled four big cookie tins. She let me lick the bowls and the spoons. The batter tasted yummy, even before the cookies went into the oven. Shortbread cookies are my favourite.

I think about the kids at the orphanage. I wish they could have tasted the cookies, too.

It doesn't seem very long ago that I left there. It was a long drive in the car to my new house.

The matron at the orphanage was kind to me. I remember standing behind her and watching her brush her long grey hair in front of a mirror. She counted to 100. "You need to do 100 brush strokes to make your hair shiny," she said.

The morning I left, she looked very sad and I asked if I could come back to see her. She said, "I don't think so, Carol, because you will live too far away in your new home."

I was afraid to leave. I'd had other mommies and daddies and they all sent me away after a while. I'm still a little scared this might happen again.

Last week, the lady from the children's place came to visit us and asked me, "How do you like it here, Carol?"

I told her, "I like it a lot."

She said she would be back again to check on me.

My new mommy and daddy are really nice. They've never had children; I'm their only one.

Their names are Anna and Raymond, but they asked me to call them Mommy and Daddy.

I started kindergarten right after I came here, and I go to Sunday school too. At this school, we sing,

Jesus loves me! This I know,
For the Bible tells me so;
Little ones to Him belong;
They are weak, but He is strong.

Yes, Jesus loves me!
Yes, Jesus loves me!
Yes, Jesus loves me!
The Bible tells me so.[1]

I know Jesus will love me forever. I hope my new Mommy and Daddy will too.

When my teachers at school and people at the church find out that my birthday is on Christmas Day, they always say, "You must feel very special to have a birthday on that day."

I tell them, "Yes, I do, because it's Jesus' birthday too." I love Jesus.

I hear a noise outside my door and poke my head out of the blankets. There's a light under my door, and I can hear Mommy and Daddy whispering in the hallway.

Daddy says, "I wonder if she's awake yet?"

I giggle a little. I swing my feet over the side of the bed, tip-toe to the door, and slowly open it. Mommy and Daddy are both standing there with great big grins on their faces. They start to sing.

Happy birthday to you,
Happy birthday to you,
Happy birthday, dear Carol,
Happy birthday to you.

After they finish singing, Mommy squats down and gives me a hug.

I'm so excited this morning. It's finally Christmas Day. It's my birthday, too! Now I can say, "I'm five!"

Our small brown dog, Chum, runs down the stairs. Chum runs in circles every day when I arrive home from school because he's so glad to see me. I like having a dog again. There was a large black dog at one of my other homes. Dogs love you all the time.

  Christmas with Hot Apple Cider

"Do you want to see if Santa came last night?" Daddy asks.

I nod my head.

Daddy takes my hand and we slowly go down the stairs to the living room. Mommy follows behind us. It feels magical and exciting.

As we enter the room, I can smell the branches of the Christmas tree Daddy and I picked out a few days ago. We bought the tree just down the street from our house, and Daddy and I decorated it together.

I had to be very careful with the pretty Christmas balls, because they're made of glass. I handed them to Daddy, and he put them on the tree. We did it that way because the branches were prickly and hurt my hands when I touched them.

This morning, the living room is dark and only the tree lights show. They're shaped like candles with bubbles moving up and down inside the tubes. Daddy says this happens when they get hot enough.

We move closer, and in the tree lights I can see silver icicles glittering and swaying gently on the branches. I can also see presents piled under the tree and spilling into the middle of the floor. The presents weren't there last night when I went to bed.

I look over at the table where we'd left a snack for Santa. Daddy helped me make the snack just before I went to bed. We filled a bowl with chunks of white bread, poured warm milk over the top, and sprinkled everything with sugar. Daddy called our snack "pap." The bowl is empty.

The kids at school told me they were going to put out cookies. I bet Santa liked ours better because it was different.

"He ate it," I say. "You were right, Daddy, he must have liked it."

I turn my head and spot a small table with two little chairs. A large red bow is hanging over one chair. I run over and sit down.

Daddy says, "What do you think?"

I smile. "It's just the right size for me."

Daddy puts a large box with a green ribbon on the table. The wrapping has pictures of Santa Claus all over it. Daddy reads the note on the tag to me. "To Carol, with love from Santa."

I pull off the paper and open the box. Inside is a beautiful doll.

The doll has blonde hair and blue eyes like me, and she's wearing a blue dress with frilly white lace at the neck. Her eyes open and shut when I tip her up and down. I hold her close to me. I love her so much.

Then I shut my eyes and remember last Christmas.

My other mommy held her new baby like I'm holding my doll. After the baby came to our home, she seemed to be mad at me all the time. She took me to the orphanage and told the matron that I didn't like her new baby and I couldn't live with them anymore. I cried and said I *did* like the new baby, but it didn't help.

I try to stop thinking about that and look up.

Mommy comes over beside me and kneels down by my chair. She hands me another present and gives me a hug and a kiss.

"This one is for your birthday, Carol," she whispers.

It has a large blue bow on top. I open the box, and see white paper wrapped around something. I tear off the paper and find a small teapot with matching cups and saucers. I run my hand over each piece. The tea set is white with tiny pink and blue flowers around the edge.

I look at all my new toys. They're so special and just for me. "I've never had so many things!" I say. "I can have a tea party with my new doll."

Now Daddy gives Mommy a present; it's in a very small box. I kneel close beside her as she opens it. "Oh, it's so beautiful!" I say.

It's a large pin with matching earrings made out of glass; they twinkle with lots of colours.

"Thank you, Raymond. It's lovely," Mommy says.

Then Mommy reaches behind the tree and brings out a present for Daddy. This present is bigger, and as she hands it to him, she says, "I hope you like it. The lady in the store said it was the most popular one there."

I move over beside Daddy while he carefully takes off the wrapping and lifts the lid. It's a new black Bible.

"What does that say, Daddy?" I ask, pointing to the gold printing at the bottom of the cover.

"It's my name, Raymond A. Jamieson," he says, running his finger over each word.

He looks up at Mommy and smiles. "Thank you. This is the one I was looking at the other day. It's perfect."

Light is now coming through the front window, and I can see big soft snowflakes falling from the sky—gently floating to the ground. Last time it snowed, I went outside and let the snowflakes land on my cheeks and eyelashes. I stuck out my tongue to catch them, too, but I could hardly taste anything.

I feel excited again. If I go outside today, I can wear my new matching hat and coat! They're a pretty, dark red colour, and Mommy told me to save them until Christmas. She also bought me a green velvet dress to wear later, when I get dressed.

Daddy makes us a nice breakfast of eggs and toast. Then we get dressed and I play with my new doll and tea set at the small table until after lunch, when Auntie Nita, Uncle Fred, and their son Ronald will arrive. Auntie Nita is Mommy's sister, and one of my favourite people. She likes to play with me. Mommy told me that she'll be coming to our house with Uncle Fred and Ronald in the afternoon.

Ronald is a big boy and won't be interested in playing with toys; he likes to bounce a basketball or play hockey. I'm glad when they come to visit, or when we go to their little house. At their place, Uncle Fred always asks if I would like a chocolate, and then pulls out a box from under his favourite chair. I look for the biggest one.

As they come in the door and stamp the snow off their boots, they hand Mommy and Daddy more presents to put under the tree.

While we wait to open these presents, I show Auntie Nita my tea set and we both sit at my new table and sip pretend tea. It's so much fun, and I feel like I must be the luckiest girl in the world.

After a while, Daddy calls everyone around the tree and says, "It's time to open more presents."

Uncle Fred hands one to Daddy, and inside the box is a nice blue-and-white tie. Auntie Nita gives Mommy an apron she has made. I can't wait to give Auntie Nita the present that Mommy and I bought for her. It's a special pin to wear on her coat, and it has large glittering pink stones in it. We bought Ronald a new sweater with stripes, but he's more interested in playing with Chum.

When Mommy calls us to dinner, we go to the table. Once we all squeeze into our spots, we bow our heads while Daddy thanks Jesus for our gifts and our family. Then we take turns pulling the ends of our Christmas crackers and laughing as we put on the coloured hats. Inside each cracker is a small prize and a piece of paper with a joke. My prize is a little red top that spins if you know how to do it.

I hand my joke to Daddy to read.

"Why was the turkey in the band?" he says. He looks around the table and everyone just shakes their head like they don't know. "Because he was the only one with drumsticks!" Daddy says.

Everyone says, "Aww."

Ronald says, "That's so corny."

They all laugh, so I laugh, too.

Mommy puts the big turkey in front of Daddy's plate. Daddy is sitting at one end of the table with a large fork and knife held high in the air, waiting to cut the first piece. It's all brown and looks really good. Daddy asks me, "What part of the turkey do you want, Carol?"

Uncle Fred says, "She'd probably like the leg."

I nod.

Daddy goes around the table and asks everyone what part of the turkey they want, and then he cuts that piece for them.

When we finish the turkey part of our dinner, the Christmas pudding arrives, and it's sooo good—it has a special sauce on top that's very sweet.

After dinner, the adults go to the kitchen and talk and wash dishes. I like being close to them and listening. Ronald is in the other room playing with a small puzzle that he brought in his pocket. I'm still holding my doll. I've given her a name. I'm going to call her Betsy because she reminds me of a baby at the orphanage.

Later, when everyone has gone home and I'm feeling tired, Mommy and I climb up the steps to my room. Mommy is letting me take Betsy to bed with me.

When I'm ready for bed, Mommy kneels down beside me and we say my prayers. Then I climb under the covers and she kisses me goodnight.

  Christmas with Hot Apple Cider

I tell her, "This was the best birthday and Christmas I have ever had."

"I'm so glad, Carol," Mommy says. "Daddy and I love you very much and we want you to stay with us forever. Last week when the Children's Aid worker came to visit, we signed all the papers to make this happen. You're our little girl now. Forever."

I hug her tightly. "Living here with you and Daddy is the best Christmas present of all."

1. Song "Jesus Loves Me," Verse 1 by Anna B. Warner, 1860, Refrain by William B. Bradbury, 1862 (Public Domain)

Author's Note:
I found my birth family at age 50. I also learned that prior to settling into this permanent home in 1948, I had lived in my birth home as well as two other homes. The couples in both of these homes changed their mind about adopting me. I was then placed in an orphanage for a few months.

A Blessed Christmas

Fiction

Sally Meadows

Jasmine clicked the button to log out of her account and sat back in her chair, worry furrowing her brow. Their credit cards were officially maxed out.

With the downturn in the oil industry and Fort McMurray still reeling after the wildfires, money was scarce for many families, and theirs was no exception. Jasmine had lost her job months ago when the employment agency she worked for had closed its doors. When Tanner received his layoff notice two weeks before, he had immediately left for Calgary, hoping to find a contract job in the technology sector. With barely enough money left in their bank account to cover the bills and Christmas less than a week away, there simply wasn't going to be any gift giving this year.

Jasmine's four-year-old son, Charlie, shuffled into the room. Jasmine couldn't help smiling at his crinkly, fresh-out-of-bed hair. He climbed onto his mother's lap, one chubby arm curling around her neck, the other reaching down to touch the floppy ear on his bunny slippers, an endearing habit that seemed to bring him comfort.

Jasmine pressed her lips to Charlie's forehead, lingering there for a moment. Then she sighed. "Time to get the girls up," she said as she eased Charlie down and headed up the stairs, her son trailing behind.

Later, as she spooned yogurt into three small bowls, Jasmine couldn't stop thinking about her family's troubled finances. She barely listened as Ava and Scarlett chattered away; that is, until the conversation turned to Christmas.

"I want a rocket kit," said Ava, the eight-year-old, bespectacled blonde who was a budding engineer. Lining up her astronaut figures on the table, she said, "I'm going to put them in it when Dad and I launch it."

Six-year-old Scarlett nodded with excitement. "I wanna get that tree house for Elizabeth; the one I saw on TV!" She hugged Elizabeth, her soft-bodied baby doll with red hair and freckles, just like her own.

Not to be left out, dark-eyed Charlie piped up in excitement, "I want—I want—a play car I can drive around in!"

Jasmine felt sick to her stomach.

That evening, during her much-needed one-on-one Skype chat with Tanner after she had put the kids to bed, Jasmine could feel tears pricking at her eyes as she bemoaned, "I never dreamed we'd ever be in this situation."

Tanner nodded. "I'm so sorry, Jas. But, hey, I've got good news! I landed a short-term contract with an IT consulting firm." He paused. "The bad news is that they need me to be here over Christmas. But I'll be able to Skype you guys Christmas Eve, and I'll pick up some things for the kids before I leave the city. We'll have a nice little celebration when I get home in January, okay?"

Jasmine willed her tears not to spill over. The last thing Tanner needed was to see her falling apart. Murmuring assurances that she and the kids would be fine, she said good-bye.

After the call ended, she buried her face in her hands and let the tears flow freely. But a few moments later, Jasmine jumped and whirled around when she felt a light touch on her shoulder.

She took a deep breath and hugged her older daughter. "What are you doing up?"

"Is it true, Mom? Daddy's not going to be here for Christmas? And there won't be any presents?" Ava's sorrowful face tugged at Jasmine's heart.

"I'm so sorry you heard that, Ava," she said, rubbing her daughter's arm. "It'll still be a great Christmas. We don't have to spend money to have a special time together, right? It'll be fine and…" Her words trailed off as Ava turned around and quietly went upstairs and back to bed.

Jasmine sighed and pushed herself away from the computer, then sat for a long time looking at the Christmas tree lights. Through the branches, her eyes rested on the nativity scene on the window ledge behind the tree.

She walked over, picked up baby Jesus, and rubbed her thumb over the cool ceramic. *Remember,* she told herself, *there's so much more to Christmas than gifts under the tree. But I'm still going to pray for a miracle!*

The next day was the start of Christmas break for the kids. After breakfast, Jasmine tried her best to be upbeat as she explained the situation to her two younger children. "We're still going to have a great Christmas, guys. I've got hot chocolate with marshmallows in the cupboard, DVDs from the library, and we can go tobogganing and make snow angels. Dad will bring presents when he gets home. Okay?"

Scarlett and Charlie pouted at first, but by the afternoon their disappointment seemed to have faded.

Over the next few days, to Jasmine's surprise, the children's usual enthusiasm for the holidays didn't seem to be diminished. She was also thankful that Ava seemed to have taken it upon herself to help out by playing with her younger siblings in their rooms while Jasmine was making meals and cleaning up.

On Christmas morning, Jasmine woke to find three cherubic faces beaming down at her.

"Mommy! Mommy!" Charlie said with a big smile. "Come see all the presents!"

"What? But I said we won't—"

"Come on, Mom," Ava said. "There are presents. Really."

"But—how?" Jasmine sputtered, pulling on her robe as she stumbled down the stairs. Sure enough, under the tree, wrapped in coloured pages and newspaper, sat a small pile of presents.

The children excitedly pulled Jasmine down to her knees.

Ava reached into the pile. "Here's one for you, Mom!"

Inside was a beautiful marbled ornament. "I made it at school. Isn't it pretty?"

Jasmine cupped her daughter's face and kissed her nose. "It's beautiful, Ava. Thank you."

"Me next!" Charlie said as he handed a package to his mother.

Jasmine unwrapped the gift. It was a picture of Charlie framed by coloured craft sticks. "Ava helped me make it," he explained.

A smile crept across Jasmine's face as she pictured the now-blank spot in the photo album. "It's wonderful, Charlie. Thank you." Jasmine pulled him close and wrapped her arms around him.

"My turn," said Scarlett. She dug into the pile and pulled out a small package. Inside was a barrette adorned with paper flowers.

"It was my idea," said Scarlett proudly, "but Ava helped with the gluing."

"It's so pretty," Jasmine said as she clipped the barrette to her hair, noting that the flowers were from her craft box. "Thank you! But my loves, I don't have anything for you!"

"Don't worry," Ava said, "those last three presents—well, they're for us! Charlie, you go first!"

Excitement shining in his eyes, Charlie picked up his present. As he peeled back the paper, Jasmine caught a glimpse of a floppy bunny ear. "Look, Mom!" he said as he put his slippers on, tapping his feet together.

Scarlett was next. Her face lit up as she opened her present to reveal her beloved Elizabeth. Her joy was as palpable as the first time she'd unwrapped the doll on her birthday, months earlier.

"My turn," said Ava. She opened her package to reveal a rocket made out of recycled materials. "Look, Mom," she said, holding it up. "My lady astronauts fit inside!" Then she whispered solemnly, "It's only a pretend rocket. Until I get my real one."

Jasmine drew her precious children close, her tears flowing freely. As she stroked their hair, she was filled with joy at being on the receiving end of a love so tender and unselfish it was almost too much to bear. It was a love that came into this world with the birth of a special child over two thousand years ago, and flowed to her through her own children on this very special Christmas Day.

"Their children will be a blessing" (Psalm 37:26).

That Time When Arnold Palmer Lost His Foot

Nonfiction

Martin Smith

When I was growing up, my family had its own set of Christmas traditions. These were tried-and-true customs that we held dear over the years.

Christmas stockings always contained a mandarin orange, a tooth brush, and either socks or underwear.

Under the tree, we were likely to find a new set of pyjamas and a magazine from a relative from Scotland we had never met.

Christmas music was Bing Crosby, Nat King Cole, or Perry Como. There was no room on the turntable for the "rockin'" sounds of The Carpenters.

We opened gifts one at a time and only on Christmas morning. The wrapping paper was saved to be used again the next year.

Candy canes were hung on the Christmas tree, but we were not allowed to eat them. They were decorations. Amazingly, they'd been purchased when Louis St. Laurent was Prime Minister (1948–1957) and remained intact well into Pierre Elliott Trudeau's reign in the 1980s.

The tree was real and decorated with a loving mishmash of lights, balls, tinsel, and an angel that looked as if she'd survived a back-alley rumble. Bits of wood or paper were carefully positioned under the legs of the rusted tree stand so that the tree wouldn't resemble the leaning tower of Pisa.

Turkey dinner was placed into the oven sometime during the middle of the night by my mother. The bird was usually the size of an ostrich. The turkey was accompanied by gravy, carrots, Brussels sprouts, cranberries, stuffing, and turnips. The economy of Prince Edward Island was kept buoyant by the mountain of mashed potatoes we consumed.

There was always a box of Black Magic chocolates, complete with a map of all the flavours. I did everything I could to avoid strawberry creams.

On Christmas Eve, we went to church for the midnight service. I believe part of the reason for this was to keep us up late in hopes that we would sleep in. With four boys in the family, this never worked. One of us would wake up at five a.m. and begin to poke and prod his still-slumbering siblings. Within an hour, the four of us would sound like a deranged marching band riding an out-of-control locomotive.

My parents would bark down the hall, "Go back to sleep!" This would sustain us for two or three minutes, but inevitably our volume would build and build until it registered on the Richter scale.

Once my parents had conceded defeat, they'd drag themselves to our bedrooms and wish each of us a Merry Christmas. We would then form a line, with each brother covering the eyes of the brother ahead of him, and move slowly toward the Christmas tree. It was like a giddy, clumsy Conga line. My father would dash ahead of us to turn on the sparkling lights.

As we entered the room, we knew that all the glorious splendour that was Christmas would soon be revealed. The stockings. The pyjamas. The magazine from Aunt Haggis. And the other tradition—the one that we were truly salivating for—the BIG gift!

Each year, over and above the mandarin oranges, tooth brushes, and Stanfield's underwear, we would each receive one big gift. This was the gift we whispered into the ear of Santa Claus at the Eaton's store. This was the gift that consumed our dreams, pushing aside any thoughts of dancing sugar plums. This was the gift we would tell every kid in the neighbourhood about. This was the gift we'd cherish for the rest of our lives.

The year I turned 13, I received what I still consider the ultimate big gift: the Arnold Palmer Indoor Golf game. I had yearned for it since playing the game one Christmas at the Browns, family friends of my parents.

The most important part of the game was a metal stick with a plastic handle. On the end of the stick was a figurine of Arnold Palmer. The figurine held tiny golf clubs, including a driver, a putter, a five-iron, a three-wood, and a wedge. On the upper part of the stick was a ring that slid up and down and caused the figurine to swing like a golfer. The figurine genuinely looked like Arnold Palmer (circa the late 1960s).

The game came with a large piece of foam that acted as the golf green, two plastic sand traps, out-of-bounds markers, and two sets of tiny golf balls. The foam golf balls were for driving and chip shots. Once a player landed on the green, the foam ball was switched for a little white marble.

What made this so remarkable was that you could set up your own golf course. You could put the green in the living room and the tee box could be in another room, up the stairs, down the hall, on top of a pile of dirty laundry…. The possibilities were endless.

My brothers and I played the game for hours, moving the green into every nook and cranny we could find and shooting the foam golf balls—which came in white, soft blue, dusty pink, and yellow—wildly about the house.

I say "wildly" because, unlike real golf balls, tiny foam golf balls are impossible to control. Actually, now that I think about it, so are real golf balls.

The Arnold Palmer foam golf balls tended to spray willy-nilly. If the furnace kicked in, the sudden burst of hot air coming out of the floor vent might push your perfect approach shot clear out of the room and into the chip dip in the kitchen. If you hit the ball with a twitching motion, it was just as likely to land on top of Dad snoring on the couch as on the green. That always made for a difficult "play it where it lies" shot.

The marble was equally challenging. First off, the putting green rarely lay flat. Ridges would form in it that in my mind resembled the ground after the San Francisco earthquake of 1906. Not only that, but the motion of the Arnold Palmer mechanism wasn't always smooth. Sometimes the slightest touch would cause your two-inch putt to jettison across the room. If you weren't careful, the ball might end up under a bed or in another time zone. And that's how Arnold Palmer lost his foot.

The competition between me and my younger brother, Lawrence, had been fierce and neck-and-neck for the better part of two hours. On the sixth hole he had pulled ahead of me by two strokes when my golf ball ricocheted off a lamp and ended up behind the chesterfield. Three holes later, Lawrence met disaster when his high-arching wedge shot boomeranged on an invisible gust of wind, struck the hassock, and careened behind our octagon-shaped side table.

The score went back and forth during the back nine, with catastrophe striking each of us in equal measures. Golf balls defied physics and landed on nearly every piece of furniture in the house. At one point, I recall standing on top of the coffee table hitting a five-iron off an old copy of *The Hamilton Spectator*.

In the end, it all came down to the hole and my final putt.

It was a two-inch putt that would secure my bragging rights. Even if I missed it and ended up with a par for the hole, I'd still win. It was simply a matter of gently swinging the Arnold Palmer putter and guiding a little white marble into a hole that was only two inches away.

I took 10 to 20 practice swings. I made sure Arnie was feeling loose and moving freely. I gently placed him on the foam green. I lined up the putter behind the ball. I eyed the hole. It looked like the Grand Canyon—gaping and inviting. All I had to do was pull back the club slowly, tap the marble, and begin my victory dance.

I slid the mechanism slowly. The putter moved backward with ease. My confidence was high. But then, during the forward motion, it happened. It was as if I'd been struck by lightning. My finger jerked in an uncontrolled spasm. The putter released like a jack-in-the-box spring and hit the marble violently.

The marble shot like a bullet off the green and across the room, striking the leg of a planter, hitting a vase, and coming to rest underneath a pair of fuzzy slippers. It made pinging noises the whole time as it shot right, then left, then right again.

I gasped in terror. A two-inch putt had turned into a thirty-foot journey across the terrain of our living room. It was like watching a wild beast that had escaped from a cage.

Filled with horror, I bellowed and howled, sustaining a long moaning "Noooo!" similar to the death scene from Don Giovanni. In anger, I slammed Arnold Palmer down on the floor. One of

Arnie's white plastic golf shoes snapped off, popped into the air, and landed next to a sand trap.

My anger immediately turned to shock. It was Boxing Day and I had just snapped off the foot of the best Christmas gift I'd ever received.

My brother's mouth opened in an unflattering manner. Normally, he'd have been rejoicing that he'd just won the game, but he understood the ramifications of what I'd just done. "Why did you do that?" he asked. "Are you crazy?"

I looked at the figurine, not quite believing what I'd just done, myself. Although Arnold had the same pleasant smile on his face, he was missing a foot.

I began to utter words that contained no consonants. Odd, gurgling noises. And then I lied. "It was an accident! It was an accident!"

It was no accident, of course. Anger had gotten the best of me. I hadn't dropped Arnold. Arnold hadn't slipped from my fingers. No, when my marble disappeared under the slippers, I'd slammed him down on the ground.

Panic set in. I begged my brother to take an oath of silence. "Where's the glue? Find a staple gun! Do you know a good podiatrist?" Although I was close to crying, dread kept the tears at bay. I had to do whatever I could to mask the incident and prevent my parents from discovering the truth.

Beads of sweat rolled down my forehead, and I moved back and forth like Buster Keaton being chased by a runaway train. I picked up the plastic shoe. Maybe it would just snap back onto the end of the leg. I fussed and twisted the shoe. I pushed and tapped it with the palm of my hand. I licked the stub of it, as if saliva would be an adhesive. It was clearly broken, but beyond all hope I wanted it to magically reattach itself. I asked Arnold for forgiveness.

I looked at my brother in desperation. No words could express the frenzied alarm that washed across his face.

And then, from behind me, hovering just on the edge of the room, I heard my mother's voice. "What's going on, boys? It got awfully quiet." I'd forgotten that parents recognize unnatural silence—the silence that is birthed during calamity.

  Christmas with Hot Apple Cider

Lawrence and I looked at her with big eyes that would put an owl to shame. "Nothing," I muttered.

"Nothing" is always the wrong answer. She could tell it was laced with guilt. She started to walk toward me. "I heard someone yell."

I immediately slid Arnold's foot into my back pocket.

"How is the new game?" she asked.

"Great," I said. "We're really having a lot of fun." My voice changed octaves three times in one sentence.

She reached out her hand. "May I try it?"

I didn't know what to do. Slowly, I handed her the Arnold Palmer golf stick.

She looked at it for a moment, then at me. "I believe Arnold Palmer has two feet, does he not?"

I shrugged as if I didn't know what she was referring to.

"What happened, Martin?"

My heart was pounding in my throat. I thought briefly of blaming my brother. He would, of course, deny it, but perhaps it would buy me time. I thought of lying and saying the foot just fell off like a tree dropping a leaf in the autumn. I thought of playing dumb and saying, "I have no idea."

Instead, I began to weep. Loud, remorseful sobs. The kind of crying that sounds like a person is having an asthmatic reaction to disgrace. During the wailing and gasps for air I kept mumbling, "I'm sorry. I'm sorry!"

Somehow, in the moments that followed, my brother vanished into the shadows and I found myself sitting on the couch, my mother's arm gently holding me around the shoulders.

She gave a speech about controlling my anger. She reminded me that it was just a game. She reprimanded me for breaking Arnold's foot. But she also fetched some glue and tape. She helped me attach the foot to Arnold Palmer's left leg. She put tape over it to keep the foot tight while the glue dried. And then she put the toy away for 24 hours—partly so the glue would dry and partly as punishment. No mention was ever made of the incident after that.

The Arnold Palmer Indoor Golf game is the only toy from my childhood that I still own. It remains in its original box underneath my bed. I've played it with my children and now with their children.

The foam green still refuses to lie flat; the foam golf balls are not really round anymore; and all but one of the marbles have disappeared.

When I pull out the game, I still have incredible memories of the endless hours I played with my brothers and my now-departed parents. How the golf balls would take on a mind of their own. How we would laugh at the wonderfully ridiculous nature of the game.

But I'm also reminded, every time Arnold is pulled out from the box, that I learned a difficult but important lesson that Christmas long ago. There's still a yellowed piece of tape on the bottom of his foot more than 40 years later.

  Christmas with Hot Apple Cider

The First Gift of Christmas

Fiction

Judi Peers

When the Turner family returned home from the Christmas Eve service at church, they all gathered around the fireplace in the living room, eager to open the first gifts of Christmas.

That's what Sarah's dad called it. His family had done the same thing when he was a boy. His father's family before. It was a Turner family tradition—everyone was allowed to open one present on Christmas Eve.

Grandma was there, and Mom and Dad, ten-year-old Sarah, her little brother Josh, and even Maggie, Sarah's dog, who lazily stretched out on the carpet.

Sarah's attention had been captured by the gift from her grandmother ever since it had been set under the tree. Amidst the colourful ribbons and wrappings, the tinsel and trim, that one parcel called softly to her. It was bulky, yet squishy. What could it be?

Finally, it was her turn to select a gift. She carefully undid the wrapping, and there lay a beautiful patchwork quilt. Each large square block in the quilt had a little red square in the centre, flanked by thin, dark rectangular pieces of fabric on one side and light-coloured pieces on the other side.

Sarah gently fingered the narrow strips of fabric. One felt rough and stiff. Another was soft, smooth—almost silky. When she ran the palm of her hand over the entire surface, each piece rippled into the next, like the waves of the ocean.

"It's a log cabin quilt," Grandma said. "It was made by my grandmother and her friends at a quilting bee." She carefully laid the quilt out to show them how the light and dark sections created different-sized diamond shapes. "There are many kinds of log cabin quilts," she added. "This design is called Barn Raising. It was popular in the 1800s. Think of it, child—this quilt once belonged to your great-great-grandmother."

Sarah smiled with satisfaction. She loved to learn more about her family and was thrilled that her grandmother had entrusted her with this treasure.

Grandma pointed to a tattered piece of creamy silk. "This was my grandmother's wedding dress. You can tell from old family photos." She glanced up at her granddaughter, and her eyes brightened. "You look a lot like her, Sarah, what with your long, dark hair, and that same lovely smile."

Sarah's smile broadened. She could hardly wait to look at the old photos and see if it was true.

Grandma's silver head bent over the quilt. Her fingertips traced a small dark patch of material, and her gaze grew distant. "This is from the blanket your great-great-grandfather always kept in the cutter." Suddenly, she laughed. "Did you know he dumped his bride in the ditch on their wedding day? The horse bolted and his bride flew into the ditch! But Grandpa stayed with the horse. Eventually, he came back, but Grandma always said that at least she knew where she stood with Grandpa right from the start—he valued his horse more than he did his wife! She was only joking, but she teased him about it for years."

Sarah's mom and dad, and Josh, too, had gathered around the quilt and were listening closely to Grandma's stories.

"This piece looks like it's from a shirt," Grandma said as she touched a smooth white strip. "Did you know that the women would buy shirting material from the general store, then make their own?"

"Sounds like a lot of work," Mom said. "It's hard enough just ironing a shirt!"

"What's this?" Sarah asked, pointing to an unusual bit of fabric.

"An old sugar or flour bag," Grandma said. "You can still see the faded lettering." Grandma laughed again as she gently touched another swatch of material. "This thick coarse cloth might have come from my Uncle John's trousers. Mother told me that whenever he was planning to get into mischief, he made sure he was wearing his thickest pants, or maybe even an extra pair. That way, if Grandpa caught him and took a switch to his backside, he wouldn't feel it quite so much."

  Christmas with Hot Apple Cider

"What's a switch?" Josh asked.

"Back in those days, a parent might use a thin branch from a bush to spank a naughty child," Grandma said. "I'm glad no one uses switches these days."

"Me, too." Josh grinned.

"Speaking of those days, did you know that they never threw material away? Anything that couldn't be worn or used would be thrown into the scrap bag to be made into a patchwork quilt. Old clothes, ties, curtains, suits, Sunday dresses…they're all here, worked into the quilt—made into memories."

Grandma stopped speaking and frowned. Then she stroked a triangular patch of black material. "I'd almost forgotten," she began.

"What is it?" Sarah asked.

"It's about the black." Grandma took a slow breath and sighed. "We always wore black when someone died. And my grandma used to make black arm bands for the men to wear."

Sarah noticed one small tear slowly make its way down the wrinkled, weathered cheek.

Grandma's voice trembled. "I…I was thinking this piece—this might have been worn when Grandpa died. But no. This quilt was made years before. But, you know…Grandma never seemed quite the same after Grandpa's death."

Sarah's grandma quickly brushed aside the tear and took a deep breath.

Her blue eyes twinkled and a wide smile returned to her face and burst into her voice. "Ahh…but I haven't told you about the green percale. My grandma told me all about it the year before she died. It's from the dress she wore when she was kissed by the good-looking scamp who worked on the next farm. Nothing ever came of it, but it was her first kiss. So she stitched pieces of that dress into the quilt—her own little secret—a reminder of the summer she was sixteen and young and pretty."

"Kissing is ooey, gooey, yuck!" Josh interjected. "What are all those little red squares?" he asked.

"Trying to change the subject, eh Josh?" asked his dad.

Grandma laughed, then settled back in her rocking chair. "At first, quilts were made to provide warmth. Then people started building stories with their quilts. The log cabin quilt tells the story of the pioneers."

She pointed to several of the small red squares. "See how they form the centre part of each square block?"

Josh nodded.

"They represent the fire in the log cabin. The pioneers not only needed fire for warmth, but a lot of their family activities centred around the hearth: cooking, mending, reading, studying, even visiting with friends and relatives."

"Sounds like our house tonight." Dad chuckled.

"The narrow strips of fabric are the logs of the cabin," Grandma continued. She carefully outlined a dark triangular half of a square with her bent index finger. "See how this section is dark?"

The others nodded.

"That's the part of the cabin where the family slept."

"And the light part?" Sarah asked.

"That's where all the windows were. That's where the family did all their daytime activities. Each morning, they would come out of the darkness of night into the light."

"Just like in Bethlehem," Sarah added. "Jesus' birth brought the world out of darkness into the light."

Grandma clapped her hands in delight. "You're right, child! I never thought of it before, but if you use your imagination, the whole story of Jesus is right here in the log cabin quilt. The red square in the centre of each block reminds us that the blood of Jesus brought our world out of darkness into the light."

Later that night, Sarah switched off her night light and snuggled under the covers. The heaviness of her new quilt made her feel safe and warm. So did the familiar smell of her grandmother, who had helped her spread out the quilt and then tucked her into bed. Sarah's hands moved slowly in the darkness to find a smooth red centre patch, and then moved forward to find another.

It's amazing, she thought, *how a quilt can tell a story. Not just one story, either, but many. Maybe hundreds! Each small piece of cloth has its own story to tell.*

  Christmas with Hot Apple Cider

Sarah lay back and pulled the quilt up around her chin. She loved the log cabin quilt. She loved Grandma, too.

And she would do what Grandma had suggested—use it tonight, on Christmas Eve, and then put it away for safekeeping. That way, she could give it to her own granddaughter someday. She'd tell her about the special dresses, the ride in the cutter, and the thick pants Grandma's uncle had worn.

And she would tell her, too, about how her first gift of Christmas this year had reminded her of that first gift on the first Christmas, so many years ago.

Oh, Christmas Tree!

Fiction

Marcia Lee Laycock

It was only the first week of December and already the cold drilled through Ben Ferrel's coat, all the way to his bones. *Looks like the Yukon is going to live up to its reputation for severe winters,* he thought, as he ushered his wife, Liz, and their ten-year-old daughter, Kylie, through the front doors of the Whitehorse General Hospital. They had tried to prepare Kylie for this visit. Ben knew it might be the last time they'd see his mother alive.

Kylie dashed into the hospital room, threw herself into her grandmother's arms, and began to cry.

"Shh, shh. Don't cry, little one." The old woman stroked Kylie's hair. "You don't want to be sad at Christmas."

The girl raised her head. "Will you be coming to our house for Christmas, Gran?"

Her grandmother let her head drop back onto the pillow as Kylie's parents approached the bed.

"I don't think so, Kylie," Ben's mother said. "I don't think so." The old woman roused herself and looked into her granddaughter's eyes. "But just remember, sweetie, I'll be so much better with Jesus. I'll be healthy and glowing, just like your lovely Christmas tree. So, when you look at your tree on Christmas morning, you remember that and don't be too sad, okay? Promise?"

Kylie was trying hard to keep from bursting into tears again, but she managed to nod and whisper, "I promise."

Her grandmother smiled. "I have something for you."

"What is it?"

The old lady waved Ben closer. "Help me sit up," she said.

When her son and daughter-in-law had made her comfortable against several pillows, she turned to Kylie.

"Now, there's a small box in the top drawer." She motioned toward the dresser in the corner.

  Christmas with Hot Apple Cider

Kylie retrieved the box and brought it to her grandmother, who took it in her thin, pale hands, removed the lid, and peeled back the bright red tissue. "I made this when I was about your age, Kylie," she said. "I thought you might like to have it to put on your tree this year." She lifted out a delicate white crocheted star with silver threads wound through it and held it out to her granddaughter.

Kylie took it and held it up by the string attached to one spike. "It's beautiful, Gran."

Ben's mother smiled again, leaned back, and closed her eyes.

Ben let Kylie stay by her side for a while, then gently took her hand and led her away.

"When are we going to get the tree, Dad?"

Ben couldn't help but sigh. Kylie had asked the same question every day since they'd returned home from Whitehorse after his mother's funeral.

Yesterday, he'd cut down a nice tree up on the hill in back of their house, but, as he'd known would happen, by the time he got it to the house there wasn't a needle left on it. It was just too cold to move a tree.

He said, "We still have two weeks. We have to wait for it to warm up a bit."

"But what if it doesn't?"

Ben saw the desperation in his daughter's eyes. "We'll see what it's like tomorrow, okay?"

Kylie dropped her head, but nodded.

A couple of days later, after dinner was over, Ben announced, "I got the job."

Liz looked relieved, and smiled, but Kylie just stared at him.

"Murray wants me to start the renovations on the kitchen in his restaurant right away. So we'll move to Dawson tomorrow." Ben glanced sideways at Kylie.

She groaned and jumped up. "No! We can't move, not now!"

"I'm sorry, sweetheart, but we have to. We need the money and it's just too cold to drive back and forth."

Kylie looked at her mother. "But it's all wrong! Everything is all wrong!" She burst into tears and ran to her room.

Ben gave his wife a pleading look, but she just shook her head. "We just have to give her time, Ben," she said.

If it would just warm up for a while, he thought.

It had been hovering around –50°C (–58°F) for more than two weeks. He didn't want to move into town any more than Kylie did, but he saw no way around it. His new boss would expect him to be on the job early in the morning, –50 or not. Last time he'd tried to get into Dawson, it was so cold it had taken him two hours just to get his old truck going.

Ben frowned. *What am I going to do about a Christmas tree?*

Later that night, he tried to console his daughter. "We'll still have Christmas."

Kylie rolled over and looked up at him with red-rimmed eyes. "With a tree?"

Ben sighed. "The forecast isn't good, sweetheart."

"But God can make it warm up, can't He?"

Ben tucked a strand of dark hair behind her ear. "Yes, He can, Kylie. But He doesn't always answer our prayers just the way we want Him to."

"But we have to have a tree, Daddy. We just *have* to!"

As Ben closed the door on his daughter's room, he heard her muffled sobs.

The weather cooperated the next day by warming up to –35, so the move to a couple of rooms above the restaurant was accomplished without too much stress, if little joy.

"Tomorrow, you and Mom can spend the day putting decorations up," Ben said to his daughter in an attempt to brighten the mood.

"But what about a tree?"

  Christmas with Hot Apple Cider

"Well, if the weather keeps warming up, we'll tramp up the hill behind town tomorrow and find us a good one."

Kylie's eyes lit up. "Really, Daddy? Tomorrow?"

Ben nodded. "Right after work. If you get to bed right now!"

Kylie scurried to her room.

When he woke up the next morning, the temperature was the first thing on Ben's mind. He pushed the curtains aside and peered out. Ice fog hung thick and heavy, blotting out the street. He groaned.

Liz rolled over. "What's wrong?"

"Looks like the temperature's dropping. Again."

By noon it was –40. And by the time Ben finished work, it was –51. Christmas was only two days away.

That night, Ben tried to cheer Kylie up by coaxing her to guess what might be in the brightly wrapped gifts piled in a corner. She played the game half-heartedly.

The morning of Christmas Eve, Ben went to work early because he didn't want to see Kylie's face.

Murray, the owner of the restaurant Ben was renovating, noticed. "Hey, you didn't need to come in today. Where's your Christmas spirit?" he asked.

"Gone the way of all miracles, I guess."

"Oh? Why don't we have a coffee while you tell me about it?"

They moved to the front of the restaurant, and Ben told him about his mother's last gift to Kylie of a star to hang on the tree.

Murray frowned. "You've got a problem all right. Just moving a tree in this weather will strip the needles."

"Believe me, I've tried."

Murray clapped him on the back. "But Christmas is the season of miracles. You never know."

Neither of the men noticed the smile on the face of a third man who was standing near them waiting to pay his bill. But they did hear him whistling softly, and as Ben went back to work, he found himself singing the same tune. "O Christmas tree, O Christmas tree, how lovely are thy branches..."[1]

After Ben returned to the kitchen, the man approached Murray. "You believe in miracles?" he asked.

Murray's eyebrows sprang up. "Well, yeah, as a matter of fact I do."

The man's smile broadened. "How would you like to participate in one?"

That evening, it warmed up to a balmy –48. There was no way they could get a tree.

After supper, Liz coaxed Kylie into making shortbread cookies.

Ben was enjoying the smell coming from the kitchen when the doorbell rang. He was surprised to see Murray on the doorstep, and even more surprised when Murray introduced the man behind him.

"This is Jeff Forrester, Ben. He's a naturalist, working with the government here for the past while. He has something for you. Or rather, for Kylie. Where is she?"

Ben frowned, but answered the question. "In the kitchen, with Liz. What—?"

"Can you keep her there for a while?" Murray's blue eyes almost sparkled out of their sockets.

"Sure, but what—?"

Jeff held up his gloved hand. "You'll see."

The men disappeared back out the door and Ben poked his head into the kitchen to tell Liz and Kylie to stay put until he called them.

Murray and Jeff came back, hauling something tall that was wrapped in a horse blanket and swathed in plastic.

Ben frowned as they set the bundle down in a corner and began to unwrap it. Finally, the wrappings fell away to reveal a tall spindly tree.

Ben stared. "What's this, some kind of organic coat rack?"

Jeff chuckled. "You said you needed a tree."

"But it's not—"

"Not a Christmas tree," Jeff finished. "I know. It's a birch."

He pulled the last bit of the blanket free. "She seems to have weathered the drive over okay." He turned to Ben. "I never cut a tree down for Christmas," he explained. "I just don't like destroying a living thing for the sake of decoration. So I take a cutting and grow a new one each year. This one has just started to leaf out."

Ben was staring at the tree, mesmerized by the small, bright green leaves on every branch. It had been months since he'd seen that colour, and it was a feast for hungry northern eyes. But it wasn't a Christmas tree.

"Dad? Can we come out now?"

"No!" All three men yelled at once, then grinned at one another.

"Not yet, Kylie. I'll let you know," Ben called out.

Jeff opened a bag and pulled out a string of tiny white lights. He handed one end to Ben. "You'll be surprised how good it looks," he said.

Ben sighed, but he began attaching the lights to the thin branches.

Then they hung a few small silver stars and stood back.

Jeff nodded. "Done." He turned to Ben. "Could you turn out the lights?"

The room went black for a few moments. Then a blaze of light lit it up.

Ben stopped breathing. The tiny white lights twinkled, reflected on the stars, and made the fresh green leaves gleam. "Liz! Kylie!" he called, his voice bursting with excitement. "Come."

The kitchen door swung open. Kylie stepped through first and Ben heard her intake of breath. Liz was next and he grinned as she did the same. Then he felt a small hand in his. He looked down at Kylie's face. Her mouth was slightly open, her eyes huge.

Murray and Jeff quietly arranged the gifts around the tree.

"Kind of fitting, isn't it?" Murray said quietly. "This little tree was a bare and homely thing. In fact, it was pretty ugly, something to ridicule, like Jesus Himself when He hung on that cross. But now it's a blessing. In fact—" he grinned at Ben "—you could say it's a miracle."

"Leave it to Jesus," Jeff said. "He makes all things new."

Kylie pulled her hand out of her dad's and dashed to her room. She came back with the crocheted star her grandmother had given her. "Can I put this on the very top, Daddy?"

Ben nodded. "You sure can, sweetheart." He lifted her up and she attached it.

They all stood in silence for a while.

"Daddy," Kylie whispered. "She's so beautiful, all new and glowing."

Ben squeezed her hand. "Yes, she is, my girl. She certainly is."

1. "O Christmas Tree," traditional German carol, author unknown (Public Domain)

The Queen of Fair

Nonfiction

Kimberley Payne

My mother is the Queen of Fair. Not the queen of *the* fair but of *being* fair.

I was the only girl in the family, with three older brothers. To make sure I didn't go hungry at dinner, Mom dished out the same amount of meat, boiled potatoes, and vegetables on each of our plates.

She also made sure we all did our part with chores and alternated the nights we had to wash the dishes.

Although I didn't feel it was fair at the time, my mom felt it right to give us our allowance according to age. The oldest brother, Roger, received one dollar a week; Dan got 75 cents; Andrew got 50 cents; and I, as the youngest, received 25 cents.

My mother also made sure that although we received different gifts at Christmas, the dollar value was always the same. She filed all the receipts and kept a handwritten ledger to help her track her purchases.

The Christmas when I was 12 started out much the same as all the previous Christmas Eves we'd celebrated in our home in Peterborough, Ontario.

Our tradition was that after midnight mass, the six of us would return home for our Christmas "breakfast." That might seem strange, but it was our tradition. Since it was officially December 25 by then, we had our breakfast at night before we went to bed.

Mom set the dining room table with a white linen table cloth and the good china. Dad lit the last of the Advent candles and led us in a prayer before sitting down to enjoy the Dutch tradition of *uitsmijters*—an open-faced sandwich made with iceberg lettuce and Black Forest ham topped with a fried egg and eaten with knife and fork.

Then, before we went to bed, we each got to open one gift.

I inevitably picked something boring like socks or underwear, and that year was no different, but I knew that in the morning the Christmas tree would be bursting with more exciting gifts piled under it.

Indeed, the next morning when we came down, I wasn't disappointed. There were lots of wrapped packages waiting for us.

We sat in a semi-circle around the tree, and Mom carefully selected gifts, one at a time, for each of us. She'd call out a name, "Roger!" and hand him a gift. My brother would unwrap the present as each of us looked on. "Dan!" she would call, and the rest of us had to patiently wait our turn. "Andrew!" she'd call. Finally, "Kimberley!"

But this Christmas morning, as my mom doled out the gifts, she seemed to keep repeating "Roger!" and "Dan!"

I wondered if Andrew felt as left out as I did. Every once in a while, I'd steal a glance his way and notice that his smile was fading, as I'm sure mine was.

Mom continued to call out, "Roger!" "Dan!" "Dad!" "Mom!" But where were Andrew and Kimberley? Had my mother forgotten the unwritten rule of fairness? Had she forgotten us?

The unwrapped presents under the tree dwindled until all that was left was a single small white envelope sitting in the branches of the tree. Mom picked up the envelope and read the words written on the outside: "To Andrew and Kimberley, from Santa Ma and Santa Pa."

Andrew reached for it before me and tore it open. A small piece of paper fluttered out. He picked it up and read it aloud, "Go to Mom and Dad's bedroom."

Andrew and I bounded up and raced down the hallway to our parents' room. We slammed open the door and, to our surprise, found two brand new, silver 10-speed bicycles. We both screamed for joy. And then both of us broke into tears.

I'm sure my mother, who had come up behind us, thought our tears were because of the bike. But although I was overjoyed to receive a new bicycle, I'm pretty sure my tears were connected to the joy of knowing that my mom hadn't forgotten us, that she was still the Queen of Fair.

  Christmas with Hot Apple Cider

Baby in the Manger

Nonfiction[1]

Marguerite Cummings

The piano playing stopped abruptly, replaced by a fit of coughing.

In the kitchen at the end of the long hallway, 41-year-old Mathilda listened intently. *This cough! What is going on?* She turned off the stove and tiptoed to the living room.

For a minute, Mathilda stood quietly in the doorway. Her eye caught the glimmer of the decorated Christmas tree by the window, and the dim light of the miniature nativity scene she had lovingly arranged in the opposite corner earlier that day. She quickly turned her gaze to her 14-year-old daughter Lucy, still bent over the grand piano. Still coughing.

"Want to lie down, sweetie?"

Lucy looked up, her eyes filled with tears. A long strand of dark, wavy hair was stuck to her forehead.

"I don't feel too well, Mommy."

Why all these health problems? Mathilda's stomach tightened as she recalled how her daughter, tall and athletic for her age, had won first place in the school Olympics in the summer of 1971, just three years earlier. But very gradually, very subtly, Lucy's health had gone downhill, with one odd symptom after another. Out of the blue, she had started tripping over very small things. Then she'd started falling while running—for no apparent reason. Mathilda and her husband, Jack, had taken Lucy to multiple doctors to have her examined, but they'd found nothing. They'd come to the conclusion it was "all in her head." But the coughing was new.

The doctor looked sombre. "I think it's pneumonia. I'll send a nurse over to your house. Lucy will need several injections every day for the next 10 days."

He wrote down a few notes. "Six injections a day should do it."

Mathilda gasped. "Six injections—every day?"

"I'm afraid so. It's pretty serious. Oh, and please try to keep her away from her siblings."

Christmas passed in a blur. Visit to the grandparents? Cancelled. Lucy's friends from school coming over? Cancelled. Concert at the local hall? Cancelled.

It took all of Mathilda's energy just to keep Lucy's two younger siblings quiet and away from their sister; keep the dog quiet; keep the house quiet. Even Jack had to postpone his daily violin practices. *Lucy needs to sleep.*

Ten days and 60 injections later, Lucy's cough had stopped. Other than the site of the injections, which looked like a red pincushion, Lucy seemed quite a bit better. Although still weak, she could sit up in bed to eat and read.

However, Lucy needed help for the simplest tasks. The moment she tried to get up, she seemed to lose her balance.

Each trip to the bathroom became an ordeal. Gripping each other's arms, Lucy and Mathilda would make the painfully slow trek out of the guest bedroom where Lucy had been confined, down the narrow staircase to the main floor, across the entrance hall with its draughty front door, through the huge living room where the floor felt cold under their feet, to the only bathroom in the house. Once there, they'd wait long minutes for something that often wouldn't come.

The pediatrician seemed puzzled. "The antibiotics Lucy has received couldn't possibly have caused such side effects," he assured them kindly, but with no further explanation.

Mathilda lay awake at night wondering about her daughter, not daring to sleep.

Finally, Jack stepped in. "This isn't right," he told Mathilda one evening. "Surely by now Lucy should be able to get up by herself, don't you think, darling? All these injections—I don't know—perhaps they triggered some kind of unusual reaction—regardless of what we've been told."

Mathilda was silent for a minute, thinking. "You're probably right. It just doesn't make sense."

Jack started pacing, looking almost infuriated. "I just don't trust these doctors. I don't think they know what they're doing."

Mathilda sighed. "Let's see how she is tomorrow."

As Mathilda helped Lucy out of bed the next day, her heart sank when Lucy's deep, green eyes looked pleadingly at her as she said, "I can't feel my legs, Mommy. Can you hold me?"

Mathilda half-carried, half-dragged her daughter, who tripped over every step of the long journey to the bathroom and back. Inside, Mathilda was screaming, but she couldn't let Lucy know.

Afterward, while Lucy slept, a shattered Mathilda crumpled near the miniature nativity scene still on display in the corner of the living room. A faint light glowed inside the tiny barn.

Such a peaceful scene, Mathilda thought as she studied each of the familiar characters. *So different from what I feel.* Her eyes welled up as she focused on the baby in the manger.

Lucy was a baby just like you, you know. And we knew we had to call her Lucy—a "light." Just like you, Jesus, have been a light for me all these years.

But what is happening to my baby now? Mathilda began to sob. *Tell me! Please! What is the matter with her? What should we do next?*

As the nativity scene glowed quietly, a gentle peace began to fill Mathilda's heart. It was as if God had whispered to her that everything would be all right.

A couple of days later, Mathilda was struck by an idea. With a sudden, unexpected determination, she knew she had to make a phone call. The holidays were over. Jack was at work; Lucy's siblings were at school; and Lucy herself was settled in bed with a book. Not a moment to lose.

Mathilda took a deep breath and dialled the number for Dr. Beetey, a neurologist whom she also knew to be the director of a therapy centre for children with cerebral palsy. After a few transfers, she got through.

"Dr. Beetey?" Mathilda's voice was barely more than a whisper.

"Yes, how can I help you?" The sound of the familiar voice was reassuring. Mathilda cleared her throat and plunged in.

"Good morning, Doctor. And happy New Year! My name is Mathilda. Perhaps you remember me? I've been volunteering at your centre for about two years. I only come a couple of times a week, though, so you may not see me around."

"Mathilda? Of course I remember you! You're the one who got Rodrick talking, aren't you?" The doctor laughed, and his voice sounded warm and attentive.

Mathilda exhaled, grateful for the recognition. "Yes, that's me. Thank you, Doctor."

Getting Rodrick to talk had indeed been something of a victory. In addition to cerebral palsy, eight-year-old Rodrick had been diagnosed with multiple other conditions, including autism. Nobody—*nobody*—had ever heard him utter a word. Somehow, Mathilda, with her patient, engaging, no-nonsense, yet playful attitude, had managed to elicit a response from Rodrick.

While putting away some toys after a play session, she had asked him, in a completely matter-of-fact tone, "Did you see where that red block went?" And Rodrick, just as matter-of-factly, had simply responded "No." What a breakthrough!

Mathilda quickly composed herself and continued with the purpose of her call.

"I'm sorry to bother you with this, Doctor, but we—my family—we have a problem. In fact, we're getting rather desperate. Our oldest daughter, Lucy—well, she—" Mathilda's voice broke. "She—she keeps falling. She just can't walk anymore."

There was a pause on the other end of the line. Then Dr. Beetey said, "This sounds serious. Tell me more, Mathilda."

Mathilda took a deep breath. "She has already been examined by several doctors. They can't seem to find anything wrong. But—" Mathilda hesitated. "Doctor, the way Lucy tries to walk and then trips and falls—well, it reminds me of some of your patients with cerebral palsy. The way they walk."

"I see." The doctor paused again.

"And there's something else. A bit more...private." Mathilda swallowed hard. "When Lucy tries to go to the bathroom, sometimes it just doesn't come. No matter what we try." Mathilda could feel her cheeks getting hot. "I've seen that happen with some of the children I've worked with, too."

"That's a good observation, Mathilda," the doctor replied gently. He paused again, but Mathilda could hear some pages turning. "Would you like me to examine your daughter, Mathilda? You could come next Monday if you like. I just checked, and I'm free that afternoon."

Mathilda's heart almost exploded with joy.

"Can you bring some photographs of her from earlier?" the doctor added. "I'd like to see how she has changed."

Mathilda smiled. She had created an album of photos only a month before.

The following week, Jack drove Mathilda and Lucy to the appointment. They expected the consultation to last just a few minutes—Dr. Beetey was, after all, an important and busy man. However, minutes turned to hours as the neurologist spent the entire afternoon talking with Lucy, examining her, asking her questions, and observing her perform simple tasks. Mathilda felt a tinge of pride as the doctor studied the photograph album.

Finally, Dr. Beetey sat with Mathilda, Lucy, and Jack in his consulting room and shook his head. "I'm sorry. I just can't make sense of this. I can see from the way Lucy walks that something is not right, but I just cannot figure it out."

Reading the disappointment on their faces, he continued, "One thing is for sure, though. Whatever it is that's causing Lucy's problems, it's serious. It's certainly not just 'in her head.' So, please give me a couple of days. I need to read up on it."

Looking straight at Mathilda, Dr. Beetey added softly, "I promise you I will think about this."

His words felt like a warm blanket around Mathilda's heart.

Two days later, Mathilda, Lucy, and Jack sat frozen in the neurologist's office.

"I think I've found what could be the matter!" The doctor paced in front of them, excitedly pointing at a textbook on his desk. "There are three possibilities that would make sense." He smiled. Then his voice turned grave. "All of them are very serious. But we can find out for sure which one it is by doing a simple test."

Mathilda's face turned white as he explained the next step.

Things moved quickly from that point. One phone call. One referral. And the very next week, a terrified, screaming Lucy received a very painful injection. She was then strapped to a huge machine and turned upside down for several minutes.

What are you doing to my child? My baby? I can't stand it! Please, God, help us. Please! Mathilda sobbed uncontrollably as she buried her face in Jack's shoulder. Jack had to practically hold her down to prevent her from becoming hysterical and running to Lucy.

Tears flowed freely on all their faces.

But the test worked.

Jack, with his engineering background and love of machines, explained it with a flourish to the whole family later that night. "The spine is like a tube. They put in some coloured liquid at one end, turn the tube upside down, and watch the liquid flow. And if it stops flowing—well, that's when they know there's a blockage."

A blockage.

A tumour.

Growing inside Lucy's spine. Compressing her nerves. Blocking the signals that would enable her to walk.

Now that she could visualize the enemy, Mathilda felt like a mother bear, ready to attack.

  Christmas with Hot Apple Cider

A week later, Lucy was in the hospital for surgery. And the tumour was out.

"It looked like a pickle. Just about the size of your thumb. An annoying, growing pickle," the surgeon explained to them after the operation. "Good thing we caught it in time," he added. "Just a few weeks more, and your daughter would have spent the rest of her life in a wheelchair."

Mathilda shivered, recalling the pneumonia that had brought matters to a head; the fact that she had been working at Dr. Beetey's centre as a volunteer; the sudden inspiration to call him; his willingness to help; the fast referral to a skilled surgeon. Everything fit together.

"Oh, and we've examined the tumour," the surgeon added. "It wasn't malignant. Just a one-off. Shouldn't come back."

As Lucy and Mathilda slowly walked out of the hospital two weeks after the surgery, the nurses lined the hallway.

Like a standing ovation, thought Mathilda. *Lucy is a walking miracle.*

Thank you, doctors. Thank you, nurses. Thank you most of all, Baby in the manger.

1. All names have been changed and the dialogue has been imagined, but the facts of the story have been kept as accurate as possible.

Author's Note:
   More than 40 years later, my parents remain thankful for the remarkable way in which their daughter's legs were saved. As for my older sister, she went on to study medicine and travel all over the world. She is now a medical doctor with an additional PhD. She still enjoys playing the piano.

The Perfect Gift for Mom

Nonfiction

Tandy Balson

In her mid-70s, my mom was a prime example of someone who is difficult to buy gifts for. There was nothing she needed, and her tiny apartment had no space for non-essentials.

Still, I wanted to do something special for her for Christmas. But what?

At the time, we were living in the Greater Vancouver area, where things could be pricey. However, my sister-in-law told me that some of the concrete picnic tables used during Expo 1986 in Vancouver had been sold to the small town of White Rock, where my mother lived.

When I heard we could purchase a sponsorship for one of these tables and have a small, engraved plaque attached, I knew I'd found the perfect gift. My mom not only lived in White Rock but she had a strong family history in the area, including many happy childhood memories of playing on the beach with her sisters.

White Rock borders Semiahmoo Bay, and the tables were being placed on their newly updated waterfront walkway. There were shops on one side of the street, and the walkway was on the opposite side, along the water. I'd spent many hours strolling along Marine Drive with Mom. She said that the salty air was like medicine to her soul.

The 500-dollar price seemed prohibitive, but I wasn't to be deterred. After contacting my four siblings, we agreed that this would be a group gift.

It was up to me to choose which of the tables along the walkway to dedicate to her. After careful consideration, I chose the one across the street from her favourite fish-and-chips restaurant.

On Christmas Day, we told Mom that she wouldn't receive her gift until everyone arrived. Before long, my sister, two of my brothers, a sister-in-law, and a nephew arrived. Her confusion was

Christmas with Hot Apple Cider

obvious when we said we had to take her to another location for her gift.

We climbed into the minivan and drove to the beach. Together we led her to the picnic table and pointed out the plaque with her name inscribed.

At first, she seemed shocked; then came the tears of joy. Moments later, she called out to a stranger walking by to show him the table her kids had given her!

This gift gave my mom untold pleasure for years. Many friends enjoyed fish and chips sitting at *her* table with her.

Mom frequently walked along the waterfront and, if anyone was sitting at her table, she'd engage them in conversation, pointing out the inscription and telling the story of how her name came to be on it.

My mom passed away many years ago, but the picnic table remains as part of her lasting legacy. I no longer live in the area, but when I go there for a visit, I always drive to see Mom's table and smile as I remember the year we gave her the perfect Christmas gift.

Explosion

Nonfiction

Shelley Norman

"Mmmm," my husband said as he wandered into the kitchen. "Something smells good in here."

With a smile, I pulled off my favourite oven mitts—the ones with the cheery red roses—and did a "Vanna" wave to indicate the glass cake pan of gooey lemon squares I'd just taken out of the oven and set on the large front element of the stove top.

"Not very Christmassy, but you know me, I never turn down a dessert," he said, making a move toward the silverware drawer. "How's about I give them a taste test?"

"Paws off, buster." I playfully smacked him with the oven mitts I was still holding. "You know it's Christmas Eve and that means an early supper so we can make it to the seven o'clock service at church."

He tried his pouty face on me, but after almost 20 years, I'm immune to it.

"Supper is in half an hour." To ease the blow of his having to wait for dessert, I added, "I'm making chicken wings—your favourite."

He grinned. "Fine. Then Holly and I will just go and watch *Elf* until the wings are ready. Won't we, girl?" he said to our Australian cattle dog cross, who was currently eyeing the tray of raw chicken wings on the counter.

Figuring the chances of the wings leaping off the counter into her mouth were slim, Holly reluctantly followed my husband to the TV room.

A short time later, after I'd put the pans of breaded chicken wings and battered onion rings into the oven, I collapsed on the couch next to my hubby and enjoyed some of the festive movie while keeping one eye on the clock. I'd set a steamer pot of broccoli on the back stovetop burner, and I needed to turn the burner on for the last 10 minutes of the wings' cooking time.

  Christmas with Hot Apple Cider

Of course, the movie was at a really good part when it was time to switch on the element under the veggie pot, so I did a quick run to the kitchen, turned the knob on the stove, and bustled back to the TV room.

I'd just got settled back to watch the show when I thought I smelled something burning. Sitting up at the edge of the couch, I sniffed. "Do you smell something burning?" I asked my husband.

"No," he answered, without even taking his eyes off the television screen.

I sniffed again. I definitely smelled something burning.

As soon as I entered the kitchen, I saw where the smell was coming from. The large front element under my pan of lemon squares was glowing bright red.

I quickly donned my oven mitts and lifted the glass pan from the burner. Tipping it slightly, I could see that the shortbread crust of the squares was burned black. *Great! So much for the lemon squares!* I looked around for a spot to set the very hot dish.

BANG!!!

When my husband came to an abrupt stop in the kitchen doorway, I was still standing in front of the stove, my hands out in front of me exactly as they'd been a moment before when I was holding the glass 9 × 13 pan of squares. But now my hands were empty. Gooey lemon filling dripped down the cupboard doors and the front of the oven. Shards of glass covered not only the stove top, counters, and floor around me, but pretty much every surface in the kitchen and the floor even into the adjoining rooms.

"Are you okay?" my husband asked, concern in his voice. I realized that only his bare feet made him hesitate to cross the room.

"Yeah." I nodded, my mind not quite having caught up yet to what had happened. "But my lemon squares are ruined, and I think this might have been the best batch I've made all year."

The sound of dog toenails clickity-clacking on the hardwood floor coming toward us snapped me out of my trance. "Quick, grab Holly! Don't let her in here. She'll cut her paws."

My husband easily caught the dog as she was about to barrel through the door. He took her back to the TV room and closed the door to keep her in there.

When he returned to the kitchen, I had started to sweep up the mess with a broom.

"Are you sure you're okay?" he asked. "No cuts or burns?"

"I'm fine. Just a blob of lemon filling on the toe of my running shoe." I held my foot up for him to see. "Supper will be ready in a couple minutes. The chicken and onion rings were in the oven, so they didn't get any glass in them and will be fine to eat. I'll bring them to the TV room since we can't eat at the table."

My hubby looked at the splinters of glass covering the table and all around it, shook his head, and muttered "Amazing!" as he went back to the other room.

As we sat eating and watching the rest of the movie, my husband kept looking at me strangely and asking, "You're sure you're okay?"

"Yes! Why do you keep asking me that?" I shook my head at him. "What isn't okay, though, is the kitchen floor. Some of the glass splinters must have been really hot because they left scorch marks on the floor where they landed. How in the world am I going to fix them? We can't afford to replace the flooring right now."

He just gave me another weird look.

After we finished eating, we quickly changed and headed off to the Christmas Eve service at our church. We'd have to clean up the mess later.

Sitting up in the balcony, we watched the little children put on their nativity pageant, joined with the choir in the singing of several lovely Christmas hymns, and listened to the minister read the story of the first Christmas from the Gospel according to Luke and talk about it.

But, to be honest, the whole time my mind was going over and over the mess waiting for me at home. It would likely take the rest of Christmas Eve to get it all swept and scrubbed. And we wouldn't get to have any of the lemon squares!

As I sat there, I started to feel rather angry about the whole thing. My original plan had been that after an enjoyable Christmas Eve service, I'd get to cuddle up on the couch with my hubby and Holly, watch more Christmas movies, and pig out on lemon squares.

Instead, when we got home, I changed back into my old jeans and sweater and went straight to the kitchen to get to work on the mess waiting there.

The whole time we'd been gone, Holly had been locked in the TV room so she wouldn't sneak into the kitchen and cut herself on the glass. My husband volunteered to take her for a walk.

They must have gone for a really good walk, because by the time they got back and my husband came to check on things in the kitchen, he found me standing by the stove, staring at the floor and muttering to myself.

"How's it going in here?" he asked, picking up a shard of glass from the counter and tossing it into the garbage can.

"Just look at the damage to the floor and the countertop! Even the oven handle! Every time I'm in here, which is all the time, I'm going to see this mess. And it's probably going to take the rest of the evening to clean up just the worst of it!" I knew I was sounding whiny and angry.

My husband just shook his head and pulled me into his arms for a hug. "You just don't get it, do you?" he said. "Yes, every time you're in here you *will* see these marks, and you should thank God for that."

I gave him the weird look this time.

"Look around you," he said. "There's glass everywhere and burn marks. You were holding the dish when it exploded, but you don't have a single little mark on you. It's a miracle. You could have been burned, even blinded. That's why you should thank God."

As his words sank into my brain, I rested my head against his chest.

"And I'd much rather spend Christmas Eve helping you clean up the kitchen than spend it sitting by your bed in the ER as they pick glass out of you. Or worse." He dropped a kiss on the top of my head.

Hating to admit he was right, but knowing that maybe this once he actually was, I looked up at him. "How did you figure that out before me?"

He smiled back at me pushing hair out of my face. "Maybe you were too close to the situation."

We both laughed.

"Okay, let's get this done," he said. "Then maybe we can still find some time to snuggle on the couch and watch things blow up on *National Lampoon's Christmas Vacation* before it's officially Christmas."

The next morning, when I got up and went to the kitchen to make breakfast, I took a good look at the scars dotting the vinyl flooring. Bowing my head, I thanked God for protecting me and keeping me safe once again, as He has before. And I thanked Him for His Son, our Saviour, who came into this world to protect us, and whose birthday I would be able to celebrate with my family today, because of His love.

The Letters

Nonfiction

Beverly DeWit

Amy Bryenton had never thought about leaving her prairie home—not even for a vacation—until her Uncle Lloyd wrote to her. His letters encouraged her to come for a visit and experience life away from the Prairies. He promised to take her to the art gallery and museums and to show her things she would never experience as a teacher in a one-room schoolhouse in Laura, Saskatchewan.

Years before, Amy's father, Leslie, had left his family in Charlottetown, Prince Edward Island, and made a homestead claim in Loreburn, Saskatchewan.

His younger brother, Lloyd, had been born six weeks after their father died from being kicked in the head by a horse. Consequently, Leslie felt it was his duty as the eldest brother to send money to help Lloyd attend a year of college in the United States.

Lloyd had always acknowledged his brother's role in his later success as a manager at Grolier Publishing, and he'd decided to repay his brother's kindness by offering to bring Amy, his unmarried 27-year-old niece, to Cleveland, Ohio, to spend the summer of 1941 with him and his family.

Uncle Lloyd kept his promises and then some! Amy enjoyed her visit and even decided to extend her stay so she could attend a family reunion, hear Pearl Buck speak, and enjoy the Cleveland Orchestra playing at the Cleveland Auditorium.

But autumn was coming, and the time for Amy to return home was rapidly approaching. She was faced with a huge decision. Should she return directly to her prairie home or should she pay a visit to her old friend, Carman, in Ontario?

She'd discovered that stopping for a short time where he lived would be only a little out of the way. But it was a big decision. She'd been only 17 when she'd seen Carman last. After 10 years, how would he receive her? Surely he'd found another girl by now.

On the other hand, she'd never met a man she liked more than Carman.

Their families had become close after his mother died from the Spanish Influenza on December 1, 1918, when Carman was just six years old.

Life on the Canadian prairies hadn't been easy when Carman and Amy were in their teens, either. The drought and dust storms of 1931 affected food supplies. Yet Amy still had wonderful memories of the many summer evenings when she'd danced with Carman in the homes of friends in their prairie community in her teens. And at Christmas that year, Amy, her siblings, and Carman had gathered in a neighbour's home to sing Christmas carols, hoping to find some joy.

Afterward, in the cold air of the night, Carman had walked her home. She could still remember the warm feeling she felt as he'd wrapped an arm around her and held her tight. At the same time, he'd looked her in the eyes so deeply that she'd felt her 17-year-old heart being pierced.

But in the spring that year, Carman's family left to find work and a better life in Ontario.

Amy had been certain her broken heart would never heal.

For many years, Carman had written to her weekly, but in the past few years, his letters had slowed down. Now, they were few and far between.

Yet Amy still spent many days dreaming of the times they'd spent together, and she still remembered staring up into the face of the tall, handsome young man.

A week from now, August 6, 1941, would be his 29th birthday. Wouldn't it be romantic to spend his birthday with him?

If she went directly home, she'd always wonder what might have been. Most of her friends were already married and had children. The time had come to see him and find out once and for all if they had a future together. Convinced, she booked a train ticket

  Christmas with Hot Apple Cider

to Sundridge, Ontario, for the following week and sent Carman a letter giving him the details of her arrival and asking him to meet her train.

As the train approached the station in Sundridge, Amy's stomach twisted and flipped. Had she made the right choice? What if Carman no longer shared her feelings? She leaned forward in her seat, anxious to see the station platform, but when it came in view, she couldn't see him.

What a fool she'd been to think he still might care for her after all these years! Why had she come here without knowing how he felt about her? She'd thought it would be romantic, but now it only seemed foolish.

She fought back the tears forming in her eyes, stood up, and walked off the train. After finding her luggage, she made her way into the station toward the ticket master. She needed to find out when the next train to Saskatchewan would leave.

As she rummaged through the purse draped over her arm, looking for her wallet to get the money to pay for the ticket home, she dropped her handkerchief. When she bent down to pick it up, a hand met hers. She looked up into the eyes she'd been longing to see.

"Carman! You're here!"

"Of course! You didn't think I'd leave you standing here at the station?" he said. "Besides, your Uncle Lloyd made sure I'd be here to meet you."

"Well—Well, I'm so happy to see you."

"Let me take your suitcase. My father, Elsie, and Ken are just outside."

"Most of your family is here?" Amy asked.

"Of course. It's not every day we get a world traveller coming to visit us."

"Oh, Carm." She laughed and nudged his waist.

He sat close to her as they travelled to his home just outside of Sundridge in a little place called Pevensey. Her heart beat faster and her palms grew sweaty as the family told her everything about their life here. She learned that Carman and his family members were working on a farm.

She was interested, but what she really wanted was to steal a few minutes alone with Carman to find out if he still cared for her.

Daylight was gone by the time they arrived, and all she saw in the moonlight was the outline of two small cabins at the edge of the woods. One cabin held a living space and Carman's sister Elsie's room; the other cabin was more of a bunkhouse where Carman, his dad, and his brother slept. Carman put Amy's suitcase into Elsie's room, where she would be sleeping.

His family seemed glad to see her, and they all showed her a grand time in the week that she spent there.

Carman took her to Crooked Lake to celebrate his birthday with Elsie and her boyfriend, Bill Dobbs. They sat next to the lake and talked about how his life had been. Before leaving, he wrapped his arms around her near a birch tree and posed for a picture. Her heart raced to feel him so close, and it brought her memory back to that Christmas dance 10 years before. Except she'd been 17 then. Now she understood her feelings much better.

They enjoyed taking moonlight walks together, hand in hand, through the woods. The number of trees astonished her. Trees were scarce on the prairies, and she imagined the comfort their shade might bring during the hot days of summer back home. She was also amazed by the maple syrup Carman's family had gathered from the trees.

One afternoon they drove to the city of North Bay and then to Corbeil to see the Dionne Quintuplets, who were now seven years of age. Amy had seen pictures of the quints in newspapers and in some ad campaigns for the war effort, but seeing the seven-year-olds in front of her, behind the glass, let her see the sadness in their eyes.

Too soon the day came for her to board the train back to Saskatchewan. She gathered up her luggage, including the maple syrup Carman's family had given her to share with her family and the students at her school.

  Christmas with Hot Apple Cider

As her feet climbed the stairs onto the train, she couldn't help but feel that somehow she belonged here and that she'd be leaving part of her heart behind. By the time the train pulled away from the station, tears were flowing down her cheeks.

Back home, summer drew to an end and Amy began to make preparations for her next year of teaching.

Letters between Amy and Carman became more frequent than in the past couple of years. The tone of the letters changed, too, becoming more private and personal than any of Carman's previous letters.

That fall had been warmer than usual, and news of the war raging on in Europe had brought concern into the lives of everyone on the prairie. Many young men had enlisted in the army, prepared to go and fight. People everywhere were looking more seriously at their relationships with others. Carman couldn't enlist because an illness with high fevers some years before had permanently affected his health.

As fall turned to winter, there were fewer hours of daylight. Since there was no electricity, and there was a need to conserve kerosene, lanterns were used only when necessary. People went to bed when it became dark and got up with first light. This meant Amy had less time to prepare for her class and also less time to write replies to Carman.

Before she knew it, work on the Christmas pageant took precedence over anything else in her life. She carefully wrote lines so each of her students could participate. The children giggled and laughed together as they tried to pretend to be someone different.

The weekend before Christmas, the children performed for their parents, grandparents, and neighbours. It was a delightful Christmas pageant that depicted the birth of Jesus.

With the pageant over, Amy could finally find time to write a letter to Carman. She sat at her desk that night pouring her heart and soul onto the paper.

On Christmas Eve, Amy's father went to town to get the mail. Amy waited anxiously for his return, hopeful that Carman had written or even sent something special for Christmas. While she waited, she helped her mother with Christmas preparations and talked about everything that had happened at the school that fall.

Later, Amy had just sat down to write another letter to Carman when she heard a sound at the front door.

"Look what the cat dragged in this time, Amy," her mother said.

Amy looked up. Father stood in the doorway, as expected, and beside him was a man dressed in his Sunday best.

She stared.

"Is that any way to greet a man who just travelled halfway across Canada to see you?" Carman asked with a smile.

Amy jumped up and ran into his arms, squealing with excitement.

"Those must have been some letters the two of you have been writing," her mother said.

Her father chuckled. "That's what I thought, too, when I saw this young man in town and realized it was Carman. Can you imagine? He boarded the train in Sundridge without even making sure someone would be at the station to meet him. Good thing I went to town this morning or he might have frozen waiting for someone to give him a ride."

On Christmas mornings, Amy's family had a tradition of gathering together to open presents they'd made for each other, followed by having pancakes for breakfast. This morning, Carman insisted that he give the first present. Reaching into his pocket with one hand and dropping down on one knee, he took one of Amy's hands.

"Amy, our families have known each other a long time and been friends, but somehow when you came east this summer and saw me and my family, something changed inside me. I knew the day you boarded that train to leave that you belonged in Ontario with me. My heart has ached every day without you there, and I want you to marry me and come live with me in Ontario. Amy Bryenton, will you be my wife?"

Amy looked deeply into his eyes. Her dreams were coming true at last. "Yes, Carman, I will marry you." She looked around at her smiling family. "What a wonderful Christmas!"

  Christmas with Hot Apple Cider

And from that day forward, until death parted them, she'd spend every Christmas with Carman.

Author's Note:

This story is based on a scrapbook my grandmother made from her summer of 1941, and from stories she shared with my family about her relationship with my grandfather. In the summer of 1942, Carman returned to the prairies with a tree as a gift for Amy's parents and married Amy. They were happily married for 55 years and made their home in Sundridge, Ontario. Carman passed away January 3, 1998, shortly after spending one last Christmas with Amy.

A Bicycle for My Daughter

Nonfiction

Rob Harshman

With only two weeks to go before Christmas, the tension in our household was building as my wife, Susan, and I scrambled to finish our Christmas shopping. There were still so many presents to buy and wrap, and so little time left.

Fortunately, we had already purchased a few gifts, one of which was for our oldest daughter, Michelle, who was eight. She'd outgrown her bicycle, so we'd decided to buy a new one, a 10-speed with pink curved handles. To save money, we bought a bike that was unassembled and stored the two large boxes at the home of a friend, whose name was also Rob.

What that meant, however, was that we would have to assemble it. Rob had volunteered to help me and keep the bike in an unfinished room in his basement until Christmas Eve.

Susan looked at me with doubt in her eyes. "Do you really think you can put the bike together?"

"No problem. Bikes aren't difficult to assemble." I paused. "Look, I've ridden bikes my whole life. And this one's smaller than any I remember. I'm not worried."

"Do you have the right tools?"

"I've got my trusty toolbox and every tool we could possibly need."

"Okay, if you think you can do it."

I smiled. "No problem. Besides, Rob's more mechanical than I am."

As I waved good-bye to Susan, I glanced at my watch. It was 7:07 p.m. "I won't be longer than an hour, so I can help with some other things when I get home."

"Be sure to read all the instructions," my wife called back.

"Don't worry. We'll be okay. See you soon."

When I arrived at Rob's house for the assembly process, the very first thing we did was empty the two boxes and lay everything out on the floor, with similar-looking pieces clustered together. Seeing it all, I knew I'd been right. I'd be home early. "It looks pretty straightforward," I said.

"I agree," Rob said. "After all, we've both ridden bikes and know how they work."

As I expected, one of the boxes contained a set of instructions. I picked them up.

"We don't need these." Rob smiled as he took them and tossed them to one side. "We can work it all out faster without them. Besides, I think the last instructions I tried to follow were written by a robot."

We both laughed.

We started off with the frame of the bike and then added the handlebars, tires, etc. As we worked, I felt pretty good about myself. The bicycle was taking shape in front of us, and I'd saved $30 by buying the assembly kit.

Not only that, but Rob and I had a great time working together. Hot chocolate and Christmas cake added to the fun as we talked about our plans for Christmas.

Part way through the process, Rob's wife called out from upstairs. "The snowstorm's just started and they're expecting up to a foot of snow."

I wasn't worried because I knew I'd be heading home in a few minutes.

We worked quickly and soon reached the last step, which was to install the seat. After we tightened it, we stood back and looked at the bike lying on the floor.

"You know, it looks pretty good for a couple of amateurs." Rob laughed his easy laugh.

"Michelle will be surprised, and she'll love the bike."

"And guess what? It only took us half an hour!" Rob smiled again.

"So simple! I'll pack up my tools and then I'll be on my way."

Rob nodded, and together we collected all the scrap paper and cardboard packing, then dumped everything in the garbage.

"Wait a minute, Rob. Are these yours?" I'd discovered a small pile of washers, screws, and clips.

"No. Where'd you find them?"

"Right here under some of the scraps of packing."

"I have no idea where they came from."

"Well, I'll save them in case you need them." I grabbed them and put them on his workbench.

As Rob lifted the bike up, I noticed that the back wheel looked a little wobbly. I went over to it and moved the wheel back and forth with one finger. "Look at this. The wheel shouldn't be doing this."

"You're right. The wheels shouldn't wobble at all."

Remembering those washers and screws, I said, "Do you think we need to check the instructions?"

"Well, I suppose it wouldn't be a bad idea. I mean…"

I walked over to the trash container and began to root around in it, looking for the instructions. I finally found them at the bottom of the mound of paper and other garbage. They were stained with hot chocolate and grease.

After a quick look at them, I said, "I—uh—I think we left some parts out as we were building the bike."

Rob nodded in agreement, a wry smile on his face.

"I guess we don't have much choice. We'll have to take the bike apart and rebuild it."

Rob sighed as I collected the "extra" parts that were on his workbench. Then we settled into the job of deconstructing the bike so we could include all the nuts, bolts, and washers that had come with it.

For the next couple of hours, we worked in total silence. Slowly, the bicycle took shape in front of us once again. By the time we were done, it looked great. Not surprisingly, all the extra pieces helped secure the wheels on the bike. Nothing wobbled.

  Christmas with Hot Apple Cider

I glanced at my watch and saw that it was 11:05 p.m. The half-hour job had somehow expanded to four hours. *Oh well,* I thought, *the bicycle's safe to use now.*

I looked at Rob. "Thanks for all your help. I'm glad we picked up on our small error before I gave the bike to my daughter."

Rob nodded and smiled as I headed out the door into a swirl of snow.

The drive that normally took seven minutes turned into an icy 25-minute adventure in subarctic conditions.

As I walked through our front door, my wife called out, "I thought you were going to be home over three hours ago."

"The instructions were lousy," I said as I ran upstairs to the shower to avoid any more questions.

Daddy's Old Shoebox

Doris Fleming

Up in the closet, a mile out of reach,
Is a shoebox wrapped 'round with string;
It belongs to my daddy, and the treasures inside
Intrigue me beyond anything.

Each Christmas morning he pulls the box down,
Lays its tokens out there on the table;
I watch as he handles and talks of each piece,
And I'm certain he's telling no fable.

I touch all the bits in his tattered old box,
And the keepsakes Dad passes to me;
I'm proud of his life and happy he gathered
These things for his children to see.

Tarnished and faded, the coins and the ribbons,
Cherished photos cast a silvery hue;
They speak of his travels, decisions, and trials,
His fears and accomplishments, too.

From youngster to manhood, they capture his days,
Depictions my mind's eye can see:
Hardworking farm boy, friend-making soldier,
Loving father, and hero to me.

"Not yet!" I cry, as he tightens the string,
And stows the box up and away;
He takes me by hand and heads for the barn,
"Shh. We'll do it again…one day."

Secret Gifts and Givers

Fiction

Carrie Seavers

"Grandma, tell us the story of the secret gift, please?"

Lulu, the grandmother of one newborn and six excited children aged three to ten, looked up from her task of spreading blankets on the living room floor and smiled. "Of course I will, just as soon as everyone has a place to sleep."

Lulu, her son Callen, and her daughter Marlee were busy rearranging Lulu's living room into a sleeping area for all but the youngest of the children. Once the furniture was moved back, six sleeping bags, blankets, and pillows were spread over the carpet.

Years ago, they had given up trying to find a bed for each family member, which suited everyone fine. Yes, it took them a bit longer to get to sleep, but that only added to the anticipation of Christmas. Because Marlee and her family lived in another city, the cousins got together only a few times a year.

When there was a semblance of quiet in the room, Grandma Lulu got the little shoebox from her bedroom and sat down with it. But she didn't open it right away. *Look at all these little faces,* Lulu thought. *This is a sight I will never forget. Oh, how my heart loves them!*

She began her story.

"A long, long time ago when your grandpa and I were first married, we lived in a very small town. We didn't have much money to spend on fancy things for the house, but we made it a home as best we could."

"Bring out the picture, Grandma," a small voice whispered.

All the little eyes followed her hand as she removed the lid from the box and rifled around for a second. She drew out an old black-and-white photo of herself and her groom standing beside a 1957 Chevy. In a twinkling, her mind went back in time and she felt again the joy of young love they were revelling in that day.

"Now, you can all hold it, but you must be very gentle. Okay?" She passed the photo to the hands of her oldest grandson and watched as his solemn eyes looked at it closely before handing it to the blond-haired cousin beside him.

"Is this really you, Grandma?" seven-year-old Oliver asked. "It doesn't look like you."

Lulu smiled. "Yes, that's me." She waited until the picture had gone around and come back to her.

"Now, to continue my story... The people in the small town where we lived were very welcoming to us, and we felt as if they were our family."

"My friend Logan feels like that to me," one of the kids said, and all the adults in the room smiled and nodded.

Lulu nodded, too, then continued. "There was a tradition in the small town that when someone had a baby, the church ladies would plan a baby shower. That's a party where they would bring gifts of clothes, diapers, shampoo, and other things to help the new mother.

"Well, the day of the baby shower for me came, and it was just lovely. The sun was shining because it was spring time, and almost every lady in that little town showed up with a gift and a plateful of goodies to eat. We had a wonderful time eating and visiting, and everyone got a chance to hold my new baby, Callen."

The kids all turned their eyes toward the object of the story, who was smiling while he rocked his newborn son in the comfy green rocking chair.

"I'd opened all but one of the gifts that the ladies had brought. At the bottom of the pile, there was a lovely box, all wrapped in pretty gold paper with a huge blue ribbon on it. I picked it up, but there was no card on it, and no little gift tag to say who it was from, like all the presents by our tree have."

The kids turned their heads in unison toward the Christmas tree in the far corner, all lit up and spreading a warm glow. As they did, the baby closed his eyes and fell asleep. Janie, his mother, smothered a giggle from the sofa where she was watching.

"But there *was* a note!" The eight-year-old tried to keep her voice quiet and not disturb her new cousin.

  Christmas with Hot Apple Cider

Lulu smiled at her. "Yes, there was. Inside the box were two pairs of boots: one little pair of black rubber rain boots, and one little pair of outside play boots." She dug in the box and pulled out a pair of scuffed-up rubber boots. "These are the rubber boots!"

"Ooh, ahh," the young voices murmured from their makeshift beds.

Lulu reached inside one of the little boots for a folded piece of paper and then set them on the floor by her feet. "Dear little one," she read, "welcome to this big, beautiful world. I know at times you will find life overwhelming and wonder if you are on the right path and doing what God wants you to be doing, but if you seek Him in all you do, He will direct you. When it rains, wear these little boots and remember, whether it's raining or sunny, there is something to love, to be appreciated, and to enjoy in every single day; God's hand is in it all. This is my prayer for you and your parents; that you would spend time being together *and* praying together every day, and as you do, I will be praying for you every day, too."

"No one knew who had brought the gift, so I didn't know who to thank for it, but it was *exactly* what I needed to hear. There were times I was unsure of myself as a mommy, but I would remember that the letter said 'God's hand is in it all,' and I could trust Him to help me do the right things.

"Many days I would bring the letter out, and Grandpa and I would read it together and pray and talk about what we had seen and done that day, especially those days that were rainy and gloomy.

"And we stomped around in our rubber boots in the puddles together!"

"I have rubber boots too!" shouted the three-year-old. "I love to jump in the puddles!"

Lulu smiled and continued. "That was the first of the surprise gifts in our community. For the next few years, every time there was a new baby, there would be a gift that didn't have a card with it. Inside would always be something very special that the parents needed, and there was always a little letter with some wise words of wisdom with it—but never the name of who it was from. We often wondered who it was, and how she or he knew just what to say to the new mommies. It was such a mystery!" She leaned forward and slowly said, "We would all watch very carefully at each baby shower to see who brought in the surprise gift, but we never could tell who it was! Someone was very, very sneaky!"

"What about my mom?" said the boy closest to her. You got another secret gift when she was born, right?"

"I sure did." Lulu reached into the box and gently pulled out a ragged-looking book. She opened the front cover and took out another letter.

"Dear Mom and Dad, how exciting that your beautiful baby #2 will be here soon. This book is for you so you have something for just the two of you to do together. Life changes with each baby that comes along, so make sure to take some time for this little one. Never let life get so busy that you neglect to give your full attention to these children together and to each one individually. And always, always, pray together. And I will pray for you every day, too."

"Well, it was just what I needed! It was a very good reminder to me when the new baby arrived," she pointed to her daughter, "that I had to make time to be alone with Marlee and not always have her big brother along.

"Meanwhile, all of us young moms in town talked about the secret gifts we'd received, and every single one of us said, 'It was just what I needed.'

"After a while, we gave up trying to find out who it was. For some reason, whoever was giving the secret gifts didn't want anyone to know. It took me a long time to understand why, but now I know that sometimes it's as much fun to give a gift as it is to receive one. Even if no one knows it was you."

Lulu put the items back into her little box. "Now let's sing a few carols and then it's time for sleep. Tomorrow is Christmas Day! Birthday cake for baby Jesus!"

A few weeks later, Lulu was working at her computer, downloading photos from yet another wonderful Christmas, when her phone rang. It was her son, Callen. "Mom, are you busy? Can you come down to the school? You're never going to believe this."

"Okay, I will." Fear filled Lulu's stomach. "Is something wrong?"

"Everyone's fine. But please come to the school office. You'll want to see this."

Lulu quickly made her way to the school. She was filled with panic when she rounded the corner and noticed several police cars and the black police van parked outside. She'd been there to pick up Oliver on several occasions, so she knew her way around and could go straight to the office.

"Grandma!" Oliver jumped up from his chair and threw his arms around her. "I wanted to be a secret gift giver too, like in your story, but it didn't work!" His eyes filled with tears. "The police are here!"

"Yes, I see them." Lulu hugged him and sat down on a chair in the already-crowded principal's office near Callen and his wife Janie. A police officer was there as well—Greg, if her memory served her correctly. She knew his mother well. "Hello, Barb," she addressed the principal, who was the daughter of a good friend.

"Thanks for coming, Lulu. We've had a bit of an incident this morning. I'll let Oliver tell you." She sent a small smile to the little blond boy who was trying not to cry as he sneaked a peek at the police officer standing nearby. "Go ahead and tell your Grandma, honey."

Oliver sniffed. "I made a gift for my teacher, but I forgot it on the bench by the door when I took my boots off. I had just remembered it when the alarm went off and—and—" He erupted in a new wave of tears.

"Oh, dear!" Lulu exclaimed as Callen picked up his son and held him tight.

The principal finished the story. "The janitor spotted it first and came to my office. Protocol dictates that we must sound the alarm for anything suspicious and put the school on lockdown. It didn't take long to figure out what happened, but the police have to do a general sweep before we can lift the lockdown."

"Am I going to jail?" Oliver asked through his tears.

"No, you're not." Officer Greg bent down to eye level with him. "But if giving secret gifts is something that you want to do, get your

Grandma and Mom and Dad to help you figure out how to do it, okay? It's very nice of you to want to give gifts to people, but we don't want this to happen every time, right?"

Oliver nodded his head.

Officer Greg smiled and gave Oliver a friendly little pat on his shoulder. "I'll just finish up the paperwork and then be on my way." He left the room.

"Do you want to go home with your parents now, Oliver?" the principal asked him.

"No, I don't want to miss school! I want to stay. Can I stay, Mom?" He looked at his parents. "Please, I don't want everyone to know it was me!"

"Well, it may be too late for that," Callen said, "but you can stay if you're okay with it. No more tears?"

"Nope, I'm good." He bravely wiped his eyes.

"Okay, you can go now," his dad said. "We'll have Grandma come over so we can talk about this more when you get home. See you later, buddy."

After further discussion among the remaining adults, Lulu left the school and drove to her son and daughter-in-law's house. *How times have changed!* she thought. Then she smiled.

Callen, Janie, and Lulu spent the rest of the day discussing how they could help the soft-hearted Oliver nurture his desire to give gifts safely. One of the decisions they made was to introduce a "secret gift" game next Christmas for the whole family to participate in.

When Oliver burst through the door at 3:20, he announced, "What a great day! Officer Greg came and talked to my class about how to be safe and how police officers help people. Then my class spent the rest of the day talking about what we want to be when we grow up. You know what I said?" Without pausing, he went on, "I'm gonna be a police officer! I want to be just like Officer Greg. I want to help people, and save them when there's secret packages that may be dangerous. Yeah!"

He grabbed a couple of cookies from the plate on the kitchen table. "Where's my Tonka policeman?" He ran to his room, where he played with his police toys until dinner.

Yes, they did have a talk about surprise packages, but not that day.

And on Christmas Eve every year since then, when the grandkids are tucked into their beds on the living room floor, first Lulu brings out her special gift box and tells her story of the secret gift giver, and then Oliver takes centre stage and tells his story.

One Red Christmas Apple

Nonfiction

Laureen F. Guenther

In July of 1995, I left Canada to teach for a year in Dhaka, the capital city of Bangladesh. I'd taught in Saskatchewan for five years, and travelled in the United States and Europe, but I'd never taught overseas, and living in Bangladesh was my first experience in Asia.

I didn't live there long before most of my understanding of life and humanity was turned inside out.

This tiny Asian country is lush and beautiful, rich in history and culture. The people were welcoming and hospitable, and they celebrated my efforts to speak the Bangla language. However, Bangladesh is also poor and overcrowded, and the patterns of Bangladeshi life were often unpredictable and frustrating for me. The country was also unsettled politically, and our little international school had challenging internal politics of its own. In my inexperience and immaturity, I didn't always respond wisely.

Before leaving Canada, I had promised a church friend that I'd spend Christmas with her and her family at her sister's home in Chiang Mai, Thailand. It was an easy promise to make, although I had no idea what travel from Bangladesh to Thailand would be like. In addition, I didn't know this friend well, and I'd be joining her whole family, none of whom I'd met. But when she invited me, it seemed like a nice thing to do at Christmas.

I had no idea then that, long before December arrived, the trip would feel like a lifeline. I was so looking forward to spending the Christmas holiday in Thailand with other Canadians—even if they were strangers.

I soon discovered, however, that accepting the invitation was much easier than making the trip happen.

Because I didn't have my own phone, and the Bangladesh phone system was unreliable, it was tricky to get in touch with my friend's sister in Thailand to make travel plans. I sat for hours in a tiny office at my neighbours' house, repeatedly dialing the number in Thailand. After more than a dozen tries, I decided the problem might not be Bangladesh's phone system, but my having a wrong number.

Since my friend was travelling in Asia before going to Thailand, I had to make several expensive calls to Canada in an attempt to find an extended family member who knew the right phone number. Finally, I had it—I'd been out by one digit.

I soon had the long-awaited talk with my friend's sister in Thailand, and she gave me dates and travel guidance for getting to Chiang Mai.

I was ready to buy my plane tickets.

That turned out to have its own Bangladeshi-style complications. There were many travel agents in Dhaka, but the only one that experienced expatriates recommended had a kiosk far from my apartment and worked limited, irregular hours.

It took several trips across the city, but I eventually got my plane tickets.

So far, everything had been many times more complicated than it would have been in Canada. Yet that was the easy part.

Although I'd already been in Bangladesh for five months, my work visa was still pending. I discovered that, while it was legal for me to work there, if I left the country on my visitor's visa, I wouldn't be able to return.

I had several conversations with the school official responsible for visas, and he continually assured me my work visa would be ready long before December 22, the day I was booked to leave.

As Christmas got closer, he began to specify the date when he'd bring me the completed visa. But he kept pushing the date back while still assuring me with calm cheerfulness that it really would be ready then.

I bought gifts and packed my suitcases. I was ready.

Suddenly it was December 21, and school was out for the holidays. My ticket was for the next day, but I still didn't have my visa!

On the day of my intended departure, I sat for hours in the school official's office, surrounded by my luggage, while he repeatedly told me he'd have the visa in a few minutes, or perhaps a few hours.

Despite my being too timid to complain, the official's assistant—whom I'd never met before—gently admonished me to "take it easy" on the official—as if I were the one who'd created this problem.

Minutes passed. Hours passed. My hopes faded. No visa appeared. At the time I should have been flying out of the country, I was still sitting in that unfriendly little office.

At the end of the day, the official took me to the airline office and charmed the staff into postponing my missed flight for two days, till the morning of Christmas Eve. He told me, with his usual cheerful unconcern, that my visa would absolutely be ready by then.

I trudged back to my empty apartment with my suitcases. All of my colleagues had gone off on their own Christmas adventures, and I was alone. God comforted me with the company of expatriate neighbours who were also unable to travel, but I hoped fervently that I wouldn't be stuck there for the whole holiday.

I never knew whether the bureaucratic wheels truly took that many months to turn or if the school official finally did the work he should have done long before, but somehow, some way, by the morning of December 24, Christmas Eve, the visa was actually ready and I was on board an airplane flying out of Dhaka, on my way to Thailand.

In the early afternoon, I walked out of the Bangkok airport and, following the instructions from my friend's sister, crossed the street to the train station, where I'd catch a train for Chiang Mai.

My heart sank when the young man at the ticket booth told me the next Chiang Mai train didn't leave until late evening.

I sat down on the bench nearest the tracks so I could watch the trains rush in, pause only briefly, and hurry out. I didn't dare walk away for fear of missing my train, but I was also afraid I wouldn't recognize it when it was right in front of me.

Thai people bustled around me and Thai words buzzed in my ears. I quickly realized that, unlike in Bangladesh, English wasn't widely spoken in Thailand.

This was before the days of cell phones, and I didn't know of any public phones nearby, so I had no way to contact my Chiang

Mai hostess to let her know I'd made it to Thailand and would arrive in her city early Christmas morning.

Exhausted, lonely, and worried, I had nothing to do but soak up the humid Thai sunshine and wait. I kept scanning the crowd, searching for a western-looking face—someone who could offer a tiny bit of English conversation, maybe assure me I was in the right place, and help me get on the right train.

At last, when it was getting dark and nearly time for my train to arrive, I saw a middle-aged man with skin as fair as mine. He was talking with a Thai man.

I wondered and hoped—did he speak English?

I approached him, excused myself, and was delighted when he answered with a British accent. We had only a few minutes to talk—long enough for me to learn he'd lived in Thailand for years and had come back to visit the friend who was with him, and long enough for me to tell him I was from Canada and teaching in Bangladesh.

We discovered we were going on the same train, and I asked his help in making sure I got on it and found the right car. Soon after that, our train to Chiang Mai rushed in. The British stranger found my car and helped me onto it. We wished each other a Merry Christmas, and he and his friend went to their own car.

As I settled into that unfamiliar seat on the unfamiliar train, heading for an unfamiliar city, my load felt immeasurably lighter than it had been just half an hour earlier.

And then the British man was standing before me once more, holding a shiny red apple in his outstretched hands, in the Asian way of giving a gift of honour.

I don't remember everything he said. He might have again wished me a Merry Christmas. He might have said something about the apple's being all he had to offer. In my surprise and delight, I hope I thanked him. All I remember for sure is that he said, "And it's even the right colour."

I still wonder if he meant that red was the right colour because it was Christmas, or because he was thinking of our Canadian flag. I had no chance to ask. I do know that, after he'd gone back to his seat, I savoured every bite of that juicy, red apple. I ate it with a very full heart—nearly overwhelmed by the simple kindness that had brought it to me.

Soon after, train attendants came to fold my seat into a bunk, and in that strange little cage, I slept surprisingly well.

In the morning, soon after the attendant reconverted my bunk into a seat, we arrived in Chiang Mai. I phoned my friend's sister from the train station, she picked me up on a motorcycle, and I began a lovely two-week respite in Thailand.

My friend and her family welcomed me as if I'd always belonged with them, and they gave me several lovely, thoughtful gifts. I've always been grateful for their kindness, and for the oasis of that restful holiday in the middle of a wonderful, often difficult, year.

God gave me several other unexpected gifts on that trip, including meeting a college friend I hadn't seen for years. Yet, when I look over my memories of that Thailand Christmas, the most miraculous moment is always the one when a stranger, whose name I never knew and whose face I never saw again, reached out to me with both hands, offering one shiny red apple.

Christmas with Hot Apple Cider

The Christmas We Almost Forgot

Nonfiction

Ramona Furst

A few years ago, my New Year's resolution was to reorganize the photo albums we'd begun to fill with family pictures before the age of digital cameras. Before long, our living room floor was covered with old albums and boxes of loose photos.

Since the task felt daunting, I enlisted my husband Per's help.

We began by laying all the photos out in order. First, of course, came our wedding. Then the births of our daughters. Other milestones followed. Now and then a picture would make us pause and share a memorable moment in our children's lives.

Peeling away the clear plastic cover from one of the album pages, I lifted a photograph from its tacky backing and smiled at the memory it evoked. "I think you were at work when this happened," I said to Per.

I held out the photo of our daughters, who at the time were aged two and four. We both laughed. I had taken the photo the day the girls decided to play hairdresser. They had cut each other's bangs in a ragged mess up to their hairlines before I discovered what they were doing and took the scissors away from them.

Per smiled at the photograph of the girls, clad in snuggly Dr. Denton pyjamas. "It's a good thing hair grows back in. They sure kept us busy."

I continued removing photos from the album and arranging them in order while Per rifled through a stack of loose photographs on the sofa between us.

We worked in companionable silence until Per said, "That's funny. I'm sure we celebrated Christmas soon after their new hairdos, but where are the pictures? They should be with these ones, shouldn't they?"

I thought for a moment, then took a close look at the other photos I'd removed from the album. There were some from

Thanksgiving that year, and some from Hallowe'en. "You're right. It was only a month or so before Christmas."

Together, we did a quick search of the albums and boxes with photos from when the girls were young, but didn't find a single picture from Christmas that year. Strange. We *always* took pictures at Christmas. What could have happened to the ones from that year?

The winter light was waning, so we gave up our search for the missing pictures. I prepared dinner while Per put the placemats on the kitchen table and found the plates and cutlery. The whole time, we were both trying to remember what had happened at Christmas that year.

Later, as we ate our dessert, Per teasingly asked, "Are you sure we *had* a Christmas that year?"

I just looked at him.

Not until later that evening, when I was under our comforter ready to go to sleep, did a memory begin to surface.

Per was still reading with the light on, so I pushed myself back into a sitting position with one elbow and poked him with the other one. "Remember, we were living in Toronto then, and you were working long hours, seven days a week?"

Soon, we were both sitting up in bed. Pieces of the puzzle had begun to fall into place.

"It all seems like a dream," I said, "but didn't all four of us get sick that year? And wasn't it around Christmas?"

"It must have been," Per said. "But if we were both sick, how did we look after the girls? And if we weren't able to look after them, who did?"

The only person I would have called for help at such a time was my mother, and yet neither Per nor I remembered a phone conversation.

Because we'd recently returned to Ontario after 15 months in Newfoundland, and had moved to a new area of Toronto, we hadn't had time to establish any close friendships yet. Since my parents lived only 20 minutes away from us, my mother was the one person we'd have called.

"If Mom found out we were both sick, and couldn't come herself," I thought out loud, "she would have moved heaven and earth to get us the help we needed. She would have contacted her church friends."

Slowly, piece by piece, we filled in the blanks of the Christmas we'd forgotten.

All four of us had become ill with the flu within hours of each other. Even Per and I had been very sick—fevered, bedridden, and at our wits' end. We must have taken turns seeing to the needs of the girls, at some point managing to get out of bed for brief periods of time to change a diaper or prepare a meal.

It was odd, but one of the things we both remembered was hearing cries from the girls' bedroom which mysteriously stopped.

"I do vaguely remember," I said to Per, who seemed to be dozing off to sleep, "the sound of whispered voices assuring me we were no longer alone. After that, I must have fallen back to sleep."

He nodded, then turned off the light as we both settled back into bed.

But my mind was still awake. "I remember hearing sounds of happy chatter," I said. "And I'm sure I smelled something fragrant and heard the sound of pots and pans coming from the kitchen. But I'm not sure which came first."

As I rearranged my pillow one last time before going to sleep, I was still trying to make sense of the vague memories.

"You could have been hallucinating," Per's muffled voice replied.

I knew he was half asleep, but I wanted to solve this puzzle. "If I was hallucinating, then who," I asked, "left the refrigerator full of prepared meals for when we were back on our feet? And don't forget the pot of soup on the stove when we first got up. Plus, the downstairs was nice and tidy."

I barely caught Per's last words before he fell asleep. "Yeah, I don't remember putting clean clothes on the girls either."

Now that I remembered that strange Christmas, I recalled asking my mother several times if she knew who had come to help us out, but all she would say was, "I don't know what you're talking about."

We never found out what happened that year. Per and I finally decided that our home must have been visited by Christmas angels.

Christmas Memories:
Past and Future

 ## Patricia Anne Elford

I curl up in our old La-Z-Boy, waiting for my apple cider to cool…

When I close my eyes, I *smell* Christmas—
wet woollen clothing, pure icy air,
freshly shampooed children in clean pyjamas,
pine tree's scent, burning maple logs,
cinnamon, nutmeg, savoury turkey.
Sweet perspiration by the cast iron wood stove.
Mom's favourite Tweed and Dad's Old Spice,
bought by us each year on special occasions.

When I close my eyes, I *hear* Christmas—
squeaky-snow footsteps; the front walk's being shovelled.
Whispers of secrets, rustling wrappers,
tape zipped from the roll.
Tinkling tree-bells pawed by the cat.
Laughter and chatter, "snap, crackle, pop" fire,
Scripture readings and carols, familiar, yet new.
Nighttime prayers and Mom's soft lullaby.
Dad's wind-up alarm clock clangs early "good morning!"
Slippered feet thump down, skipping some steps.
Toys chug and whir and play tinny music.
Exclamations and thank-yous and excited wows!
Christmas crackers burst; groans acknowledge weak puns.

When I close my eyes, I *taste* Christmas—
daily cod-liver-oil pill. Yes, even then.
Spearmint leaves and licorice mini-sandwiches,
hard candy mixes and peppermint canes.
Creamy potatoes, buttered and peppered.

Freshly cooked carrot coins lightly sprinkled with ginger.
Peas, barely cooked, burst fresh mint on the tongue.
Turkey with gravy; cranberries, pickles, and olives.
Steamed Christmas pudding submerged in rich sauce.
Hot raisin mincemeat pie melts its ice cream.
Shortbread, gingersnaps, and sweet macaroons.
Ginger ale, eggnog, wine, and hot tea.

When I close my eyes, I *feel* Christmas—
at the church, inside-my-boot snow dampens my socks.
At home, toes explore lumpy stocking at the foot of my bed,
I thumb-nail the skin from a stocking-toe orange,
seam-split a walnut for making a shell boat.
My tummy feels full enough for a week.
Prickly tree needles jab fingers and soft-slippered feet.
The kitten's tangled fur is smoothed by love-strokes.
Enthusiastic hugs squish stuffed toys and real people;
Christmas is a warm embrace.

When I open my eyes, I *see* Christmas—
at home, I see faces reflected in red, gold, and silver—
ornaments stretch our silly smiles.
The gently blown tinsel glitters its reward.
Eight blocks away, at night,
I see the nativity scene the lighted church window
paints on the snow.
The candlelit choir illuminates the warm inside darkness.
Families and singles join in the singing,
suspended in these moments of peace and of joy,
kissed by the rays of Love come down at Christmas.[1]

1. "Love Came Down at Christmas", a poem by Christina Georgina Rossetti,
   1885

The Christmas Forest

Nonfiction

Glynis Belec

I crossed my arms. "No way!"

Gilles, my always practical husband, had dared to suggest we invest in an artificial Christmas tree.

I wasn't impressed. It was important to me to keep the "real tree" tradition alive. Growing up, I'd always had a real tree. Since our first Christmas together, Gilles and I had had a real one. An artificial tree? What was he thinking?

It was fun for the children to help us lug the tree indoors and put it up. They couldn't wait until Daddy anchored and tied the fragrant blue spruce into position. And decorating it was the best part.

Okay, there were some negatives. But the messy needles didn't matter to me. And the daily watering wasn't really a chore. For me, having a real tree helped set the tone for the true Christmas spirit.

So, for years, that's what we continued to do. We made popcorn strings and carefully blew out eggs to decorate and hang as ornaments. We created other wonderful handmade ornaments and collected pretty angels, carefully placing them all on the perfect branches of our real trees.

Then, something happened. Our children grew up and moved out. They got married and put up trees of their own. Yes, they came home for Christmas every year, but somehow our tree lost its importance. No one cared much about it. Not even me.

Trying to get the blue spruce to stand up straight in the stand seemed to involve more frowns than giggles. The needles started to irritate me. Sometimes I forgot to water the tree, so more needles fell, and that irritated me even more. I started to wonder if it was time to reconsider my husband's idea from some years earlier.

Don't get me wrong. I still loved celebrating Christmas. It's a wonderful time of the year. But did a tree really represent the true

  Christmas with Hot Apple Cider

spirit of the season? After all, there's no mention of real or artificial Christmas trees in or near the stable where the Christ Child was born. So why did I think we needed one?

One day early in November, I was wandering around a thrift store when I noticed a sweet little tree that looked so realistic I had to touch it to find out it wasn't the real McCoy. I spotted the three-dollar price tag. Something nudged me into coughing up the money, and I bought it.

A few days later, my daughter asked me if I wanted a small tree. She and her husband had purchased a little three-foot tree one year, and had been using it, but they'd decided to opt for a real tree that year.

Gratefully, I accepted the little tree.

I've always liked putting up our Christmas tree in the first week of December, so, on cue, I got ready to set up the two small trees. However, I quickly realized I had a problem. While an eight-foot tree would easily house our many decorations, my new mini-acquisitions—a skinny two-footer and a gleaming three-footer—would barely balance a solitary angel on each branch, let alone 20 years of collectibles.

I sat in our living room surrounded by oversized plastic containers filled with precious memories just begging to be hung. What was I to do?

I headed out to the thrift store again. This time, the shelves were filled to overflowing with greenery and what I had come to think of as alternative Christmas trees.

I got a few funny looks as I pulled up to the cash desk with six mini trees of various sizes, but I just smiled. I had a plan.

I began with the mini lights. Mini lights for mini trees. Perfect. Then the decorations and the garlands. Finally, an angel perching proudly on top of each tree.

The first tree—I called it "The White Tree"—was adorned with every white decoration I could find in my boxes, from little snowmen to handmade snowflakes. That tree represented the purity of Christ, the sinless One, the One who creates in us a pure heart.

The second tree was "The Teal Tree." One Christmas, after a year-long battle with ovarian cancer and the rigours of chemotherapy, I'd been given quite a few teal ornaments. That tree represented good health and good friends, beautiful gifts from God.

The third tree held the fragile, hand-blown, decorated egg ornaments that my two children had made 26 years before, along with popcorn strings made a few years before that. It also held some other little handmade ornaments made by my offspring. I called it "The Heart Tree." Unto me were born some pretty wonderful children who found their way into my heart forever and ever. This tree reminded me to be grateful.

Tree number four boasted all kinds of interesting ornaments—handmade and otherwise—from my students. I had tutored for more than 18 years, so I had a large collection of lovelies for this special tree. I called it "The Learning Tree." It reminded me about the responsibility I have in teaching others about why Christ came to earth.

Tree number five sported a mixture of creations made by students, friends, and our children. A homemade Styrofoam popcorn-type string, made by my niece 40 years ago, was the treasure of that tree. I called it "The Treasure Tree." It made me think of the treasure of family and how much I love spending this holy holiday with them year after year.

Because tree number six was a little misshapen—I hadn't noticed that when I bought it—I could adorn its tiny branches only with mini decorations. Luckily, I had lots. For years, our pastor and his wife, before they retired, would give every family a small decoration containing a beautiful, etched, Christmas-themed Scripture. A perfect tree for these wonderful gifts, it became known as "The Imperfect Tree." A big reminder to me about how Christ was born unto this world to save imperfect people like me.

The seventh tree was for leftovers. In other words, whatever didn't fit the theme of one of the other trees in my forest. I have ornaments that I inherited from my parents and precious glass balls that were given as gifts when we were first married. Then there were those wonderful gingerbread men I made years ago. One is missing a leg now, but that's okay. He gets tucked behind a branch and no one is the wiser. Naturally, this one was named "The

Christmas with Hot Apple Cider

Leftover Tree." It reminds me that God picks up our broken pieces and makes us whole again.

"The New Tree" was what I called the eighth and final tree. I called it that because we're always getting interesting new Christmas ornaments, so this is the "overflow" one. "The New Tree" represents new life in Jesus. I like to have this tree close to the nativity scene so that when I glance from the baby in the manger to the tree, I'm reminded about our new life in Christ. God sent His Son, and that makes me want to sing, "Joy to the world, the Lord has come!"

We might have given up our real tree a few years ago, but it seems the trade-in was a good one. The true spirit of Christmas didn't lie in a prickly, pungent evergreen after all. Nor does it lie in my new artificial trees. But it sure does permeate my heart and fill me with the true spirit of Christmas when I gaze upon my little Christmas Forest and think about the meaning of each tree.

Maybe I should have listened to my husband sooner!

Three Christmases I'll Never Forget

Nonfiction

Bill Bonikowsky

Though it was almost half a century ago, I can still see the store. Bogardus Gaul Pharmacy, on Wyndham Street just north of Quebec Street, in Guelph, Ontario. Displayed in the window of that store, one autumn day in 1967, was what would become the most important purchase of my life up to that point—an "orange blossom" solitaire diamond that sparkled in its elegant yellow gold setting.

It was surreal—me shopping for an engagement ring for the girl of my dreams. Especially after she'd spent her teenage years avoiding me. Just the thought of a possible engagement by Christmas made my pulse quicken.

The girl was Joy McCallum. Born in Belfast, Northern Ireland, she had immigrated to Canada with her family when she was about nine. We met in church, and this dark-haired girl with hazel eyes and a mischievous smile gradually drew my attention away from Pastor Boyd's sermons.

Though Joy agreed to a first date when she was 13 and I was 14, I'd failed at further attempts to get her attention during our teen years. One Sunday afternoon, on a solitary drive through the countryside, I had a talk with the Lord. "Father, I give up," I said. "If anything is ever going to happen between Joy and me, You'll have to do it. I lay this whole thing in Your hands." I recall the feeling of a burden being lifted from my shoulders.

At the end of my first year at college, everything changed. I was visiting Joy's brother when she asked if we could have a talk. I was stunned, but managed a matter-of-fact, "Sure!" Then came the question that turned my world upside down: "Where do I stand on your list?"

I was dumbfounded. Pausing a moment to corral my thoughts, I blurted out, "Pretty near the top." Truth is, I didn't have a list. Or if I did, hers was the only name on it.

That seismic shift happened in the spring of 1967. By fall, things were serious enough that I began my search for an engagement ring. Once I had found—and managed to buy—that glittering treasure, the quest became to find the best time and place to ask "The Question." Just the thought of it took my breath away.

I wanted to find a spot where the lighting would sparkle in the facets of the diamond. And, of course, a place where we would be alone. The front seat of a car on a moonlit night seemed perfect. So I headed down a country road by myself in the moonlight to try it out. But that diamond, special as it was, needed more than a moonbeam to reflect its beauty.

My parents' home had been decorated for Christmas. Late one night, when no one was around, I sat on the end of the sofa next to the tree with its multicoloured lights and pulled out my treasure. The diamond sparkled with the colours of the rainbow. It was beautiful.

I had my answer. Christmas Eve, on the sofa by the tree, seemed the perfect time and place to propose. The challenge was to devise a way to make sure my Mom and Dad, brother, and two younger sisters were out of the house. It was complicated, being Christmas Eve. But I somehow worked it out.

On the night before Christmas, when the time was right, I ushered Joy into the house. My heart sank to find my sister Barb still at home. On her way out the door she said, with a twinkle in her eye, "Good luck, Bill."

Thanks a lot, Barb, I thought. Ignoring this momentary irritant, I brushed the comment aside (Joy later claimed she didn't think anything of it), and pressed forward with quickening pulse.

As we entered the living room, the setting was perfect. The silence, the lights, the ambience, the promise of Christmas in the air—all are etched in my memory. We sat briefly, then I turned to the only girl on my list. With trembling fingers, I opened the box containing the orange blossom diamond and asked, "Will you marry me?"

With her "Yes," the years of waiting dissolved into nothingness. The thoughts of Christmas—one of my most treasured times of the year—were eclipsed by the excitement of the pact we had just made, and we rushed off to tell our families and anyone else we could find on this Christmas Eve.

We were engaged for almost 18 months—a seemingly endless stretch of time. Too long, in our opinion. We were married on June 7, 1969 at Calvary Baptist Church in Guelph, Ontario.

The years rolled by with all the joys and challenges commonly found by married couples. Joy stood by my side as I completed Bible college and seminary. She followed me as we stepped out in faith, moving across the country to Vancouver, BC, where we ministered with Youth for Christ for 27 years. She supported me through two and a half years as a pastor and over 11 years of service with Alpha Ministries Canada.

During those years, we had three boys—Mark, Tim, and Jonathan. Between Tim and Jonathan we had a stillborn child, and the heartache it brought.

In 1998, Joy endured a serious encounter with breast cancer. Cancer cells were found in all 18 lymph nodes removed during surgery. During six months of heavy chemo followed by 13 weeks of radiation, Joy's constant prayer was that the Lord would allow her to see the marriage of at least one of her sons. She survived to witness three weddings and the births of nine grandchildren.

In all that time, I never contemplated life without her. And then the cancer returned. In February 2013 it was discovered that the breast cancer had metastasized to her bones. Joy was immediately listed as palliative, but once again God gave her extra time— partly, I believe, for my sake. By the end of the year I was on a list for heart by-pass surgery, which took place January 10, 2014. She summoned the strength to see me through.

On June 7, 2014 we celebrated our 45th anniversary. On June 16, Joy welcomed the birth of our ninth grandchild. By the end of August she was in hospice care, and she was called home by her Saviour on September 28.

That led to another Christmas Eve I will never forget.

On Christmas Eve, 2014, I stood at the graveside of my beloved Joy, where her body had lain since October 4. I recalled the 45 Christmases we'd celebrated together. Now alone, I'd needed to come here tonight.

Through tears, I said a few words to her. Then I looked up and talked to my Heavenly Father about taking good care of my girl, and if possible, letting her know I still loved her.

A light, cold breeze was blowing across the deserted cemetery. I looked up at the night sky and noted how brightly the stars were shining. It occurred to me that those were the same stars that shone on Bethlehem the night Jesus was born. They'd been a silent witness to all of our Christmases past, including the first Holy Night, and the one when I held that ring in the light of the tree and presented it to my love.

The death of the only woman I'd loved ushered me into uncharted waters. Change and loneliness were frequent companions. Much as I'd enjoyed living in our 2,100-square-foot townhouse in Surrey, British Columbia, I decided to sell and downsize. On January 19, 2015, I met with my realtor and signed the papers.

It was a watershed moment. Until then I'd been losing Joy in pieces: removing her name from bank records, cancelling her Save-On grocery store card, giving away her clothes. Now, the place where we'd shared our lives was about to be sold.

To process things, I went for a walk in the dark on the pier in White Rock. There was a familiar tug in my heart as I retraced steps Joy and I had often taken together, sometimes huddled close to ward off the chill of the night air. But this time, rising above the sea of emotion, I felt something new—the awakening of anticipation.

On the way back to my car, I glanced across the parking lot. The words "Boathouse Restaurant" shone against the night sky. It stirred memories of meals shared with Joy at this restaurant through the years. I crossed the street and climbed the stairs.

"Table for two?" the hostess asked.

"No. Just one," I smiled.

As I sat at my little table by the window, I stared out into the night, thankful that, to the Lord, the night is as bright as day, and confident that He would show me the way.

And He did. Before long, I moved into a perfect little 900-square-foot condo in the White Rock area. I rubbed shoulders with seniors living in my complex. I attended the grandkids' sporting events. And one of the highlights of my week was the time spent looking after my youngest grandchildren, Simon, Ruby, and Harriet, while their parents worked.

While I had lived my life with Joy, a parallel love story was being played out not far away.

On June 18, 1945, a baby named Shirley Booth was born in Victoria, BC. She was raised in Victoria, attending Victoria High School and Glad Tidings Tabernacle. During her high school days, she was pursued by a young man named Ken Birch—a story bearing some resemblance to my quest for Joy.

Following completion of her nursing training at Vancouver General Hospital, Shirley and Ken married on September 10, 1966. They immediately moved to Pasadena, California, where Ken attended Fuller Theological Seminary and Shirley found employment as an obstetrics nurse.

For 40 years they ministered together—in Pasadena, Hong Kong, Toronto, Saskatoon, Langley, Mississauga, and Nairobi, Kenya. Ken served as pastor, missionary, and college president as well as in administrative roles with the Pentecostal Assemblies of Canada (PAOC). They also raised two children and had five grandchildren.

In 2006 Ken and Shirley left Kenya to return to Vancouver Island, where Ken continued his work with the PAOC while they lived in Sooke and then Nanaimo. During these latter years Ken had recurring encounters with melanoma, a skin cancer that took his life on November 9, 2011.

After 45 years of marriage, Shirley Birch was now alone.

In May 2016, I received a message from Brian Stiller, Global Ambassador of the World Evangelical Alliance. I knew Brian from my years with Youth for Christ (YFC), when he served as director of YFC in Montreal, then Toronto, and finally as Canadian president.

Brian and his wife, Lily, were also good friends of Shirley and Ken. At that point, Shirley had been a widow for almost five years.

I received my first note from Brian on May 21, 2016.

> Dear Bill. You are often in our thoughts. We have much history together. Periodically I get your Facebook notices and it seems that you are dealing with your aloneness in a remarkable way.
>
> I've been thinking about writing this note for some time, but have been reluctant to, but today feel it's appropriate. I don't want to intrude on your life, but I do know that in time you will want to live in a relationship, because friendship provides an amenity for your soul that matters so.
>
> We have a very dear friend who lives in Nanaimo. Her husband passed away about five years ago, and we are very close friends both working here in Canada and while they spent time in Africa. If at some point you would be open to an introduction, we would be happy to provide that.
>
> Peace my brother and may this summer be one when you experience the shalom of the Lord.

I replied:

> I've never had a blind date, but am open to having one. I haven't been pursuing a relationship at all, but it certainly wouldn't hurt to meet your friend.

Brian got back to me right away.

> Thanks Bill. Would it be okay if I contacted her? Her name is Shirley Birch. … She's a marvellous

person. Very attractive and a lovely, gentle spirit.…

Love and blessings, Brian.

After Brian got Shirley's agreement, we surreptitiously checked each other out on Facebook while corresponding by email.

I didn't tell her that, after my first email to her, I went to the grocery store and caught myself walking down the aisle flexing my muscles.

The day before I caught the ferry to meet Shirley, I stopped by my daughter-in-law's home. Sarah has always been a prayer warrior, and I was so much wanting God's guidance in this huge matter that I asked if she would pray for me.

She must have been in shock, as she had no idea there was a woman on my radar. But pray she did.

Our first meeting was at the White Spot restaurant at Woodgrove Centre in Nanaimo for breakfast on June 10, 2016. Each of us listened intently as the other gave a brief life history. It was significant to learn that we were both 70 years old, had both been married for 45 years, had both lost our spouses to cancer, and had both come from full-time Christian ministry backgrounds.

After breakfast, we went for a walk at Neck Point Park and along the Nanaimo Marina, where Shirley bought me an ice cream cone, which I promptly dropped on the floor.

On the second day, I went to church and had lunch with my friends, Ron and Jan Dyck.

I met Shirley around two in the afternoon. We went to Coombs Old Country Market, famous for the goats that graze on its grass-covered roof, and went to Cuckoo's restaurant for a coffee and a sweet treat. Then we enjoyed a hike at Englishman River Falls Provincial Park. The date was June 11, 2016.

Afterward, I sent a message to Brian Stiller:

> Hi, Brian. Have had a nice time with Shirley for two consecutive afternoons, and plan to have coffee one more time before I head home tomorrow evening. She's a lovely lady.

Brian responded:

> Lily and I are thrilled. May the gentle and all wise
> Spirit guide your lives into His plans.

Our third date started with coffee and a chocolate-and-cara-mel cookie at Serious Coffee in Nanaimo, followed by a stroll through beautiful Pipers Lagoon Park. Near the end of our walk we sat on a log. I asked Shirley if she minded if I prayed that God would guide us in our relationship. She agreed. I took her hand. Suddenly she slid over next to me on the log. It felt like a spark jumped from her to me.

When I finished praying, our hands remained connected. We finished the walk down the beach arm in arm, and we hugged before I left for the ferry.

"That feels so good," I said.

"Yes, it does," she agreed.

I ended up missing my ferry and having to wait two and a half hours for the next one. But somehow it didn't matter.

As I waited in the ferry line-up, I texted my daughter-in-law Sarah, the one with whom I had prayed before meeting Shirley:

> Hi Sarah. Thank you for your prayers. I am returning tonight. Have had three long "dates" with Shirley Birch…a very special lady. Let me just say this for now…like the Grinch who stole Christmas, my heart grew three sizes today. It was so nice knowing my experience was shared with you.

Shortly after I got home, I met with my three sons. I was full of enthusiasm. They were still somewhat stunned. While this growing friendship was foremost in *my* mind, it was new territory to my kids, who were still grieving the loss of their mother. It had been 21 months since Joy had left us, but the river of sorrow still ran deep beneath the surface.

As my sons and I sat around the table, I tried to paint a picture of what was happening. I quoted a line from Lord Alfred Tenny-son's poem "Break, Break, Break."

> But O for the touch of a vanished hand,
> and the sound of a voice that is still!

I explained how God had brought another hand to hold and another voice to hear.

One son said, "It's just endorphins, Dad."

Another suggested, "I want you to think of the darkest times in your first marriage and ask yourself if you are willing to go through that again if necessary."

The third son said he had noticed a sparkle in my eye and, although it was hard, he was happy for me.

Thus began the emotional tug of war that so often accompanies the process of opening hearts torn by grief to the possibility of the surviving parent exploring a new relationship. I tried to be sensitive while, at the same time, not deny the feelings that grew stronger each time Shirley and I met.

I recall visiting the cemetery where Joy was laid to rest. I knew she wasn't really there, but it just seemed fitting to thank her for the many years we had together, to tell her about the new woman in my life, and to thank her for understanding.

As my love for Shirley grew, once again I found myself standing in front of a display of diamond rings. Once again, one particular ring called out to me. Once again, I faced the decision of where and when to present that ring.

I've always loved the drive to Mount Baker in Washington State in late summer or early autumn. By then, the high-level snows have largely melted and it's possible to drive right up into Heather Meadows, an alpine area that marks the eastern end of Highway 542.

Wednesday, August 17th will live in my memory as a particularly special trip to Mount Baker. This time I took my friend Shirley along. By the time we returned from our hike toward Artist Point, she had become much more than a friend. She had agreed to become my fiancée!

The ring I pulled out of my backpack has special significance. The white and yellow gold holds three small diamonds set at different levels. I was told that they are meant to represent the past, present, and future. Shirley and I are grateful for the past, in which God blessed each of us with 45 years of marriage with loving spouses. We thank God for the present, for the way in which He brought us together, for the happiness we have found with each other. And we embrace the future, trusting God to work out the intricacies of merging our lives, homes, families.

Brian first asked us about connecting on May 21, 2016. Shirley and I met on June 10. We were engaged August 17. That's fast. They say life speeds up as you get older. It appears that can be true of relationship-building at this stage, too. When we looked at our hearts toward each other, then looked at the calendar, the two didn't match. We chose to follow our hearts.

In the afterglow of our engagement, I had set aside our biggest challenge—where would we live? Shirley lived in Nanaimo, a two-hour ferry ride from my home in Surrey, BC. Her two children and five grandchildren live in the Toronto, Ontario, area. I lived within a half-hour drive of my three sons and their families.

The solution seemed simple. Shirley would just move to the mainland. My condo would be a bit tight, but we could look for another place to live. But the woman I was growing to love felt strongly that, when we married, we needed space and time to grow in our relationship as husband and wife.

The thought of "leaving" my children and grandkids caused me deep angst.

To help us get clarity of thought in this huge decision, Shirley and I went to a counsellor recommended by a friend. He was very pointed in his advice. Our marriage needed to be our priority. Moving to the Island would mean finding new ways to stay connected with the kids and grandkids, but it could be done.

I was quiet for the rest of our time together that day.

As I drove Shirley to the ferry, she said, "So what are you thinking?"

I said, "My mind is telling me that the counsellor's advice makes sense, but my heart is having trouble catching up."

I dropped Shirley off at the ferry terminal. As I drove away, I began to sob. All that night and the next day, I was in turmoil. My thoughts ran deep as I contemplated postponing the wedding or not getting married at all. I fasted and prayed and read. Then I went for a walk at Crescent Beach.

As I continued to pray for direction, I heard in my heart an almost audible voice saying, "Shirley is a treasure to you." Then, one after another, God reminded me of the many ways in which she had already enriched my life. There followed a sense of peace and the knowledge that, difficult as it would be, I could leave my life as I had known it and cleave to this woman God had prepared for me.

From that point on, there was a sense of wanting to wring every last drop of enjoyment from each encounter with my kids and grandkids, and a growing sense of commitment to finding ways to keep our bond strong after my move to Nanaimo.

In November, I invited Jonathan and Jennifer and my three youngest grandchildren to the Island for a few days. I was house-sitting for my friends Ron and Jan Dyck, whose house was right on the water. We had a delightful time.

After a fire on the shore one evening, eight-year-old Simon and I found ourselves alone.

"I love Nanaimo!" he exclaimed.

"What would you think if Grandpa moved to Nanaimo?" I asked.

"Well…I wouldn't see you as often. And who would drive us to school? And I would miss your apartment."

"Simon, do you remember the townhouse where Grandpa lived before the apartment?"

"Yes."

"You really loved the townhouse, didn't you?"

"Yes."

"And now you love Grandpa's apartment. You know, Simon, sometimes change is hard, but then you discover that you really like what you have changed to, right?"

He became thoughtful as we stood in the mix of moon and firelight.

Weeks later, two-and-a-half-year-old Harriet was looking at photos as I flicked through them on my camera. As a picture of a lighthouse on a small island flashed by, she exclaimed, "Nanaimo! Shirley!" And she mentioned one-word descriptions of that visit to the Island: water, fire, marshmallows, dinosaurs. (We had hiked down Cable Bay Trail, where someone had hidden scores of plastic dinosaurs for kids to find.) It was heartening to sense that my youngest grandchild was already, in her childlike way, beginning to embrace the changes to come.

Our Christmas wedding was coming fast. In just over six months from the day we first met, we would become husband and wife. December 29 was the chosen day, placing it between the busyness of Christmas and New Year's celebrations for the sake of our guests.

The morning of the 29th dawned with wind-driven rain spattering against my window. But, despite the weather and the tremendous emotional significance of this being my wedding day, I was filled with a peace and calm.

By noon the rain had stopped, and soon I was standing in the sanctuary of a century-old church with my new love, in front of close friends and family. When each of us had first married, the words "till death do us part" seemed to speak of a time so far distant as to make them almost irrelevant. It was a solemn experience to repeat those words again, at 71 years of age, having experienced the pain of separation from our first spouses by death.

And so, Shirley Birch and Bill Bonikowsky began their new lives together.

I didn't know if I would be able to love again. But love doesn't come in finite packages. God's immeasurable love poured out that first Christmas in the gift of His Son should have been my clue.

On this, my most recent Christmas, the God whose nature is love, and who is the giver of life, reminded me of the capacity of the heart to love again.

The Angel in King's Place

Nonfiction

Esther Rennick

The day was typical. Same work. Same processes. Same telephone calls. Same, same, same... Nothing new. And now it was lunch time. On this particular snowy December day, I decided to eat out—something I often did, particularly on very busy days. At this point, eating out for lunch was another case of "same" for me.

I'd started my career as a young lady fresh out of school, and now I was considered a rarity in the workplace for having stayed with one employer so long. After working for the same financial company in Fredericton, New Brunswick, for 20 years, I'd moved into the role of general manager. But after 10 years in that position, there were no additional accomplishments to work toward.

As I plodded through the fresh-fallen snow to the food court at King's Place, the downtown mall, my face was downcast. I was so tired of my life.

I planned to grab the forbidden fruit of a burger and fries. Actually, it was going to be a double burger and large fries, the real forbidden fruit.

I ordered my food, put it onto my tray, and started looking around for the most uncrowded, solitary place to sit in the food court. I didn't want anyone nearby to bother me.

I found an unoccupied, two-seater table next to a window and sat down. Through the window, I could see the Christmas decorations on the street. It seemed like they were exuberantly beckoning all who beheld their beauty to be filled with Christmas joy, but, for me at least, they failed miserably. They were the same decorations as the year before and the year before that. Their joyful beckoning had grown stale and mouldy like an old loaf of bread.

I dumped my fries into one side of the burger box, took the dill pickles off my burger, and threw them into the empty fry box. I took the paper off my straw and started to put it into my diet pop.

A woman's voice interrupted my most precious solitude. "Excuse me, dearie. Would you mind if I sit with you at your table?"

Unbelievable! Who would interrupt my quiet lunch! Then I thought, *How selfish can I be?*

I looked up and saw an elderly lady with a cane. She was a few feet from my table, and her movements were slow and unsteady. She didn't have any food with her, so the only explanation I could see for her being in the food court was that perhaps she needed to sit and rest.

Why? Why? Oh, God, why this? I so wanted to eat in peace today! You know I need time alone. God, I do not want to eat with this person today. Couldn't she find another table to sit at with someone who actually wants to talk to her?

My silent prayer went unanswered. The woman continued slowly moving toward my table.

I had no choice but to get up, saying, "Sure! Sure you can sit with me." I then saw to it that she was comfortably seated. No matter what my selfish inner prayer had been, I have good manners, at least most of the time.

Now that we were seated, I saw she had a sweet, angelic face with eyes that crinkled in the corners when she smiled. She exuded happiness and joy. Her presence gave off a fragrance of strength but also gentleness. There was an aura of mystery about her.

Curiously, she seemed to bring a change in the atmosphere around me. Instead of the turmoil I'd been experiencing, I felt a sense of peace.

I didn't have a clue what to say to her, but I shouldn't have worried. She asked me what I did and some other ordinary "get to know" you questions. Then, she asked if I usually ate in the same place when I went out for lunch. *A strange question.*

I told her I did.

"Why?"

I shrugged my shoulders.

"You don't want to live a boring life, dearie! You weren't made for that. You need to live a life of adventure!"

When she said the word "adventure," it was as if months of boredom rolled off my back. The land of "same" fell away, and hope stood up. Life of adventure! That was it. I craved change. I craved adventure!

The lady then went on to tell me all about her life and how years and years ago she'd made the decision to live a life of adventure. She told me that even though she was now crippled, she still travelled a lot. In fact, she had just returned from overseas.

I was amazed. Would I dare to hop on a plane and travel if I were as old as she was, never mind if I had trouble walking?

She then told me that the next time I ate lunch out I should eat at a different restaurant. "Forget the food court for a day. Do something different!" she pleaded.

Something inside me made me wonder if this woman was more than what she appeared to be. I mean, it was Christmas, and somehow angels seem to be spoken of more often at Christmas. *God, why do I seem to be hearing Your voice through this lady? Could she be an angel in disguise?*

It occurred to me that if she was an angel, perhaps no one else could see her. That would mean when I spoke to her, people sitting near me would see me talking to an invisible person. My facial expressions wouldn't make sense to them. They'd think I was behaving very strangely. Let's face it, if this lady was an invisible angel, people around me might be thinking I needed transportation to the psych ward at the hospital!

Ah, well. If it happened, it happened.

My lunch companion went on to tell me more about her adventures travelling all over the world. She said she'd worked at challenging jobs that women didn't do years ago, but she'd persevered and done the seemingly impossible. She told me that adventure was a choice, and that I needed to go where others didn't go.

In all, she talked for about 45 minutes, and her story was incredible! I kept stuffing fries into my mouth every now and then; however, my mouth was hanging open by the time I was ready to go back to work. This lady had interrupted my world of same and literally told me off for living a boring life. She'd challenged me in ways no one else ever had.

I left King's Place a different person. The lady had planted a seed. I'd realized how much I longed to live a life of adventure. I

  Christmas with Hot Apple Cider

didn't want to live in the land of same and boredom. I began to pray about it. I knew that God would help me find a way. After all, He'd already sent me an angel!

The next day, I decided to eat out again, but following her instructions, I went to a restaurant instead of the food court burger joint.

The waitress who came to my table stared at me and said, "Esther! Are you Esther?"

"Yes," I said. "And you're Susan!¹ We went to school together in grade eight."

What an awesome catch-up conversation we had. Amazing! A new adventure! I would never have met up with Susan while stuffing down double burgers in the land of the food court.

I never saw my angel again, but her words still challenge me to live a life of adventure every day, even if it's just eating at a new restaurant.

Since that Christmas encounter, my life hasn't been the same. I didn't understand until much later that boredom was the cause of my frustration and unhappiness.

One little step at a time, I started making life changes. Then, I started taking huge giant steps of faith into the unknown world of God-adventures.

Eventually, I left my career of 34 years and went to Bible school in Prince Edward Island. I then became an assistant tour manager for a travelling evangelistic musical family, The Sky Family, who toured all over North America. We lived out of suitcases while going from one city to another. Three months on the road and three months off became my life.

For one tour, we drove from the east coast of Canada to Vancouver Island on the west coast. Then we drove all the way down the west coast of the United States to the Mexican border, across the bottom of the United States, and up the east coast, returning home to Prince Edward Island.

After three and a half years living and touring with the Prince Edward Island musical family, God had me return to Fredericton. Today, I actually live by faith. In other words, I haven't had a full-time paying job in almost four years. I gave up my career, my home, my car—everything—to live a life of God-adventures, and He has daily provided for me.

I'm presently living with a pastor and her husband while helping them in their church and their music ministry. Where I'll be in six months, I don't know. And no, the arthritis in my knee won't stop me! I know that the God who sent a Christmas angel to change the direction of my life is very capable of taking care of me as I continue to live the adventures He has planned for me.

I still don't know if my Christmas angel was a real person like me or an actual angel, but I do know that she was the catalyst who helped me realize I was being stifled by a life of boredom, and led to my getting in touch with God's much better plan of hope, adventure, and joy.

"For I know the plans I have for you," declares the Lord,
"plans to prosper you and not to harm you,
plans to give you hope and a future" (Jeremiah 29:11).

1. Name changed

  Christmas with Hot Apple Cider

Master of the House: A Christmas Fantasy

Fiction

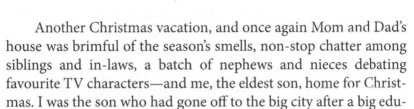

John Paul Tucker

Another Christmas vacation, and once again Mom and Dad's house was brimful of the season's smells, non-stop chatter among siblings and in-laws, a batch of nephews and nieces debating favourite TV characters—and me, the eldest son, home for Christmas. I was the son who had gone off to the big city after a big education to land a big job.

My sister always said I was like the older brother in the movie *It's a Wonderful Life* if he had actually left town. "You're the corporate Jimmy Stewart," she said. "Nice, but a little distant." She never told me what she meant by "distant," but that's Siss. She doesn't spear you; she plants annoying slivers and lets them fester.

Don't get me wrong. I enjoy coming home. But for some reason, that Christmas, everything seemed too much. The combination of garish ornaments, the blaring TV, fits of raucous laughter bursting from the kids, one too many mushy songs seeping from the stereo, inescapable family conferences, topped off by the steamy odour of half-cooked cabbage rolls set my head spinning and my stomach churning. I had to make an exit.

I slipped through a side door into the crisp, quiet air of my parents' unheated, and, more to my aim, uninhabited, two-car garage.

It might have been the overwhelming quiet or the refreshing cold air that splashed against my face, but I was struck with an urge to walk across the field behind our house and plunge into the woods. I nabbed one of my dad's work coats from a peg on the garage wall, pulled on a pair of warm boots, and briefly popped into the kitchen to announce that I'd be gone for an hour. I returned Mom's concerned look with a meek smile, slunk back into the garage, and passed like a thief through the door leading to the backyard.

As I crossed the field, the call of the approaching woods hastened my steps. My heart was thumping harder than usual and I'm pretty sure it wasn't because of my shabby fitness. I was returning to the place where I'd spent my best times as a kid, and it had already set its hooks in me.

There'd been a light snow overnight, but a strong sun had melted half of it away. I skirted the long white islands amid the sea of brown, knotted meadow grass, jumped a creek that ran along the edge of the woods, and wandered through a stand of tall, eerily familiar White Pines—the best climbing trees in the world. I found a path I had trod many times—an abandoned horse trail, as I recall—that led further in.

When I was young, in mind as well as body, these were enchanted paths. Every one of them might as well have been leading to a gingerbread cottage or a hobbit hole. But those days were gone—long gone. Now my head was crowded with overseeing development of new application software, marketing, suppressing the urge to avenge myself on an underhanded co-worker, making flawless presentations to prospective clients on half a tank of enthusiasm—and yes, Siss, the wild hope of a promotion. How out of place those things seemed there.

When I'd entered those woods as a 12-year-old, I'd felt as if I were entering Someone's domain, and that every living thing was watching me, weighing my every move, even listening to my thoughts.

Now, with every step, I was falling under the forest's spell anew. The tops of the fir trees began whispering their secrets. The chipmunks skittered about, frantically announcing my trespass. The tall, straight hardwoods loomed overhead like wizened elders. And the richly scented earth gently cradled everything. Here were influences that seemed as strong as my family.

I followed the trail along the edge of a beaver pond until I spotted a small clearing where leaves and pale grass had nestled around the horizontal trunk of an old, fallen beech tree. I'd been warmed by the sun, so without hesitation I accepted the invitation to sit down in front of the broad trunk, leaning back against its weatherworn side under the gentle heat of the winter sun, with the iced-over pond peeking through the trees.

In the past when I'd been still, and very patient, the woods had forgotten my intrusion. Birds would begin first, with their conversations and jubilant exultations. Next, the nattering antics of squirrels. And if I kept quiet for long enough, the chipmunks would pop up. Those curious brown and black striped burrowers were always the last to abandon their hiding places and give the all clear. On lucky days, a heron would float down and stand among the cattails.

I sat in the warm bright sun with my coat open, legs stretched out, and my back resting against the trunk. I'd forgotten about this world in the woods. Everything melted into a delightful haze and I must have dozed.

I remember an icy breeze creeping up my back, and standing up in the shade of a bleak slow-moving cloud. I zipped up my coat and, to stave off a chill, broke a trail further into the back woods.

I was curious. This was territory I'd never explored as a boy. It was too far, and the woods close to home had been enough to keep me endlessly curious and entertained.

But, now, I felt compelled to walk further on. Perhaps if I walked far enough I'd discover that my so-called enchanted forest had a name on a map—that it had been scooped up by a developer who had, as the song goes, "paved paradise and put up a parking lot."[1]

In 10 minutes, I could see that the trees gave way to a clearing of low mounds of bedrock, bordered by a crowded grove of tall, plush cedars. Though the slate-grey sky was bright, the muffling conifers appeared dark and forbidding. Thick with enchantment. I had a distinct hunch they were guarding a secret. I couldn't resist. Hands shielding and head down, I plowed into the firs. I pushed through and stumbled out into a flat area completely encircled by evergreens that had the feel of an empty, if not solemn, courtyard. Except for what stood in the middle.

For a minute, I stood gazing at the object before me the way I might gawk at a peculiar painting. *Was that here when I was a kid?* Against the dark green background, like a pale spectre, loomed an old, two-storey, wood frame house. The weathered wood siding looked like it might have been green at one time. The glassless windows reminded me of the hollow, dark sockets of a skull.

It's odd to have turned up here, I thought. *But what a find!*

My dad was a bit of an amateur antique hunter. He'd track down long-forgotten roadside dumps to unearth hand-blown, coloured bottles, or ask local farmers for permission to dig around foundations of long abandoned buildings on their properties. When I was younger, I was right at his side.

My dad would say that the foremost pleasure in exploring one of these old houses was in discovering the treasures that lay within. If the house hadn't been utterly ransacked, it usually yielded some remnant from the past: an old match tin, a medicine bottle, or if you were really lucky, an old magazine or letter lining a chest of drawers or tucked under a floorboard.

The front door had no stairs, and there was a hollow in front where the ground had possibly caved in—perhaps because of a root cellar. I looked around, and in a moment, I'd scrambled over the sill of the glassless front window. I found myself in what once must have been the living room. Surprisingly, it was bare to the bones: not a shred of curtain, a table leg, or even a patch of lurid graffiti tagged by some kids staking claim to a clubhouse. Nothing.

I scoured every corner until it occurred to me that the room was unlike any other abandoned house I had explored. This one was *too* empty. The wood was parched and cracked, and the wallpaper was peeling, but there wasn't a screw, a wood chip, or a fleck of dust in sight. It was as if the room had never been lived in; merely built and then deserted.

I ventured into another room—dining room, maybe? Also bare. On to the kitchen. Surely that busy place would have left behind a small token. Nothing. Empty, knobless cupboards, a hole for a sink, and no telltale scars of a fridge or stove. The vinyl floor covering was peeling up at the corner; water stains blotted the ceiling and walls; but not one room on the main floor offered a solitary scrap from the past.

I climbed up the stairway, testing each step as I went, then walked across the floor of the empty front bedroom and peered out the window. Nothing but mounds of snow and the high fence of fir trees, but I was beginning to feel closed in, as if I were being squeezed in a trap.

  Christmas with Hot Apple Cider

It was the house. Something wasn't right.

The moment I'd decided to scramble down the stairs and launch myself through the hole that was the front door, a cry stopped me in my tracks. Not a loud, desperate wail, but a pitiful whimper. The second one stole my breath. It was very faint, yet distinct enough to be coming from inside the house. I drummed down the stairs to the first floor.

Since the first floor had been deserted, my first thought was that some kid had gotten trapped in the basement. Off the kitchen, I found a doorway leading down a gloomy set of wooden stairs. As expected, no light switch. All I had was the meagre light offered by the small kitchen window. I hovered over each step before trusting it with my full weight. That's all I needed, to fall through some rotten stairs and break my leg before Christmas dinner.

Halfway down, I was encouraged by feeble streaks of light pooling on the basement floor from two half-buried basement window wells. I reached the bottom, which wasn't far, maybe a six-foot head space, a hair between me and a headache.

The basement was divided by one thick supporting wall down its centre. There was no one and nothing in the first section where the stairs were, so I ducked under an arch into the darker space beyond. In the far corner of the basement was what appeared to be a loaded burlap bag. It was just sitting there, so I ventured closer and gave it a tug.

It wasn't a sack at all. Huddled under the coarse material was a small, shivering kid. I snatched off my coat and wrapped it around the tiny curled back, but the kid shook it off and let it slump to the floor. I picked up the coat to try again.

"The child is not easily comforted," a voice said from behind me.

I involuntarily jumped and smacked the crown of my head on a wooden joist. I turned around, nursing my head. In the corner, seated on what looked like an old kitchen chair, was an old man.

"Who are you?" I blurted out, believing I'd stumbled on a kidnapper. "Do you know this boy?"

"I do not know the child, but I watch over him nevertheless," the old man said. "The child refuses me. If I try to help him, he only thrashes and kicks and runs back to his corner."

The old man spoke deliberately and kindly, but that made me all the more suspicious. Was this some sort of abuse case?

I anchored myself between the old man seated in one corner and the kid huddled in the other. It was a least a half hour run to Mom and Dad's to call the police. *No,* I thought. *Rescue the kid and then call the authorities.* I approached the kid again. "Do you want to come with me?" I asked.

"No," came the reply. "I live here."

What sort of bizarre cruelty had I stumbled on? If God had any hand in this world, he must have sent me here to rescue this kid. "You can't live here—in a deserted basement."

I turned to the old man. "You both have to come with me," I said with all the corporate authority I'd accrued since I'd first clutched a briefcase. "I'll arrange to get help."

"I am the child's refuge and he refuses," the old man said. "You can do nothing—in fact, you have tried and failed."

"Failed?" I flashed back. "What are you talking about?"

"You have failed to provide the very thing he is wanting, and yet you are sure you can help."

"I can save him from you!" I shot back.

"But who will save him from you?" returned the old man.

This strange, incoherent conversation had gone on long enough. I moved to pick up the kid. I had determined to take him against his will, even if he did kick and thrash about. I gripped the boy's shoulder, then stood blankly staring into the face that stared back at me. He wasn't a kid at all, but a shrunken old man.

I stumbled back. His features were familiar to me, but I didn't recognize the dark, fear-filled eyes.

The backs of my hands glistened with sweat. I moved away, and bumped hard into the wall. Stumbling, I reached the basement stairs and fled the horrible scene.

Forgetting there weren't any steps, I rushed out the front door, narrowly clearing the hollow, and hit the ground heavily. For a moment, I lay sprawled on the snow, my dad's jacket still clutched in my fist as if it were all I had to transport me back to the real world.

When I regained my wind, I got up and turned to see the old man. He had abandoned his basement chair and was standing in

 Christmas with Hot Apple Cider

the doorway as if nothing strange were happening, as if he had lived there all his life and was seeing off a friend.

Shaking my head, I staggered back, looked for the path I'd come by, and tore off into the cedars. When I reached the place where I'd been sitting, I stopped to cast a glance back, half expecting the spectre of the old man floating along the ground in pursuit. But I saw no one.

Had I wandered into a dream? Had I fainted or had some other kind of terror come to haunt me? Was it possible I was in the middle of a mental breakdown?

The edges of the darkening long tree trunks were ablaze with gold. The sun was setting, and the long trunks of the wood had drawn crooked shadows across the old beech. A breath of icy evening air swirled around me. Yet I was panting and sweating heavily.

My coat draped over my shoulders; I tripped along the trail home, reviewing the menacing images of the house in the woods as I went. As a boy, I'd always believed these woods were enchanted, but now they seemed threatening, as if they hung over me in judgement.

When I reached home, the house lights were brilliant in the twilight. The lamp over the back door into the garage was on; that was Mom.

I had been gone too long. My absence would have been noticed. I would need to present a reasonable explanation. But it wasn't as if I was late for a budget meeting or surrounded by colleagues.

On the other hand, there was no hope of fooling my mother or Siss. They would see trouble in my eyes and cast questioning looks at me for the rest of my visit. I had to do what I'd always done; pull myself together.

But my return to the house was a lot easier than I'd anticipated; my nephews and nieces instantly surrounded me, shouting, "He's back! He's back! Now we can start."

Two of them ushered me to the table and shoved me down to Christmas dinner.

I muttered a feeble apology for being late and no one, except maybe Mom, suspected anything other than a prolonged walk, or perhaps a lost wandering in the woods.

After too much of everything, I nabbed a rocker by the Christmas tree while the others went to the family room for dessert.

I rocked and retraced the strange events of the afternoon against the backdrop of the brilliantly lit tree. I hadn't called the police. Somehow, I knew that there would be no old man, no shrivelled child, and maybe not even the spectral house.

When I'd finished the reruns and focussed on the present, I had wandered from the tree to the warmly lit nativity on the mantel. I'd never given it more attention than any other ornament, but now I was suddenly struck by it. I got up to examine it more carefully.

It was typical. Crafted from barn board with crudely carved little statuettes and a manger that held something that looked like hay. But it was the kid in the manger that caught my attention. A happy baby surrounded by a bunch of happy people.

I'd always heard people talk about the stable as if it were a shabby place for a baby to be born, but poverty wasn't what I saw. The shed was full. Full of company, gifts, expectation, warmth, and light. Even the animals seemed happy.

The life in that simple stable cast a deathly chill over the barrenness of the house I'd visited in the woods. I suddenly knew that *I* was that tomb of a house, or the shrunken little man I'd found huddled in the basement, or both. An empty house without the resources to fill it. The old man was right; I had tried and failed.

"Could that be my older brother gazing at the nativity?" It was my sister.

I swiped my cheek.

"Christmas miracles never cease," she said.

Because I hadn't turned, she poked her face around my shoulder. "Hey, are you—?"

My eldest niece and nephew charged into the room, calling for their presents.

Rescued—at least for now.

The others joined us, and soon we were all seated and opening gifts. But after the exclamations for five-star presents, after-dinner treats, and refills of spiced cider, my thoughts steered my gaze back to the nativity.

  Christmas with Hot Apple Cider

The image of the shrewd old man lingered in my vision like a stubborn ghost. Maybe old Scrooge had arranged a visit by some unknown Christmas spirit? However it had come, by a strange Christmas miracle, the Master of the house in the woods had offered me a rare gift—a glimpse into the "me" who existed beyond my carefully staged resumé.

And that revelation wasn't the only miracle that Christmas. The other was that I prayed. Not a long prayer, but I'm pretty sure it would have turned a few heads at a prayer meeting. "Lord of the stable," I said, "fill up my house."

I knew what I meant. I figured He did, too.

In the days or months that followed, I can't say anyone would have noticed anything dramatic. The changes were subtle, but there was definitely, what we call in marketing, a disruption.

Of course, Siss was the first in my family to notice. It was the following summer on a walk in the woods. I'd had to see if the house was still there. Anyways, Siss said, "It's the wrong season, Jimmy Stewart, but welcome home."

As I said, with her it's slivers, not spears.

1. From the song "Big Yellow Taxi," Joni Mitchell, 1970

My Pork Chop Christmas

Nonfiction

L. June Stevenson

It was the first Christmas after my husband and I separated. We'd been married for more than 25 years, and our son and daughter, both in their late teens and well on their way to careers and marriage, lived with me.

Since we were breaking new ground, in the second week of December, I decided I wasn't ready to be around people who would fuss over me. I asked my kids what we should do on Christmas Day. "Do you want to have dinner at home with me?"

"For sure," came the response.

So I bought a turkey and began thinking about the trimmings and treats for the dinner.

A week before Christmas, it occurred to me we could have a few other people over to lighten what might be a stressful day. The kids agreed.

I suggested brunch. We had done it before, successfully. They would invite their cousins and several friends to come early Christmas morning. *Great,* I thought, *that will help to occupy my day.* I planned grapefruit, champagne, a frittata, and some new and different breads.

Three days before Christmas, I asked what vegetables the kids would like to have for Christmas dinner, and got a blank stare. They looked strangely at each other.

"Duh! Well, Mom," my son said tentatively, "we thought we were having brunch instead of dinner." He glanced at his sister as if to make sure she was there to back him up.

"Oh, yeah," she confirmed. "We made plans to go to Dad's for Christmas dinner."

I stood perfectly still, digesting what I had just heard. My first Christmas alone—not only without my husband, but also without my children. I didn't know what to say.

The kids were quick to react, as they had been in those early days after our separation. "Uh, we can change it," they both said at once, again looking at each other for support.

By then, I had recovered from the shock. "No, no, of course not. Brunch it is, and it will be the best brunch we've ever had."

So I prepared for brunch, wondering how I would cope with the rest of what I knew would be a long Christmas Day by myself.

The next morning, I got on the phone to the Scott Mission in downtown Toronto. But they told me they didn't need any help; they had plenty of volunteers. I called Evangel Hall, another mission in Toronto. Same response. But they did give me some good advice. "Go to your local hospital," they said, "and ask who could use a visitor." *Great*, I thought. *I have a plan.*

Christmas brunch was a success. We all relaxed, filled our stomachs, and chatted. Most of the kids had been away at college or university, and this was a great chance to catch up on their adventures since the summer.

After brunch, my kids and their guests continued their conversations while I prepared to go out. I put some magazines and a few paperback books in a bag—some Christian, some not—and dressed for the mild winter weather. Then I interrupted the kids' chatter to say good-bye.

"Where are you going, Mom?" They seemed concerned.

"To the hospital," I answered.

"Are you okay?"

"Of course," I said. "I'm just going to visit some patients. Have a great day."

The streets were bare and dry. Since Sunnybrook Hospital was only about six blocks away, I added a nice, healthy walk to my Christmas adventure.

At Sunnybrook, I stopped inside the main door and simply asked the receptionist on duty, "Is there a ward that has some patients who can't go home today?"

She never even blinked an eye. "Go to Ward 2, second floor, and ask the nurses at the desk."

I did, and was surprised when they quickly gave me a short list of patients' names.

Smiling, I poked my head into the first room to see a young woman lying comfortably in bed. "Merry Christmas," I said, "Would you like a visitor?"

Politely, she replied, "No, thank you," so I continued down the hall. My next stop was more challenging. An older woman sat beside the bed of a male patient who seemed to be sleeping. He looked very fragile and pale.

"Oh, how nice," the woman said, "to have someone to talk to. My husband doesn't say much anymore. He doesn't have very long to live. I come every day just to sit with him. Sometimes my son comes, too." She sighed and wiped a tear from her eye. "We've been married fifty years." She shook her head and blew her nose.

I sat with her for quite a while. We didn't talk much, but I was glad that I could be there if she wanted to say something.

Next, I encountered a woman resting in a small room set apart for family who are visiting a patient and need a place to go. Her feet were up, but her eyes were open and sad. "We have to tell my husband that he'll never go home again," she said. "He's going to a nursing home. I worry so much about how he'll take the news."

"That must be hard," I said, sitting down beside her. "Tell me about it."

I let her talk as I sat quietly beside her, encouraging her but not intruding, hoping my calm would give her some comfort. Soon, the rest of her family arrived and I bid her best wishes.

Next I found a woman, quite young, who had a weighty contraption on her head. She didn't seem to want to talk, but she admitted how much she missed her husband and young children, who were unable to visit due to distance.

I wished her well and left a book of poetry beside her.

The next woman couldn't have been happier to welcome me. A Christian, she seemed to need reassurance that God was with her in her illness. She gladly accepted my gift of several Christian paperbacks, and we chatted about many things, both secular and religious, for about 20 minutes. It was a very satisfying time for both of us.

Soon after that, I left the hospital with mixed feelings. I was saddened by the burden others had to carry at such a special time of year, and I was also humbled, hoping that perhaps I had made a little difference in a few lives.

Everyone needs someone to greet them at this special time of year. Most people need someone to talk to—especially someone who will listen—someone who is there just for them. I hoped my presence had helped. I certainly felt better for the experience.

Home again, I hunted for something to eat. My turkey was still frozen. Nothing else had been made. At last, I spied a leftover pork chop in the refrigerator.

I heated it up, added a few vegetables, put my supper on a tray, and turned on the television to watch something Christmassy.

"Merry Christmas" flashed across the screen.

Indeed, I thought, *it has been a merry Christmas!*

Remembering the old adage, "When life gives you lemons, make lemonade," I looked at my plate, smiled, and said aloud, "When there is no turkey, eat a pork chop!"

Missing You

Lynne Collier

Your cane and walker stand forlorn
Beside the kitchen door.
The closets hide your
Purses inside
And the wigs you need no more.

Those who love you feel the sorrow—
Christmas without you here.
But we'll muddle through
This ache that's new,
Grieve our loss of you, my dear.

We'll miss the homemade Christmas cards,
The visits and the tea.
Your warm embrace,
Your smiling face,
All from a heart so free.

You always thought of others first
And hid your pain inside.
You gave so much
So we'd feel blessed.
And when you left, we cried.

But though we grieve your presence lost
Our thoughts cannot stay grim.
We'll sigh awhile
But also smile
For now you dance with Him.

"You turned my wailing into dancing;
you removed my sackcloth and clothed me with joy,
that my heart may sing your praises and not be silent.
Lord my God, I will praise you forever" (Psalm 30:11,12).

  Christmas with Hot Apple Cider

Advent of Healing

Fiction

Shelley Norman

Six-year-old Sarah stood on a scarred old wooden kitchen chair that had been dragged out into the hallway, balancing precariously on her tippy toes as she reached to hang the evergreen wreath on a hook on their apartment door. "How's it look, Mommy?" she asked, setting her little fists on her hips as she studied her work.

"It's perfect, honey." Her mother wrapped an arm around Sarah, giving her a gentle squeeze. "Now, how about we go back inside and start putting the lights on the tree before Daddy gets home from work?"

"Yippee!" Sarah squealed, hopping off the chair and almost crashing into an elderly lady coming down the hallway from the direction of the elevators.

"Hi, Mrs. MacGregor!" Sarah chirped. "Do you like our wreath? It's an Advent wreath. That's why it has three purple and one pink bow on it instead of red bows."

Mrs. MacGregor looked at the door decoration and grunted before turning toward her own door across the hall.

As Sarah's mother picked up the kitchen chair, Sarah followed Mrs. MacGregor, leaning against the wall as the elderly lady searched her mammoth handbag for her key. "How come you don't have a wreath on your door yet?" she asked. "Everyone else on our floor has Christmas decorations on their door—well, except for 3B, but everyone knows they celebrate Hanukkah instead."

Finding her key, Mrs. MacGregor opened her door and stepped inside.

"I don't do Christmas," she said before shutting the door, leaving Sarah's question more or less unanswered.

"Mommy, what does Mrs. MacGregor mean by she doesn't 'do' Christmas?" Sarah asked as she followed her mother inside their third-floor apartment and closed the door behind her.

Sarah's mother placed the chair back at the kitchen table before turning to her daughter. "Remember how I told you that Mrs. MacGregor moved to Canada many, many years ago with her family?"

Sarah nodded.

"Well, she moved here with her husband and son. Her son was probably around your age. He had just started school. They hadn't been in this country long when one night they were driving home from somewhere and they were in a car accident. Her husband and son both died in the crash. Because it happened close to Christmas, she hasn't celebrated Christmas since. For her, it's a very sad time."

After moving into the living room, Sarah's mother started searching through a box for the Christmas tree lights.

Sarah followed quietly behind.

Having found the lights, Sarah's mother looked over at her daughter to see how she had processed the information about their neighbour.

"Do you mean her husband and little boy are in heaven now with the angels?" Sarah asked quietly.

"Yes, and she misses them a lot, especially at Christmastime." Sarah's mom reached out a hand and pushed a strand of Sarah's fine brown hair behind the little girl's ear, praying she'd never have to experience the pain the elderly lady must have gone through and no doubt still felt when the holidays rolled around each year.

All of a sudden, Sarah's eyes lit up. "Mommy, do you mind if I go to my room while you get the lights ready? There's something I need to do."

"Of course. I'll let you know when I've got this mess sorted out." Sarah's mom began to untangle the strings of lights as Sarah bolted from the room.

The little girl reappeared about 20 minutes later, a piece of paper in hand as she headed for the front door. Opening the door, she disappeared into the hall for a moment before coming back empty-handed.

"What was that about?" her mother asked.

"Oh, nothing," Sarah said. "Can we put the lights on the Christmas tree now?"

  Christmas with Hot Apple Cider

They had just finished hanging the lights on the tree when Sarah's father came in the door.

"Daddy, come see the tree!" Sarah called excitedly.

"In a minute, honey," her father replied. "But first, could you come here for a second?"

Sarah ran to the door, where she found Mrs. MacGregor standing beside her father. "Hello again, Mrs. MacGregor."

The elderly lady pointed to a piece of paper hanging on her own apartment door. The paper had a picture of a Christmas wreath drawn on it and decorated with glitter glue and shiny red and gold bell-shaped stickers. "Did you put that on my door?" she asked Sarah.

"How did you know it was me? I was really quiet," Sarah said, slightly annoyed. "It was supposed to be a secret."

"Hmph!" Mrs. MacGregor responded. "If you want it to be a secret, next time don't use the back of old school work with your name on it."

"Oops!" Sarah thunked herself on the forehead with the heel of her hand.

"Good job on the spelling test, though," Mrs. MacGregor said. Sarah smiled, "Thanks. I love spelling!"

Mrs. MacGregor nodded and made a grumbly sound, then went back into her apartment.

Sarah's parents looked at each other over Sarah's head, not sure what to make of the exchange, but Sarah smiled widely. After all, Mrs. MacGregor must have liked the drawing since she hadn't taken it down. And she really should have a wreath for her door, too. It must be hard being old and not having any family to help decorate for the holidays. If Sarah was living with the angels in heaven, she'd want some kid to help her mommy decorate for Christmas.

Over the next few weeks, Sarah continued to make and leave little drawings and gifts on Mrs. MacGregor's door: the dove she made in Sunday school on Peace Sunday; tissue paper poinsettias, prancing reindeer, and cotton-ball snowmen from art class at school; a painting of a happy angel made on Joy Sunday; and, for the last Sunday of Advent, a star-shaped ornament with a drawing of the holy family in the centre.

When Sarah approached Mrs. MacGregor's apartment on the afternoon of December 23 with a Christmas card she'd just finished making, she couldn't find any space to hang it up, so she simply slipped it under the door.

A few hours later, Sarah was standing on that rickety kitchen chair again while her mother knelt beside it attempting to hem up a borrowed angel costume. The doorbell rang.

"I'll get it!" Sarah exclaimed, jumping from the chair and sending the pin cushion that had been by her feet flying across the kitchen.

Shaking her head, Sarah's mother followed her to the front door. Standing in the open doorway was Mrs. MacGregor, holding the Christmas card Sarah had delivered that afternoon.

"Hi!" Sarah said cheerfully. "Do you like my angel costume?" She did a little twirl. "I'm going to be an angel in the church pageant tomorrow night."

As Mrs. MacGregor looked down at Sarah, tears started to form in her eyes.

Sarah's mother bustled to her side. "Won't you come in, Mrs. MacGregor?" She held the door open wide for the elderly lady, then escorted her to the living room. "Please have a seat. Would you like a cup of tea?"

"No. No, thank you, dear. I just came to see Sarah about the Christmas card she left me."

Mrs. MacGregor watched Sarah as she continued to twirl around the living room in the much-too-long white robe, the gold tinsel halo on her head twinkling in the Christmas lights.

"My Liam was a shepherd in the Christmas pageant." A tear slid down her wrinkled cheek. "He was so excited. I sewed a brown robe and a headdress for him to wear. His father made a shepherd's crook for him." She reached into the sleeve of her black dress and brought out a white handkerchief to dab at her eyes.

"Liam remembered all his lines. His father and I were so proud of him. He insisted on wearing his costume home under his winter coat." She paused to take a deep breath. "We were on the way home from the pageant when a truck swerved into our lane. The driver was drunk. My husband and Liam—" She broke into sobs.

"It's okay, Mrs. MacGregor." Sarah said gently, rushing over to the elderly lady and wrapping her arms around her neck. "They're with the angels now. And Jesus. And everyone is happy in heaven and they always celebrate Christmas there, too, because that's Jesus' birthday."

They embraced for another moment as Sarah's mother looked on, speechless. Her daughter never ceased to amaze her.

When Mrs. MacGregor finally pulled back, she sniffled and wiped her eyes and nose on her hanky before clearing her throat. "Well now," she said, looking down at Sarah's dress. "If you want me to go to this pageant with you tomorrow, we'd better get this dress hemmed up all the way around."

"You'll come?" Sarah said, clapping her hands in excitement.

"That's why I came by; to thank you for the invitation and make sure your parents were all right with me coming." Mrs. Mac-Gregor looked up at Sarah's mother.

"It would be a pleasure to have you attend the service and pageant with us," Sarah's mother said, smiling.

"Thank you, dear." Mrs. MacGregor smiled back, then turned to Sarah. "And thank *you* child for helping me remember there's still hope, peace, joy, and love in Christmas, even though I may have forgotten for a long time."

Connecting at Christmas

Nonfiction

Marian Shehata

It's an unusually warm Thursday evening for a Toronto winter. Today marks five days before Christmas. Scarborough Town Centre is packed with people of all ages rushing to the next store, hands full of gift bags, wrapping paper awkwardly sticking out of Shoppers Drug Mart bags.

A festive and buoyant hum fills the air. Red and green decorations and gold glitter hang from the ceiling. Christmas music is blaring in the background. The young men and women working at the customer service desk are wearing Santa hats. I can see a long, winding line-up of parents and squirming children waiting impatiently for a picture with Santa.

My first attempt to brave a mall this holiday season finds me ambivalent. Four months ago I lost my dad, and without him, I'm not quite sure what to do with Christmas. While I look forward to celebrating the Lord's birth, part of me has been secretly dreading the boisterous joy of the season. Yet, after convincing myself that I needed to pop by the mall for a few brief errands, I'm pleasantly surprised to find that I'm able to enjoy the Christmas cheer around me.

I'm almost done picking up a few gifts and am rushing to my last stop when I pass by the Kernels kiosk with its many varieties of popcorn. Suddenly, I stop.

And remember
how much my dad loved
popcorn.

I look at all the enticing flavours—salt and vinegar, ketchup, BBQ—on and on until I reach his favourite:
caramel.

Brown sugar,
caramelized,
sticky and shiny,
glistening on golden kernels…

I'm a little girl again, opening up one of my favourite treats—a
box of Cracker Jack, caramel popcorn in a small box that also contained some caramel-covered peanuts and a surprise "prize." My
favourites were the tattoos and the little toy games and spinners.

I remember sharing those boxes with my dad when I was a
little girl. I remember digging as fervently for the toy at the bottom
of the box as I did for the sweet and salty peanuts. Gobbling up
the popcorn and feeling cheated that those roasted peanuts weren't
evenly spread out. Complaining about the toy that took so much
trouble to find.

I can see Daddy laughing or smiling, patiently waiting, receiving only a few gooey kernels if he was lucky, even though he loved
the popcorn much more than I did.

Just as suddenly, I'm transported back to the present moment.
I'm standing in the way of busy shoppers who are walking around
me in a crowded mall as I stare, smiling and frozen in time, in front
of the Kernels store.

Even though as an adult I've felt neutral toward most popcorn,
suddenly
that caramel popcorn
starts pulling
on my
heart
strings.

Which reminds me of the time
two weeks ago
when we were ordering from
Swiss Chalet
and I decided

to get a
burger.

Why?
Who really orders a burger from Swiss Chalet?
My dad!

Missing him now as we turn to the holidays. But today reminds me that I can still keep my connection with him alive in all sorts of sweet and surprising ways.

Love and miss you, Daddy.

No Greater Gift

Fiction

Sally Meadows

Never in a million years could I have imagined that a dog would create such havoc in my marriage. Especially a dog that didn't even exist!

I've always liked dogs. When I was out walking, I enjoyed watching them with their owners. When I saw a dog that appealed to me—usually one that was small and cute—I would even comment on it. But I didn't grow up with dogs, and I was never interested in owning one after I had allergy-prone kids and their doctor recommended against having pets.

True, once the kids left home, I could have had a dog, but I had no interest in getting one. I guess I didn't want the responsibility. After years of putting my own needs and wants aside for my family, I enjoyed the freedom of not being tied down.

My husband, on the other hand, has always loved dogs. For the sake of our kids' allergies, he did without. But when my daughter and her husband bought a dog shortly after they got married, my husband's long-buried yearning bubbled to the surface.

And that's when the nonexistent dog became a huge problem. I was as bewildered by his insistence on getting a dog as my husband was with my digging in my heels in opposition.

"Why don't you want a dog?" he asked me repeatedly. "Did a dog hurt you when you were young or something?"

"No!" I said. "I just don't want the responsibility. I have enough distractions as it is. I'm in a season when I need to focus on building my website design business. I don't understand why you don't get it! You're working in your downtown office during the day and away on business often. If we get a dog, most of the caretaking would fall on my shoulders. I don't want to have to take that on!"

The argument raged on and off for weeks. It was clear my husband longed to have a pet, and I struggled to understand why I couldn't put his wants ahead of my own. I wanted to be a good wife, but I couldn't get past my own feelings of being robbed of my hard-won freedom. However, finally, I broke down and agreed to see a dog my husband had his eye on.

The minute I met the owner outside her home on her acreage, I was turned off by her loud voice and even louder clothes. As I entered the noisy trailer of caged show dogs, I felt even more uncomfortable. While Penelope, an eight-year-old purebred Lhasa Apso due for retirement was cute enough, the whole situation didn't feel right, and I got out of there as soon as I could. Penelope was not the dog for us.

On the drive home, my husband complained that I hadn't even tried to get to know the dog. Later, when he received a phone call from the owner, saying she didn't think this was a good match—because clearly I didn't want a dog—it fuelled my husband's frustration even more.

I knew that we needed to find a compromise and not let this get between us. "How about this?" I said. "Why don't we look at getting a dog when you retire in a few years? That way, you'll be here to take care of it."

"So that's it?"

"Yup," I said with finality, despite feeling guilty.

Later, my husband quietly said, "One of the reasons I wanted a dog was to keep you company during the day. I know it's lonely for you with the kids gone and all."

I felt even worse. My husband was being thoughtful and I was shutting him down.

As time went on, I prayed that God would open my heart to the possibility of adopting a dog, and I trusted that it would happen in His timing.

Several months later, when my husband showed me another dog he'd found online—clearly he'd forgotten that we'd agreed to wait until his retirement—I told him we could take a look at her.

  Christmas with Hot Apple Cider

Patricia was a mature black collie mix, very different from Penelope. As we sat chatting with the foster family, my heart went out to their own dog, a blind Labrador retriever. But with Patricia, I felt no connection.

On the way home, I tried to explain to my husband that if we were going to get a dog, it had to feel right to me. The arguments started all over again, and I began to wonder if a nonexistent pet was going to sabotage my marriage. Would we ever be able to get past our differences?

In late November, I was knee deep into a study of the Book of John. In Chapter 13, Jesus takes on the humbling position of washing his disciples' feet. His intention was to set an example of serving and humbling ourselves before others.

I got to thinking. How often had I missed the blessing of serving the person who was closest to me in the world? With the Holy Spirit's nudging, I quietly began to research dogs on my own.

The moment I saw Scottie on a dog rescue website, my heart leapt. When I was nine years old, I'd hand-sewn a small black terrier from a kit. It was the first thing I had ever sewn, and I was very proud of it. I held on to that stuffed doggie until it was so bedraggled and frayed that I had no choice but to throw it out. Scottie looked exactly like my beloved childhood friend, red collar and all.

I contacted the organization and visited Scottie several times at her foster home during December. I quickly fell in love with her and thought how wonderful it would be if she could come to live with us, in her forever home, on Christmas Day.

But adoption is a process and there simply wasn't enough time. Besides, the foster family needed to know for sure that my husband was on board with adopting her.

Not wanting to keep this from my husband any longer, I arranged for him to meet Scottie.

When I told him that I'd been invited to a small get-together with a new friend of mine on Christmas Eve, he resisted. "You know I'd prefer to stay home."

"Come on," I said. "It'll be fun!"

He reluctantly agreed.

When the foster mother opened the door with Scottie in her arms, my husband immediately reached out to pet her. I made the introductions and we followed our hostess into her living room.

"So how do you know each other, again?" my husband asked our hostess as he dipped a tortilla chip in salsa.

She opened her mouth to speak, closed it again, and looked furtively at me.

I put up my hand, turned to my husband, and could barely contain myself as I said, "She's ours if we want her."

A look of confusion came over my husband's face. "Wha—what?"

Pointing to the dog, I said, "She's ours. Scottie is my Christmas gift to you. Merry Christmas, my love."

My husband looked back and forth between my smiling face and the little tail-wagging dog, who was looking at him expectantly, almost as if she understood. "For real?"

I leaned over, picked Scottie up, and put her in my husband's arms. "For real," I said, as tears pricked at my eyes.

A few weeks later, Scottie settled into our home. It didn't take me long to realize that the sacrifice I'd made so that my husband's heart's desire could be fulfilled wasn't really a sacrifice at all. In fact, she brought much joy into our lives. She was the catalyst that deepened my relationship with my husband.

And bringing her into our lives reminded me daily that there is no greater gift than to lay down our own wants for the sake of the happiness of others.

Scottie passed away one cool September day almost four years later. Our grief was profound, and I didn't see how she could ever be replaced.

A few months later, on Christmas morning, I awoke to the warmth of doggy breath on my cheek. "Scottie?" I murmured, still half asleep.

  Christmas with Hot Apple Cider

"Unh-uh," said my husband. "I'd like you to meet Tori." He placed a beautiful white and caramel Shih Tzu puppy in my arms. "Her owner had an accident and can't keep her. They let me bring her home for the day. I realize you might prefer a different dog, but if you like her, she's ours."

I nuzzled her neck, burying my face in her soft fur. She snuggled close. "She's beautiful," I said.

Tears moistening my eyes, I looked up to husband and reached out with one hand. And for several minutes, we remained that way, hands clasped and smiling eyes locked.

My Magnificat

Nonfiction

Vilma Blenman

Yesterday, as I walked out the doors of The Scarborough Hospital in Toronto and crossed Lawrence Avenue East, I held onto my news—held on as if it might suddenly slip and fall from my hands and crumble on the sidewalk like a fragile tea cup wrapped in a single layer of tissue paper.

I walked toward the Shell gas station where I'd stealthily parked my car so I didn't have to pay the high fees in the hospital's parking lot. Pulling the flapping ends of my scarf together, I knotted them just below my chin. The wind made the –18°C (0°F) cold register on my face, but deep inside me, my heart felt as if it were close to the equator.

In the past three months, entering and leaving this hospital had become familiar, almost normal.

It had begun with the routine, then repeated, mammograms at the Breast Clinic, followed by the quick call from my family doctor saying, "There's something unusual showing on the mammograms. I've made an appointment for you to see an oncologist."

On a sunny September morning my husband, Grantley, and I, both teachers, walked into the hospital for the first time to see Dr. Krieger, the assigned oncologist. Normally, we'd have been going off to our respective schools, thinking of our lesson plans, and getting to know the new batch of students. September is the real "new year" for teachers.

It was so quiet in Dr. Krieger's off-white office that I could hear Grantley breathing as he sat beside me, motionless. I'd been told to bring someone with me. It's never good when they tell you, "Bring someone with you."

I barely heard what Dr. Krieger said. I know that he confirmed it was breast cancer, and immediately told us the date they'd scheduled my mastectomy. I know that I signed the waivers and left with forms for blood work to be done the following week. But inside, I was numb.

Afterwards, Grantley and I took the crowded elevator down to the hospital ground floor. We were the quiet couple, holding hands, squeezed into the corner, kept silent by our own thoughts. When we finally emerged from the elevator and walked outside, how surprised I was to see so much light, to hear so many sounds. Life—pulsating in the city. Life—going on as usual.

It was then that Grantley and I broke the silence. We spoke about our concerns and fears. We decided we had no choice but to do the same as others around us—to just go on with living. Yes, we'd go and teach our classes that morning, then go home and tell our two children. But after that, we'd go on being alive.

He left to find his car to get back to work, and I did the same. There were no tears. Not then. Not as I walked up Lawrence Avenue to the gas station where I'd parked. It was just me staring at the sky, a perfect pool of blue, my eyes dazzled by how much light there was outside the hospital's walls.

Oddly enough, what I remember most about that autumn day, the first day at the oncologist's office, was what I saw when I pulled into the staff parking lot at my school.

There was only one spot left up front—the one beside the growing sink hole. I took it, grateful that I didn't have to park in the back and then walk all the way around to the front. The school's doors would be locked by now.

I didn't back in. That would have required too much effort. Instead, I drove in, turned off the engine, and sat in my car, facing the fence that separates the school's parking lot from our neighbours' yards—the brown brick bungalows built in the 1950s.

I sat; I breathed; I looked up; I gasped. Right before me, trailing up and over the fence in wild abandon, were deep purple morning glory blooms, their pink throats open wide as they caught the last of the morning rays of sun before closing at midmorning.

That was the first day, the beginning of the innumerable doctors' visits leading to not one, but two surgeries.

Yesterday, I went to my appointment with Dr. Krieger alone. I wanted to go alone.

I hadn't known that before the actual day, but that morning, I suddenly told Grantley, "It's okay. Don't try to get class supervision so you can leave to come for the follow-up appointment."

"You're sure?"

"Yes, I'm sure."

Later, I came to realize that this propensity to want to reassure the world that whatever was not well with me *would be well* didn't help me to practise self-care. But in the moment, I believed it, and I went to the oncologist alone.

"It's good news," Dr. Krieger said, dispensing with any formalities of asking how I was or even asking me to sit in the sole chair in his small office. It was a different office from the first one, with pictures of Mediterranean holiday scenes.

"The test shows no indicator of high-risk re-occurrence of cancer, so you won't need chemo. It's up to you if you choose to do the drug therapy. It's not a strong recommendation since the risk factor is low."

"My early Christmas present," I replied, cracking a smile in an attempt to make the news real, to make him understand what the news meant to me. Or maybe trying to laugh because I didn't want to cry—not then, not there, not in the doctor's office. "I choose not to," I said. "*Not* to do the drug therapy."

"Okay. Then it's only radiation," he said, lowering his glasses and taking his eyes off the report in his hands. "My office will contact you about the appointment details."

I think I shook his hand and thanked him. I can't remember that part.

Only radiation! That was the news that burned in my breast as I ran across three lanes of traffic to the Shell station to get to my car, not bothering to walk down to the lights to make the crossing. I felt daring.

That was yesterday, Friday, December 13. Almost three months since that first visit.

Christmas with Hot Apple Cider

Today, I awake with an urgent need to journal—to retell my story to myself; to anchor me as I reflect on the details of both my journey and yesterday's news. I want to move my story from my head to my heart, to let the ink flow the way a river runs over rocks, meandering and curving with the bend, but still flowing, still being a river in motion.

But there's a particular image I need to journal around. I don't always know that when I set out to write, but I know today. I want to immerse myself in the pages of the Christmas story and visit a familiar Bible character whose words I've been hearing in my head ever since I learned the news from Dr. Krieger yesterday.

"My soul magnifies the Lord and my spirit rejoices in God, my Savior..."[1] The line echoes in my head. It's Mary's voice, her words as recorded in the gospel of Luke in a passage commonly referred to in church liturgy and history as "The Magnificat."[2]

The back story that precedes Mary's Magnificat is rooted in another woman's narrative of how her baby came to be. The priest Zechariah and his wife Elizabeth were old. They had no children, and now Elizabeth was past the age of child-bearing. But the angel Gabriel appeared to Zechariah and told him his wife was going to have a son. Zechariah, quite naturally, was skeptical. But Gabriel's words were fulfilled.

When Elizabeth was six months pregnant, Gabriel appeared to Mary, a young unmarried virgin, and told her she had been chosen to be the mother of the Son of God, the long-awaited Messiah. Mary was astonished, but willing to do whatever God wants. A short time later, she went to visit Elizabeth, who seemed to know from Mary's first greetings that she was carrying a child. That's when Mary spoke these words in response to Elizabeth.

To me, Mary's entire spoken word piece is pure, potent poetry about God's magnificence and munificence. The words of the Magnificat are words I'd heard and memorized from childhood, but only begun to appreciate later as I fell in love with poetry and grew deeper in my faith as an adult. The lines often come to me when I'm joyful, especially after a time of despondency.

I get out of bed gingerly, not wanting to wake my husband so early on a Saturday morning. I take my Bible and my latest journal, a flowery softcover one, and tiptoe to the study—a room that over-looks our tree-lined suburban street. It's a room that knows and welcomes me in silence whether I'm in sickness or in health. The daybed is a place of refuge and repose.

At six in the morning, the neighbours' Christmas lights are still on. They do a great display every year. Blue and white lights seem to be their theme this year, the blue outlining the roof and windows. Three neon reindeer graze on a snowy lawn, with two polar bears peacefully coexisting nearby, and a tall twinkling star surveying it all. Their giant blue spruce waves at me from across the street. I locate a pen, sit down, and pull up the fluffy throw at the foot of the daybed. Then I relax against the mounds of pillows and cushions.

First, I re-read the story, narrated in Luke 1, a long chapter with sub-headings. I skip parts. That's the truth. I just do, some-times—like most readers do. But today I notice new lines, too, even though I've read the ancient text many times.

After a moment's thought, I start to scribble in my journal, hearing only the sound of pen walking across paper, feeling my fingers curling around this most remarkable object, without which I don't think I could survive.

Saturday, December 14, 2013

Yesterday, I found out the outcome of the last test to decide on my post-surgery cancer treatment plan. The second surgery, which I dreaded more than the first, was successful. All invasive cancer tissue was removed, and they were able to get a clear margin. Nothing had spread to the lymph nodes. There won't be chemotherapy after all. And there won't be another mastectomy, either.

Sometimes, God comes with impossibly, improbably, good, life-changing news and you don't know what to say or do. You ask a few foolish questions or, if you're Zechariah, you tell God that He doesn't know Biology 101—that eggs and sperm are no longer produced after a certain age, and that he and his wife can't possibly have a child at their age.

But if you're like Mary, humble and receptive in God's presence, you don't suggest impossibility—you ask for insight. You say, "How will it happen?"

And then you wait for Him to speak, if He chooses to. You say, "It's whatever you say because you're God and I'm not; I'm your servant girl. I'm your delivery person. It's whatever You say. You do what You do best, and I'll do whatever You ask. You know me. You love me. I'll leave the rest up to You."

I think it was this awe-of-God attitude, her rock-bottom acceptance of God's sovereignty in her life, and her belief in His benevolence, that allowed Mary to face the next days and months of disgrace, disbelief, and difficulties over her pregnant, unwed state.

Make no mistake though about easy acceptance. Mary knew cultural norms, knew the likely consequences of premarital pregnancy. If her betrothed, Joseph, chose to denounce her publicly, she could be ostracized, even stoned to death at the entrance of her father's house.³

Do I have that kind of courage? How does one get it?

Mary's world was turned upside down after the angel's visit, and yet, within a short time, she got ready to go to Elizabeth's house, prepared to greet Elizabeth in full faith and joyful expectation, one mother-to-be to another, one divine carrier to another.

And Elizabeth heard that divine song welling up in Mary and felt her son, John, "leap in her womb." She then offered Mary the confirming words the younger woman needed, "Blessed are you among women, and blessed is the child you will bear."⁴

I thank God for the encouragers in my life—especially at this time.

Buoyed up by Elizabeth's words, Mary was ready to sing the Magnificat to "the Mighty One who has done great things for me."⁵

So Mary's spoken word piece spilled out, and became a classic model for us. For me.

It captures the majesty and mercy of God, and the humility and gratitude of a young woman who realizes she has been chosen to be a history maker. Was she crying and holding on to Elizabeth as she said it? I don't think she sang it, although it's called Mary's song in the subheading. Did she whisper? Was she on her knees as if in prayer? Who knows?

Me? I'd have been all gesturing and walking around, carrying on.

And here I am today, thousands of years later, me, a Black woman, reading Mary's words in tears. After first hearing a cancer diagnosis and then getting the news that the surgeries were successful, that the tests confirm no more traces of invasive cancer, I know hope. And Mary's words give me more hope. I feel that Gabriel has also been sent to me to deliver news. So today I want to sing-speak my Magnificat.

I'm mindful that it's about the Magnificent One, the Promise-Keeping One, the Mighty One, the Merciful One, who has done, and who wants to do, great things for me—for all of us. But I'm mindful, too, that such magnanimity frightens me. That I need to learn from Mary how to say with joy, "My soul magnifies the Lord, and my spirit rejoices in God my Saviour."[1]

It's not because Mary is good enough that such a blessing comes to her. Mary rejoices because she knows it's all grace—all God-initiated.

Throughout this Advent season, I want to reflect on Mary's words and respond to all of God's messengers who have been "sent" to me this year with news. Whatever the news, joyful or painful, I want to respond with courage even in the face of fear, and say, "Okay, I am the Lord's servant."

What that all means, I don't really know. But I want to find out. And I want to sing my Magnificat. 'Tis the season for a Magnificat!

I close the journal, stick the pen inside its spiral loops, and sit back, breathing slowly, feeling the familiar release that comes from writing, no matter how short the piece is.

Think it. Ink it.

That's what I often tell my students about writing. It's what I'm learning myself as I break out of perfectionism mode and try to be more disciplined to write more often.

A thing is created that wasn't before, I tell myself. A thought, a feeling, a moment—however imperfectly captured—is there now. So do it. Just start.

Sometimes I wonder if writing is a bit like gestation and child birth. Something starts, grows, keeps growing, and then there's the inevitable birthing, whether we're ready or not.

A baby is born after nine months, not after 10.

It's at this moment of thinking about giving birth that the other memory comes—the memory of that first Christmas after our baby came and went.

Funny. I didn't set out to write about—to reminisce about—that. The Magnificat. That's what was in my head. Sing the song of praise, like Mary's. And then, there it is, unbidden, the memory of the fateful visit to the obstetrician gynecologist specialist at the other hospital near where we used to live, on the other side of the city. I can still hear the doctor's voice, "This fetus is going to die."

That's what the doctor said to me. Just so. Monotone. Looking straight at me. No preambles. No medical semantics to break the fall. No whatever. Just the bare, bone-chilling announcement after the ultrasound and his hasty conference with the technician.

After the doctor delivered his verdict and left, I waited alone in the cold room, waited with gel goop still sticking to my stomach. Alone in a downtown hospital because I'd told my husband I'd be fine. He didn't need to come. I was five months pregnant, and things seemed to be going well. Little did I know.

She died a few minutes before she came to us. As the doctor had dutifully warned us, her lungs were unable to do what lungs do outside the womb. Breathe for us. Breathe with us.

Today, I decide to breathe for her, to grieve for her.

I inhale gulps of winter morning air and exhale slowly, saying goodbye to our beautiful, still-born baby girl.

Mesha. That's what we named her. We had hoped to have a five-month-old at Christmas. But at Christmas I looked wistfully at Baby's First Christmas bibs and jumper sets and photo frames and... *She's not going to have a first Christmas with us* is what I thought.

We showed up at family Christmas dinner that year, empty-handed except for the curried goat dish we were assigned to bring. The youngest child there was supposed to be our child, but while there were plenty of kids running around, there was no baby there that year. No one said anything about a baby.

Why did that memory surface on this morning of all mornings, when praise was my theme?

Maybe my Magnificat, my life anthem, is as much about sorrow as it is about joy. Both an ode and a dirge.

My heart rejoices; my heart cries. My heart magnifies; my heart identifies. Maybe the "good news of great joy" also teaches me how to live with news of great loss.

I pick up the journal again. There's more to my Magnificat. I need to keep living, keep writing...

1. Luke 1:46–47, ESV (English Standard Version). Note that different versions of the Bible use the word "praise" instead of "magnify." The King James Version also uses "magnify."

2. *Magnificat* is the Latin translation of the word "magnify," the first word Mary uses in her poetic praise response after her cousin, Elizabeth, confirms she knows Mary is going to give birth to the Messiah. Mary's entire piece is recorded in Luke 1:46–55 and is sometimes sung as a canticle in worship and often read as part of specially selected biblical readings in celebration of Advent.

3. According to ancient Judaic laws, a woman pledged to be married, but pregnant or proven not to be a virgin, was to be stoned unless there were extenuating circumstances such as rape. See Deuteronomy 22:13–27.

4. Elizabeth's greeting to Mary is in Luke 1:41–45.

5. Luke 1:49

The Gifts We Didn't Need

Nonfiction

Theresa Goldrick

"I get to play Santa," our pastor said over the phone a few days before Christmas. "Can I come for a visit in about an hour?"

"Umm, I guess so," was my hesitant response. "What is this all about?"

"You'll see."

Our family had gone through a few tough years. My husband, an electrician, was in business for himself, and jobs were few and far between. I wasn't working. I still had a toddler at home, and we'd agreed early in our marriage that I wouldn't work until all the kids were in school.

This year, though, my husband had been able to get a pretty good job, which gave us some extra money, so we'd decided we could afford to purchase bicycles for all three children. Since there hadn't been much for them the previous couple of years, we couldn't wait to see the looks on their faces on Christmas morning when they saw the bikes under the tree!

An hour after the phone call, a knock came at the door, and there stood our pastor, his arms full of gifts.

"What's this?" I asked.

"These are for your family," he replied, grinning from ear to ear.

After inviting him in, I looked over the packages. There was one for each of the children, plus a tin of cookies.

"Oh," said the pastor, "before I forget, inside the tin of cookies is something else."

After I opened the cookie tin, I became a bit emotional. On top of the cookies sat several grocery vouchers for our local grocery store. "Where did these come from?" I questioned. "Who sent these gifts?"

Our pastor explained that he knew a family who, rather than purchasing gifts for each other, pooled their money and "sponsored" a family that could use some help. This year, they'd selected our family.

Tears in my eyes, I thanked the pastor for playing "Santa" and asked if he would be willing to deliver a thank-you card on our behalf. He cheerfully agreed.

For the remainder of the day, I felt lifted up—pleased that a family would be so generous to us—but I also felt guilty. We'd already bought bikes for our children, and now they'd get more gifts. I began to feel that we didn't deserve the extra gifts.

That night, I was talking to a friend on the phone and I told her about the gifts we'd received and my feelings of guilt.

Her response to me was, "Don't feel guilty. Someone wanted to bless you with these gifts, so accept them as the blessing that they are! This year will make up for some of the years when you couldn't do much for your kids."

As I thought about it, I had to acknowledge that she was right. God had put it on this family's heart to give us these gifts, so I shouldn't spend my time feeling guilty. That would just take away from the blessing.

During the 25 years that have passed, I've often thought of that Christmas and reflected on how blessed we truly were, and how God watched over us during those lean years.

As a family, we now pool our money with my siblings and our children and donate to a worthy cause. To me, that's what Christmas is about, sharing with others, and giving them a little extra!

  Christmas with Hot Apple Cider

The Weight-Lifter

Fiction

Melissa Yue Wallace

Teresa couldn't take it anymore. After working at the shelter for 10 straight hours, she was exhausted, but she'd had to watch three packed subway trains pass by. Toronto rush hour! *Gah!* she thought. *What a way to spend Christmas Eve!*

Peering through the windows of the trains, she'd seen dozens of squashed and sweaty passengers sweltering in winter parkas and looking more than a little disgruntled. But at least they were going someplace!

As each train stopped, three or four people would burrow their way out, but the space they had occupied quickly filled up, and the train doors promptly closed.

I just want to go home! Teresa screamed inside her head.

As the fourth train screeched to a halt, Teresa decided she was getting on this time, no matter what. Her commute would take at least an hour, and she was so tired of waiting. "Excuse me," she squeaked as she pushed her way in.

She heard groans as she stumbled over shopping bags and slushy boots.

"Caution! Wide load!" a male voice muttered.

Around her, she heard snickers.

"You don't exactly *fit* on this train, Miss Piggy," said another voice.

Female, Teresa thought. She felt her face getting hot, but she willed herself to ignore the taunts. Nothing she hadn't heard before. She pretended not to see the glares from her fellow passengers who hated her for taking up so much space.

Despite the frigid temperature outside, it was uncomfortably warm on the train, but there was no room to take off her coat. Her *large* coat. Yes, she was overweight. She'd always been, ever since she was a child. In college, she'd tried a bunch of fad diets and various shakes, hoping to shed the pounds that affected her social and love life. But nothing had worked, so she'd given up.

As she walked home from her stop, she couldn't help but replay the taunts in her head. They weren't exactly original, but they hurt nonetheless. It had been a few months since she'd encountered such disdain from strangers about her weight. On Christmas Eve, they seemed even worse than usual.

Why am I so hideous?

When she got home, she threw herself on her bed and cried. The day had ended terribly and she felt so embarrassed.

After a while, she thought about calling her best friend, Brooke, but she didn't feel that Brooke was on the same wavelength any more. Brooke was also overweight, and in the past they'd often commiserated with one another when something was getting one of them down. But Brooke had recently become a Christian and that seemed to have driven a wedge between them.

"Remember when we tried going to church in high school and we overheard those 'Christians' making fat jokes about us?" Teresa had reminded Brooke the last time they'd been together.

"That was in the past!" Brooke explained. "And, anyway, I don't go to that church."

Brooke had a beautiful voice, and apparently when people at her new church heard her sing it was as if nobody saw a fat person anymore. Brooke had recently starred in a musical production at her church, and now she was busy with a new set of friends and activities.

She'd even told Teresa to get over herself and find something she liked to do.

However, unlike Brooke, Teresa felt she had nothing to offer the world. *Nothing on the outside, nothing on the inside*, she sighed and fell asleep.

The next morning, she awoke with a jolt. It was Christmas Day, and they were expecting a crowd of at least 200 for Christmas dinner at the shelter. Her role was to register and help the women and children with food, toys, and their Christmas meal. She quickly rushed out, grateful that no one at the shelter expected her to appear in fashionable clothes and makeup.

  Christmas with Hot Apple Cider

She'd left the subway—not as crowded today—and was two blocks away from the shelter when she noticed a dishevelled man in ripped clothes lying motionless on a grate. She stopped and hesitantly went over to him. "Excuse me, sir, are you okay?"

The man slowly sat up and looked at her with piercing eyes. "Yes, my child."

"Do you need some food? Warmer clothes? I work at the shelter just a few blocks from here."

The man didn't respond.

Teresa wondered if he was too cold and disoriented to understand. "Come with me," she said.

She helped the man to his feet and began walking with him toward the shelter.

When they were a short distance away, the man spoke. "Teresa, do you know who I am?"

"Judging by how cold your arms are, you're someone who's been lying outside for a long time," she said.

"Do you know I've been lying on these grates since yesterday evening and you're the only person to notice me?"

"I work at a shelter, so I guess I'm kind of trained to notice that sort of thing."

"It's more than that, Teresa," the man said.

She stopped walking and stared at him. "Wait! How do you know my name?"

"I know everything about you. I was there when you took your first step, when you won the spelling bee in grade six, when you graduated from high school, when your mother died…I saw it all."

"What? So you're…psychic?"

"Not exactly." The man grinned. "Teresa, you're beautiful. Don't ever think you're worthless. You mean everything to me."

Teresa gave the man a funny look. "Okay, then. Thanks!"

She saw one of the male shelter workers. "Hey, Paul! Can you help this man? He's been outside since last night and is freezing."

"What man?" Paul asked, looking around.

Teresa motioned to the space next to her, and then stopped. No one was there. "There was a m-man," she stammered. "He was right here."

Teresa and Paul searched the area around the shelter. The man had disappeared without a trace.

"Maybe if we look at the security cameras you'll realize I'm not crazy?" Teresa spluttered.

However, a quick look at the cameras showed Teresa talking to the air next to her as she'd walked to the shelter.

What just happened? Am I losing my mind?

She put the man out of her mind as she served guests at the shelter, and everyone had a great time.

At the end of the day, as she was getting ready to leave for home, she spotted a brightly wrapped gift on her desk. Opening it, she found a pocket-sized Bible inscribed with a message:

Dear Teresa, it was a pleasure walking to work with you today. Thank you for your heart for the poor and for noticing those who are often forgotten. It brings me joy to see you serve with kindness, humility, and compassion. You are more beautiful than you realize. I look forward to having more conversations with you.

Love, your number one fan.

P. S. I highlighted Psalm 139:13,14.

Teresa found the Psalm and read the verses:

For you created my inmost being; you knit me together in my mother's womb. I praise you because I am fearfully and wonderfully made; your works are wonderful, I know that full well.

Once more, Teresa couldn't stop the tears from flowing. But this time, they were tears of joy.

From Sea Sand to Snowflakes

Nonfiction

Melony Teague

I gasped in delight! The purple, blue, green, and gold fireworks blazed across the dark sky, their multicoloured vibrancy reflecting what I felt—as if I might explode with emotion. With each burst of light dancing across the sky, my heart brimmed with the hope and promise of the endless possibilities that lay before us, stretching from sea to shining sea across Canada.

I was at Queen's Quay, on the shore of Lake Ontario in downtown Toronto, on December 31 of 1999 AD, grinning from ear to ear as I bounced up and down on the balls of my frozen feet. My husband, Rory, and I were among thousands who had gathered to watch the fireworks on First Night, 2000.

At the time, Rory was in his early thirties and I was a few years younger. We were in a strange new country, welcoming in not only a new year and a shiny new millennium but also a new life. This city, with its unfamiliar sights and sounds, was now our home. Each shower of golden and coloured light, accompanied by music, pushed my doubts and fears further away from my thoughts.

The transition from sunny, stifling hot, South Africa to Canada that September hadn't been easy. Our new land, where we had to learn a whole new way to drive a car, brought many challenges. But we believed we had made the right decision to leave everything we knew, as hard as that was, in order for us to get to know the Canadian members of my husband's family and for us to make new friends and follow our dreams.

That fall, when we arrived in Ontario as immigrants, we'd experienced our first Canadian autumn, watching the maple leaves turn their beautiful shades of russet, orange, gold, and red before falling to the ground to crackle and crunch beneath our feet. When the weather turned cooler than we had ever experienced, in true immigrant fashion we'd shouted, "It's snowing!" and dashed outside to take pictures of snowflakes falling from the sky. No doubt, seasoned Canadians wondered what all the fuss was about—knowing this was only a small flurry and there was much more to come.

A week before our first Canadian Christmas, we found ourselves strolling the shopping aisles, my hand tucked into my husband's, searching for a Christmas tree. We had never had a real, fresh-cut tree. Not being confident enough to attempt to keep a real one alive, we opted for an artificial one. But our new Canadian tree was taller than the artificial one we'd left behind, and so pretty with more modern lights.

On Christmas Eve, we spread a blanket on the floor and cuddled in front of the new decorated tree with its twinkling lights the way one would in front of a roaring fire at a ski lodge.

"Isn't this nice?" my husband said between kisses.

With our first Canadian Christmas behind us, as special as it was, those Christmas-card-perfect snowy scenes complete with reindeer, sleds, and jingle bells that we had never quite understood while growing up had finally become reality. We were the proud owners of snow boots, jackets, and toques, and we had learned all about shovelling snow and bundling up.

Now, as snowflakes landed on my lashes, I resisted the urge to stick out my tongue and catch a few. Life in the northern hemisphere was certainly different from the tropical climate I was used to at this time of the year. But I'd take the crisp, cold air and the freedom and safety I now felt over the sweltering heat, the barbed-wire and security fences, even the beaches and seashells, any day.

Now, where we stood, the iconic CN Tower, with the Rogers Centre (then known as the SkyDome) nestled beside it, looked down on us, and the partially frozen Lake Ontario spread out before us as far as we could see.

My husband's toasty gloved hand firmly clasped mine as our breaths mingled in the frosty air. Rory turned to me and said, "Happy New Year."

As is the custom on my side of the family, because we like to make a joke out of everything, I replied, "Happy New Ears."

How sweet that midnight New Year's kiss felt as he held me tight.

  Christmas with Hot Apple Cider

Soon I untangled myself from his puffy-winter coat-clad arms and adjusted my cozy scarf to cover my frozen ears. Then I looked at the crowd surrounding us, some with Toronto Maple Leaf knitted hats on their heads, tassels and all, others wearing red-and-white Canadian flag apparel.

There were men and women, all shapes and sizes, young and old together, some carrying little ones who had long lost the fight against sleep. Beautiful, varied shades of skin colour revealed different cultures and backgrounds, all wrapped up against the cold, collectively exhaling clouds of damp frosty air.

In South Africa, the land of our birth, New Year's revellers would celebrate in the sweltering summer heat, eating watermelon in an attempt to stay cool.

To be honest, as we stood under the winter sky, the crowd made us a little jittery. When strangers said, "Hi, how are you?", as cautious and skeptical South Africans, we couldn't help being suspicious. Coming from a country where crime was a part of day-to-day life, we'd had to adjust to living without security gates and fences. But we realized that the people in this New Year's crowd were only being nice and had no ulterior motives.

After the fireworks ended, we decided it was time to head home for bed.

Most of the crowd seemed to be coming with us as we made our way along Yonge Street to Union Subway Station on Front Street West, where we felt as tightly packed as sardines in a can as we were funnelled down into the stairwell leading to the subway platform.

Once there, the flow of people came to an abrupt halt.

"Oh, boy, this could get nasty," I said to my husband. I expected the worst.

We were sharing a closed space with all these strangers, our sweaty bodies awkwardly pressed together. After my euphoria only minutes before, my heart dropped. I whispered in his ear, "We could be stuck here for hours, fall asleep on our feet, and be found frozen in the morning."

I waited for the disgruntled comments, complaining, perhaps a tiff here and there, maybe even some shoving.

My heart pounded as I gripped my husband's arm, afraid things would get out of hand and people might be injured or trampled. A moment later, goose bumps erupted on my exposed skin. But not from fear.

One voice rose up clear and strong over the din, singing "O Canada..."[1] Another voice joined in, and another, until everyone on that subway platform seemed to be adding their own unique voices to my new country's national anthem.

My heart full of admiration and respect for the people of my new country, I blinked away tears as I studied the faces in the multicultural crowd. Men and women from different nations, each one as unique as a snowflake, sang our national anthem together. I felt so proud of the Canadian way.

No wonder these people are known as some of the friendliest, most peace-loving people in the world. Such a gift for those of us who came in search of a better, safer future! For me, coming from a country of conflict, their gentle yet strong spirit was a balm to my tired soul.

As my heart soared along with the words "Our home and native land..." I felt the "true patriot love" from far and wide. I was seeing, firsthand, the strong and free people of my new homeland do what they do best—make the most of a potentially unpleasant situation, and make it better by showing respect to one another.

I lifted my voice in tribute along with the voices around me.

---

1. The original version of the Canadian anthem was written in 1908 by Robert Stanley Weir.

  Christmas with Hot Apple Cider

December Blues

Marguerite Cummings

To do!
To do!
My list is getting longer.

To do!
Yet more to do!
It's the same year after year.

As nights stretch out
But sleep time shrinks,
I dread the dire cycle
That each December brings.

I long to be on top of things
With cards, lights, food, and tree,
And, above all, find perfect gifts…
But is this really key?

To be!
To be!
I know that's more important.

To be with friends who need kind words,
To be a listening ear,
To be a light that shines in trials,
To be like God—so near.

So here's my new December list,
I'll try it and we'll see:
I'll give a gift of presence,
And let the presents be.

New Christmas Traditions

Nonfiction

Janis Cox

As the years went by and our family grew, Christmas shopping became tedious. Our three children compiled long lists of wants, and I obliged by trying to fulfill their requests. I carefully kept each receipt in an effort to make sure that we treated them equally. As a result, Christmas Eve became a stressful time of wondering if I had enough and if what I'd spent on each one balanced.

Finally, one year, it hit me that we'd fallen into the trap of "What can I get?" and forgotten that Christmas is meant to be a time of giving, not getting.

Our son was spending his first Christmas away from home with his new wife and family, so my husband and I asked our two girls, who were 18 and 14, if they'd like to help at a shelter for homeless people on Christmas morning.

Because the girls loved to help others, we weren't surprised when they became very excited and said an enthusiastic "Yes!" We wondered if the early wake-up call would deter them. However, our whole family got up super early that Christmas morning and drove through a snowstorm to get to the shelter about 40 minutes away.

In all, about eight people from our church showed up to help make and serve the breakfast. The people in charge didn't appear to be used to having volunteers, so there was a little confusion in the beginning. However, we were able to figure out our duties. We planned who would dish out the food, who would collect the dirty plates, who would rinse, and who would run the dishwasher.

As I dished out food to one homeless gentleman, he looked at me and asked, "Why are you taking your Christmas morning to come in here and serve us?"

Why indeed? What was my reasoning? Did I want to feel good about myself? Did I want to make my heart clean before God because I felt guilty for having so much? Did I just want to teach my children not to focus on getting presents? No matter what the reason was, the end result was satisfaction. We smiled all the way home after cleaning up the kitchen, washing the dishes, and putting them away.

That Christmas has stood out among all the others as the most blessed time. In fact, my younger daughter told me the other day that she would have liked to continue that every year and make it a tradition.

As the years went by and the kids grew up and had their families, I sensed the same struggle happening in their lives as had happened in ours. *Why do all this shopping? Do we need all this stuff?*

Plus, as our family grew in numbers, we didn't know what each person would like, so we started making lists of wants. That began to be a chore and it also took away the joy of surprising someone. Plus, it took a long time to watch everyone open all the presents. As a family, we talked over the problem.

Our solution was to have each family give one present to each of the grandchildren, but instead of giving presents to the adults, use the money we would have spent to bless others. Then, when we got together as a group during Christmas, each family would tell the others where the money had gone.

Some examples:

- Our son's family chose to deliver presents to new-immigrant support groups.

- While visiting El Salvador one year, our older daughter's family met a gentleman who was starting a school. The next year, they bought school supplies to help with that school.

- Our youngest daughter's husband connects with administrators from schools where he has worked to identify a family in need. They provide some ideas of where they shop and their needs/interests, and then give them a special Christmas.

The list of possibilities is endless, but throughout the year we all watch for opportunities to bless others. God has never failed

to give each of our families an idea that catches their hearts, and since we began this tradition, we've shared many tears of joy as we listened to how God led each family to give to someone special.

As a result, everyone in our family has benefited, but most of all the grandchildren as they have come to see giving as a true blessing. One grandchild in particular saves part of his allowance in order to be able to give something special to a needy person each year. Last year, he filled two backpacks for homeless people.

No longer are we stressed at Christmas. We have our grandchildren open their presents. Then each family shares how they were led to spend the money allocated for the adults. Then the grandchildren put on the Christmas story as a play. They're getting to be great actors and actresses, and are learning more about God. Finally, we enjoy eating together.

Christmas has become a special time of gathering and sharing—and not just getting—ever since we began to focus on others and not on ourselves.

  Christmas with Hot Apple Cider

My Christmas Chicken

Nonfiction

Pat Hennan

As far back as I can remember, I've had a fondness for chickens.

It probably started when I was just a little guy spending summer holidays at my grandparents' place in the country. They lived in a small stone house on a couple of acres on the edge of town. A little ways behind the house, a small hen house was surrounded by a large fenced-in area made from chicken wire stapled to posts made from railway ties.

Much of the area inside that fence was overgrown with tall grass, and I spent many hours out there, just hanging out with the chickens on those endless summer days. It made for a great place to hide, explore, look for eggs, and chase chickens!

Whenever I went to my grandparents' place for a visit, I'd choose one chicken and give it the honour of being my special pet chicken. I'd tie a ribbon around one of its legs so I'd be sure to recognize it and give it extra attention. I believed that my pet chicken came when I called, but it's more likely that it ran in terror at the sight of me. On many summer evenings, I would bring the chicken into the house with me, much to the feigned protests of my aunt and grandma. Then we would sit and watch TV while I petted my friend and rocked it to sleep.

I held my dad in high esteem because legend had it that in his younger days he was able to hypnotize a chicken and put it to sleep on command! I was later told that it was actually easy to do because chickens are incredibly stupid, but as a young child, this ability seemed amazing.

Of course, I eventually grew up and left behind my childish ways, but not my love for chickens. For many years, I prayed that God would somehow grant me my wish of having my own place in the country, with my own little barn and a few acres so I could have chickens. I wanted this badly!

Seven years into our marriage, that dream came true. My wife and I settled into our own little house on the prairie—40 acres of land a short distance south of town. As soon as we'd moved into our new house, I set about getting myself an assortment of chickens—of all sizes, shapes, and colours!

I truly enjoyed having my own flock of free-ranging birds, and when we moved to a new place five years later, I built a small enclosure and set up my chicken ranch there.

I kept up with this passion for the first few years, but then decided to take a year off. That year somehow turned into six or seven more. After all but one of our four children had left home, my wife and I made the difficult decision to leave our country home and move to town.

For me, the hardest part of the move was giving up the thought of ever raising chickens again.

My wife pointed out that I hadn't raised chickens in years, so what was the problem?

My response was, "Yes, but I always knew I could have them if I decided to."

Now, sadly, I would no longer have that option. And this thought truly took the fun out of the move for me—crazy as it sounds.

All my kids knew it too. My eldest daughter even asked me, "What's with this chicken fixation anyway, Dad?"

I thought it over and I really couldn't give a good answer other than it brought back warm memories of my childhood. Then one day it all came into focus.

A few years after my father's death, I sat down to look through his old keepsakes, including several hundred photos he'd taken over the years. It's funny that I had never noticed it before, but out of hundreds of pictures, maybe 10 per cent of them were of people, 30 or 40 per cent were of his dogs, and the rest were all pictures of chickens. This whole chicken thing was genetic!

It was quite amazing. My father and I were indelibly linked with the rare chicken fetish gene!

Time passed, and I got used to not having chickens around, although I still enjoyed reading books about them to my grandchildren. And I could still cluck like a hen and crow like a rooster. Of course, I've always been one of KFC's most devoted customers. My love knows no bounds.

Then one year, a couple of weeks before Christmas, our pastor challenged us to think less of ourselves and more of others in need. He talked about various Christian organizations that would use donations to help third-world families get a start. He mentioned how a simple gift like a goat or a couple of hens and a rooster could enable a struggling family to overcome poverty and provide for their children. This seemed as amazing to me as my father's ability to hypnotize chickens—but far more useful.

That Christmas morning was a little more exciting than usual because we not only had our children and their spouses with us, but also two wide-eyed grandchildren. It was a special time watching them unwrap their gifts and examine the contents.

When it was all over, or so I thought, someone pointed out that there was one more present—"for Dad." As my family watched, I walked around the tree and found, stuffed in among the branches, a handmade Christmas card. On the outside, it simply said, "Merry Christmas, Dad." On the inside was a coloured drawing of two hens and a rooster. Apparently my daughter—the same one who'd commented on my chicken fetish—had asked my wife what to get me for Christmas, and she'd passed along our pastor's suggestion.

Of course, as soon as I saw the drawing, I knew what it was. I just stood there for what seemed like the longest time, staring at that drawing and fighting back the tears that had begun running down my cheeks. Finally, with a shaky voice, I told them how grateful I was, and that this was probably the best gift I'd ever received.

I felt truly blessed to be able to help someone out in this way.

With a surge of joy, I realized how right Jesus was when he said, "It's more blessed to give than to receive" (Acts 20:35). My best gift was one I'd never actually see or hold.

We're already talking about next Christmas and how each of us can use "our gift" to help someone else.

Thank you again, Heavenly Father, for my Christmas chicken.

A Hum Harbour Christmas Mystery

Fiction

Jayne E. Self

I was at the grocer's stocking up on soda crackers when I noticed Buddy McLean following a woman down the produce aisle. Her black hijab made her unmistakable as our community's newest resident, a Syrian refugee who'd been relocated to Hum Harbour.

Buddy is sort of family, though I'm loath to admit that too loudly because he's not always the nicest person. It was only 10 in the morning, and his red nose telegraphed that he was already three sheets to the wind.

Glancing around to make sure he had an audience, Buddy snatched the carton of eggs from the woman's cart and dropped it. Loudly. Then he grabbed the tail of her hijab and yanked.

The woman's head jerked back, and her thick dark hair tumbled free. Tears sprang to her eyes.

"Go back where you belong!" He spat into her face.

I just stood there.

A few days later, the same woman came into my husband's clinic where I work as receptionist. This time her hijab was navy blue.

"I am Amira Rahal," she said. "My husband, Nazir, and I have come from Syria. I would like an appointment with Dr. Geoffrey Grant, if it is possible." Her dark eyes looked wary, as though she expected another hijab yank. Or worse.

I gave her some appointment options, she picked a time and date that suited, and I wrote it on a card.

I knew I had to say something. As I stood and held out the card, my hand shook. "I'm Gailynn MacDonald-Grant, the doctor's

Christmas with Hot Apple Cider

wife. I was at the grocery store the other day when Buddy McLean assaulted you."

"I remember."

My cheeks grew hotter. "I need to apologize. Buddy's actions were unforgivable, and so were mine. I said nothing and I'm so ashamed of myself because I know better. I don't know why I didn't do anything." I was talking faster and faster. "I've played it over and over in my head—what I should've said and what I should've done—and there's no excuse for how I acted. I want to say—no, I *need* to say—how sorry I am. And I hope—I pray!—I won't ever be such a coward again. And I promise I'll do my best to never let Buddy hurt you again, no matter what."

It took her a moment to sort through all I'd said. Then she nodded. "Fear is a terrible thing. I understand. Believe me." She touched my hand as she accepted the appointment card. "I forgive. Yes, of course." She caught her bottom lip between her teeth. "When are you due?"

I glanced down at my bump, which was apparently more noticeable than I'd thought. "Not till the new year."

She smiled shyly. "Me, too."

And that's how Amira Rahal and I became friends.

Four months later, Geoff was in Halifax at a doctors' conference, and Amira and I were watching Buddy McLean secure the final string of Christmas lights to the eaves of our house.

Our home's unique shape—an old stone Cape Cod attached to Hum Harbour's decommissioned lighthouse—made the task too cumbersome for me to tackle.

For over a century, the light from Hum Harbour's lighthouse had pointed sailors toward the harbour's safety. After the government automated the light, the town purchased the lightkeeper's house to turn it into a museum. Their plans fell through; the place went up for sale; and Geoff and I grabbed it.

You're probably wondering why Buddy McLean was hanging our Christmas lights, or why I'd let him anywhere near Amira after my promise to keep Buddy from hurting her again. Unlike me,

Geoff thinks compassion and Christian love are better strategies with people like Buddy than walls and turned backs. So, whenever possible, Geoff hires Buddy to do odd jobs.

Thanks to Buddy's reputation, Geoff's job offers are often all he gets, and his growing family barely survives most winters on welfare. Geoff figures that's why Buddy drinks. I figure the drinking is why he's on welfare. But, hey, what do I know?

Besides, Amira had assured me that a small-town bully like Buddy couldn't intimidate her. She'd faced much worse in Syria, had she not?

So she said. But she hadn't convinced me. I saw the shadow in her eyes whenever Buddy was around, so I never left her alone with him.

From the roof, Buddy pointed toward the end of the electrical cord that Amira was holding and shouted, "Give her a try!" Or, that's what I thought he said. Waves crashing against the rocks drowned out his voice.

I gave Amira the go-ahead signal and, nudging our beagle, Caber, out of her way, she shoved the plug into the outdoor outlet—one of the upgrades Geoff and I'd made on the old place since we bought it. Strings of white twinkle lights sparked to life, and Buddy climbed down the ladder.

"Good enough?" he asked me. He pointedly ignored Caber—who looked more comical than fearsome with his upper lip caught on a canine and his ears lifted in the wind like airplane wings. He ignored Amira, too, which was good. No one wanted a replay of their first meeting.

"You'll be back tomorrow to finish painting?" I shouted at Buddy's fleeing back. Geoff had also hired him to paint the baby's room. If everything was on schedule, we'd need it to be ready by Valentine's Day. Amira was due a month later.

Speaking of Amira, despite Buddy's presence, the swirling snowflakes, and the winter wind tugging wildly at her hijab, her eyes shone. Her first winter in Canada was full of new and seemingly wonderful experiences, and she savoured them all. Even the ones I preferred to avoid, like this nor'easter freezing the hairs in my nose and shrivelling my blood.

Amira and I headed inside for some hot chocolate before she went home. She shed her boots and heavy coat and settled into an armchair in our living room. I brought us Christmas shortbread and steamy mugs topped with mini-marshmallows. Caber flopped on the rug.

Late afternoon, and it was almost dark outside. I plugged in the Christmas tree lights and the fairy lights that trimmed the mantle. My nativity—a gift from my nan when I was eight—was on display among the lights. Seeing it always gave me a sense of peace.

Amira studied the crèche from her seat. Maybe she enjoyed the play of light and shadows as much as I did. "You really believe the Christmas story is true?" she asked.

"Of course," I said.

For the most part, we'd avoided anything beyond the most basic discussions of faith. I did my best to answer her questions honestly, but I made a point not to be preachy. I mean, she had her own faith. She might be curious about mine, but I had no illusions she'd convert. (Okay, not true. I prayed for her every day.)

"Why?" she asked.

Why did I believe? I nabbed another chocolate-dipped short-bread to give myself time to think. Indeed, why *did* I believe?

The lights on the mantle flickered and went dark before I had come up with a good response. With relief, I set aside my cocoa to fiddle with the plug. Amira adjusted the tiny bulbs. Neither made any difference.

I said, "I hate the way strings go dead even if only one bulb burns out."

"A poor design, yes?"

I nodded, embarrassingly glad to change the subject. "And it's not like poor designs are something new. I mean, look at the crooked dentil work on the mantle."

"Dental work?"

Thanks to years studying in Britain, Amira was so fluent in English that I sometimes forgot she couldn't always follow what I meant. "The wooden moulding. See these squares that sort of look like a row of teeth? It's called dentil work. When we were stripping the paint, we noticed they didn't align properly."

Amira angled her head and poked at three squares that seemed particularly out of whack with the rest of the trim. "I think these teeth need braces."

As I laughed, she bent awkwardly and looked at them from a different angle. "These are not the same as the others."

"What do you mean?" I got down beside her.

"See? They come out further than the others. There is space behind them."

"A lazy patch job when some got broken?"

She pressed the heel of her hand against the section of moulding that held the three odd teeth and pushed. I sat back and wondered why her breathing had grown shallow.

After a moment, the wood groaned. The teeth shifted a bit.

My breathing hitched, too. "Do that again."

This time she used both hands and I placed mine on top of hers, adding more pressure.

The whole fireplace seemed to moan. Suddenly, it jerked sideways.

My precious nativity figurines tumbled off the mantle. Jesus, Mary, Joseph and all three kings hit Caber, snoring on the carpet near us, and bounced off him, unharmed. The shepherd boy wasn't as lucky. He crashed onto the brick hearth. His head, his arms cradling a lamb, and his lower body rolled in different directions.

Amira gathered the pieces, hugging the broken figurine to her heart as if it were a real child. Her shoulders heaved. Tears streamed down her cheeks.

I wrapped my arms around her.

It happened like this sometimes. An unanticipated bang or a seemingly harmless smell like the aroma of barbecued meat could send her spinning. I'd learned that a quiet embrace seemed to be the best help.

She looked at me. "Can you fix him?"

"I think so." I hoped so.

I tried to remember what kinds of glue I had on hand. As I did this, my gaze went past her. That's when I noticed the hole—the *big* hole—where the fireplace had been. It looked tall enough to stand in, if you didn't mind the cobwebs and grime. "Oh, my!"

Caber sniffed the air and howled.

"What on earth?" Amira spun around. She stared, too.

I gobble local history faster than chocolate fudge, yet I was positive I'd never heard anything about a secret room in the lighthouse. Obviously, the mantle had concealed the hole for decades. Maybe even longer.

I fetched the flashlight from the kitchen drawer. Its beam quivered—or maybe it was my hand—as it passed over the space. The whole thing was crammed with cobwebs, so it was impossible to tell how deep it went. I'm known for my inquiring mind—some may even call me nosey—but my curiosity evaporated when I leaned in and spotted the unmistakable skeleton of a dead rat.

Wind rushing down the chimney into the living room sounded like a thousand ghosts chanting, "Come see, come see." However, there was no way I was going in there, at least not tonight with that storm raging.

Amira's cell took that moment to ring. "I must leave," she said when she disconnected. "Nazir is worried about the wind and the snow." She stroked her round tummy.

"Help me close up. I don't want to leave it open all night."

"You will wait until tomorrow to explore?"

I eyed the skeleton. "I am definitely not going in there by myself. Besides, who knows what else is in there?"

"I am relieved. I have heard many speak of your adventures. Risks you take."

I couldn't deny I'd done some pretty dumb things in my time. True, I'd also solved two murders,[1] but I'd learned that good results were no excuse for doing dumb things. Thanks to Geoff's influence, I'd grown a *little* common sense since we'd married. Plus there was no way I was hauling my seven-month baby bump into the unknown. Not alone, anyway. I'd wait until I had someone to explore with me. Like Amira and her six-month bump.

Together, we pressed on the crooked mantle teeth and the fireplace noisily jerked back to where it belonged.

"When I return tomorrow," she said, "I will bring a stronger lantern."

Unfortunately, the storm left the roads in a mess and most of us were snowed in the next day, so neither Amira nor Buddy came. Naturally, the power was out, too.

I got out my glues and did my best to repair my little shepherd boy. I left him drying on the kitchen counter while I perused my shelf of Hum Harbour history books. Some had come from my parents; some I'd unearthed at used bookstores. I knew several mentioned the lighthouse, so I carried them into the living room.

I stoked the fire in the wood stove, wrapped myself in a blanket, and opened the first book. The first four said nothing about a secret room in the lighthouse. The last one I leafed through, however, had a bookmark at a page that mentioned a secret treasure.

I'd grown up on tales of shipwrecks and missing treasure. I remembered one summer back in grade school, during my "Nancy Drew phase," when my friend and I'd initially read this book. We spent the entire summer searching for the treasure. Of course, we never found it. I doubt it even existed.

I guess I'd left the bookmark at that chapter and forgotten all about it.

Now I reread the story. The author believed a schooner loaded with black market whiskey had capsized just beyond the harbour in a storm in 1927. The whiskey was intended for prohibition-constrained USA. According to the author, Hum Harbour's lightkeeper at that time was believed to have rescued some of the whiskey and stashed it in or near the lighthouse. However, he had died before telling anybody if the rumour was true.

I set the book aside. Could my fireplace hold a secret hidden for almost a hundred years?

The bookmark still lay on my lap, a picture of the book's cover on one side. I flipped it over and read the back.

REWARD

Highland Ale will pay $500 for each bottle of prohibition whiskey recovered.

See our website for details.

A reward, eh? I looked at my dog, who was lying with his head on my foot. "I promised Amira I wouldn't explore behind the fireplace alone, but I didn't say I wouldn't peek. Right, Caber?"

Caber yawned, which I interpreted as a thumbs up.

I shoved myself up and out of the soft cushions. My nativity, apart from the shepherd boy, was safely positioned on a tray on the dining room table, where it would stay. On the tray. Maybe not on the table.

I gathered my equipment.

First, I squirted lubricating spray every place I could think of on the fireplace. Repeated twice, and wiped off the excess. When I finally pushed the three-crooked-teeth section of moulding, the mantle slid smoothly to the right and exposed the hole.

Caber sneezed.

Next, I put on my rubber work gloves and, using my shovel and the fireplace poker, I transferred the small skeleton into a garbage bag. I put the bag into a second one, tied them off, and opened the back door to throw the bundle onto a snow drift.

Finally, I wrapped a towel over the fuzzy head of my dust mop and attacked the tangle of cobwebs. I also bagged and tossed the towel when I was done.

I dragged my nan's rocker close to the hole and sat down to study it. My flashlight's beam showed what might be the top of a descending staircase. My curiosity swelled. Where did it lead? To the basement? Or somewhere else? We were near a cliff edge. Could it come out there? I strained my ears, listening for any sound from within. I whistled, shouted, played games with my echo.

Caber left the room.

My curiosity positively throbbed. If I was going to wait for Amira, I needed to find something else to do or I'd go crazy.

I closed the hole and decided to make mincemeat tarts. No. The power was out. Watch TV? Nope. Paint the baby's room myself? I looked around. No one was here to tell me otherwise.

My cell rang. It was Geoff, in Halifax, enjoying his lunch break. We talked until the power was back.

Plates of mincemeat tarts sat on the table beside my nativity, but Amira was interested only in the shepherd boy. She turned him over and over in her hands. "He is perfect."

"I had the right kind of glue." I fingered baby Jesus nervously. "Fixing him made me think about your question, though. You know, the one I avoided?"

"About why you believe the Christmas story is true?"

I nodded, my heart tap-dancing against my ribs. I'd prepared my speech. Could I deliver it? "It's not because I've been brought up to believe, although I have. And it's not because I've seen visions or experienced miracles, because I haven't." Uncertain, I sneaked a sideways glance at her. "I believe because Jesus healed my heart. Kinda like my broken shepherd. Jesus made me like new again." Then I did the boldest, scariest thing I've ever done. "He can do that for you, too."

Amira stared at the figurine in her hands.

I held my breath and prayed she'd consider my words.

I'm not sure what I expected. But Buddy arrived just then and tripped over the kerosene lantern Amira'd brought for our adventure. The chance to say more slipped away.

Our adventure was still on the agenda, though.

After shovelling our driveway and front sidewalk, Buddy had gone up to the baby's room with the paint, so Amira and I were free to explore.

We'd dressed for it. Boots, heavy sweaters, wind-proof jackets, phones to photograph our expedition. We geared up, lit the kerosene lantern, and opened the fireplace.

"Ready?" I asked.

Amira looked as excited as I felt.

"We'll stop the moment one of us feels unsafe. Okay?"

Amira, who'd survived war, hunger, and refugee camps, smiled as if to say, "That will not be me."

Since there wasn't room to walk side by side, I went first. Black soot coated the fireplace alcove and my hand when I touched it. At the back was a stone archway that I had to stoop to pass through, three stairs down, and then a wall. As Amira squeezed in beside me, I held the lantern high so she could see better.

  Christmas with Hot Apple Cider

"There." She reached over my shoulder and probed what looked to me like a crooked rock with her gloved hand. "Do you have that lubricating spray?"

I passed back the lantern, pulled the spray can from my pocket, and squirted where she'd indicated.

"Try now," she said.

Though almost bursting, I wedged myself into the corner. "The honour's yours." The lantern's whir drowned out my sharp, short breaths.

Amira's hands hovered over the rock. Maybe her heart, like mine, was doing a drum roll.

"No," she said. "Together. We do this together."

I set the lantern on the step behind us, covered her hands with mine, and, at the count of three, we pushed.

In the hollowness of the pit, something rumbled like thunder. A whoosh of stale air hit us hard. Our lantern light flickered but didn't go out.

In front of us was a very rough staircase leading down. We followed it to another door, and then into a sort of cavern. It might have been part of a passage at one time. There was a pile of rocks and rubble at one end that could have been from a cave-in that had closed it off from whatever lay beyond.

What was left for us to find didn't seem like much. A couple of broken barrels, a coil of rope, some stained oil cloth draped over a lump. Amira and I dragged the heavy fabric aside and found four wooden crates underneath. Three held only empty bottles, a few of which were broken. The last crate, however, contained 10 dark glass bottles with cork stoppers. I lifted one of the bottles. The liquid inside sloshed.

My heart just about exploded out of my chest. "Amira! Do you know what I think we've found?"

Her eyebrows rose in question.

"We've found the lost treasure of Hum Harbour!"

"It is…?"

"Whiskey!"

My enthusiasm obviously baffled her. "But you do not drink whiskey."

"I know, but according to my research, the bottles might be worth $500 apiece." I did a quick count. "That's like $5,000 dollars!"

"For old liquor?" She sounded incredulous.

"I know!" An idea was forming in my mind. I'd have to talk it over with Geoff, but… "Come on. Give me a hand and we'll get this upstairs."

"What are you doing?" a grumbly voice said behind us.

Amira and I spun around. Buddy's bulky form towered just beyond the reach of our lantern light, and Caber, who'd followed us, growled. I'd never heard him growl like that before.

I could feel Amira's panic.

"What are you doing here?" Surprise sharpened my voice.

"Came to ask a question and found what you'd done." Stepping closer, Buddy cast a menacing shadow. "Need help with that?"

Amira edged behind me.

I reached back, took her hand. "Yes. If you could carry it up to the kitchen, that'd be nice."

Buddy muttered something unpleasant but grabbed the crate. The glass bottles clattered as he hoisted it to his shoulder.

"Careful! You're carrying the lost treasure of Hum Harbour."

He snorted. "Yeah? What's it worth?"

"Enough to make someone's Christmas extra special."

Buddy swore under his breath.

The next day, after Geoff arrived home, we notified Highland Ale of our discovery. They came, confirmed it really was from the lost shipment of prohibition whiskey, and notified the media. The CBC covered the story. A clip showing Highland presenting us with a giant cardboard cheque made national news. Just in time for the holidays.

Amira and Nazir joined my extended family for our culturally modified Christmas dinner.

Ever tried to find a halal turkey in Nova Scotia? No easy task, believe you me.

When dessert was over, Geoff and I presented Amira and Nazir with a much smaller version of Highland Ale's $5000 cheque.

  Christmas with Hot Apple Cider

"The treasure would never have been found if Amira hadn't recognized the significance of the mantle's crooked dentil work," Geoff said.

"We want you to have this as a gift to mark your first Christmas in your new country," I finished.

My family clapped. My niece pounded the table.

Tears filled Amira's eyes.

Nazir looked gob-smacked. "We cannot possibly accept such a gift."

I shook my head. "Of course you can!"

Amira touched his sleeve, leaned in and spoke softly to him in Syrian.

"You are sure this is what you want to do?" he answered her in English.

She nodded. Her face shone.

It was snowing softly when Geoff and I drove Nazir and Amira to Buddy McLean's place. His rusty old mobile home looked almost festive under its blanket of white. Coloured lights on their Christmas tree shone in one window.

Geoff mounted the decrepit front step—we didn't think it would hold all of us—and rapped on the door.

Buddy's wife answered and called Buddy. Behind them, kids' voices rose and fell. They had seven at last count.

Nazir stepped forward.

To my surprise, Amira did too. "Merry Christmas," she said with a smile.

Buddy looked uncertain.

Nazir smiled. "In keeping with your Canadian Christmas tradition, we wish to share our good fortune with you." He sounded like he'd been practising the speech for a month instead of an hour. "Please accept." He handed Buddy the envelope containing the cheque for $5,000. "Merry Christmas."

"Merry Christmas," we all chimed in.

Nazir and Amira had told us that giving gifts was a tradition they also had. To give and not expect anything in return.

Did they realize they'd given me an amazing gift, too? Amira's smile. Her healing had begun.

1. Read more about Gailynn's sleuthing adventures in the books *Murder in Hum Harbour* and *Death of a Highland Heavyweight*.

I Knew You Would Come

Nonfiction

Eleanor Shepherd

In the late 1980s, my husband Glen and I, both Canadians, were asked to serve with The Salvation Army in France. By December, 1989, we therefore found ourselves immersed in the Christmas activities of *l'Armée du Salut*.

Our office was near the second busiest railway station in Paris, Saint-Lazare, which connected to the Paris Métro.

As in so many western countries, French Salvationists encourage contributions to Christmas fundraising activities to help those in need. In Paris, the millions of commuters are targeted during the final weeks of December. Thus, leaving our office, Glen and I joined a uniformed group singing carols around our Christmas Cheer kettle in the great hall of Saint-Lazare Station.

SNCF, the national train company, provided a storage room for our accompaniment keyboard. This allowed us to roll it out to a strategic location to catch the greatest number of passengers. The vaulted ceiling echoed with Christmas music every evening from five to seven p.m.

Two days before Christmas, Glen and I finished our shift and joined the rest of the commuters heading to the familiar track where we jumped onto the train going to Nanterre, then transferred to the train for Rueil-Malmaison, the suburb where we lived.

Tired after a long day, we were eager to get home and have supper with our family. But in the crush at Nanterre, just as we were about to board the train for Rueil-Malmaison, someone tapped Glen on the shoulder.

As we turned to look, a woman said, "Monsieur? Madame? Could I have a word with you?"

We stepped out of the streaming crowd and listened as she sketchily recounted her story of a friend who was holed up in a cheap hotel with her two children and had nothing for Christmas.

She had no food to make a Christmas dinner and no gifts to give her little girls.

Knowing our train's departure was imminent, we promised to see what we could do to help. The woman gave us her friend's address, but no contact information for herself.

As the train whistle blew, we rejoined the crowd pushing to get inside the already-crowded train, realizing we wouldn't be able to let her know if we could help or not.

Around the dinner table that evening, we told our children, John and Elizabeth, aged 16 and 11, about this encounter. We knew it was probably too late to ask for help through official Salvation Army channels. All of the names for Christmas hampers and toys had been registered, and most of the food and gifts had already been distributed to the families for whom they were designated. But John and Elizabeth seized on the idea of making this family our personal Christmas project.

When we went in to work the next day, Glen decided to ask the folks responsible for the Christmas hampers if there was anything left that we might be able to scrounge for this little family. His quest yielded a few items of food.

After school that day, our kids pooled their resources and headed over to Euromarché, a popular supermarket, to see what they could find in the way of treats for the children. Elizabeth also decided to contribute some toys she no longer needed that were still in good shape. John bought a few story books about Christmas. Glen and I looked after the groceries.

On Christmas Eve, we gathered all the things we had accumulated, wrapped the gifts in colourful seasonal paper, and placed them in Christmas baskets. Then we squeezed into our car and headed for the address the lady at the train station had given us.

To call such a place a hotel seemed ridiculous to me. It was more like a dilapidated boarding house with sparsely equipped rooms and no amenities. With wallpaper peeling in the hallways, floors bearing the marks of generations of scuffed shoes, and a damp, musty smell pervading the atmosphere, rating it with one star would be extremely generous. The woman at what we assumed was the front desk told us that the room we wanted was on the second floor, so we climbed the creaky stairs with the lifting lino leum and found the room number written in chalk on the door.

When we knocked, the door was timidly opened a crack by a skinny woman who appeared to be hardly more than a teenager. Her clothes drooped on her emaciated frame.

When she spied our uniforms, she opened the door wide and invited us into the room, which was furnished with one bed and two fragile wooden chairs. A naked light bulb was suspended from the ceiling, and a hot plate with two burners served as her kitchen. There was no refrigerator and no table.

Taking refuge behind their mother were two little girls with matted brown hair and toothpick-like limbs, their wide eyes filled with fear and expectation. Seeing their threadbare pants and T-shirts, I wished that we had thought to add some warm clothing to our gifts.

We offered the family everything we had brought and, like most excited children, the girls squealed with enthusiasm. They were thrilled with the toys and candy.

While John and Elizabeth settled on the bed to read some of the Christmas books to the children, the young mother and I sat on the rickety chairs and Glen leaned against the grey wall.

The first thing the young woman said to us was, "I knew you would come. My friend told me she had talked to someone from The Salvation Army, and when she told me that, I knew that you would come."

That tearful young woman had no idea how much joy she brought to our family—not only that Christmas, but also every year since then. There isn't a single Christmas that we don't speak about that experience and how much we enjoyed the opportunity to brighten the lives of this little family. We also learned how important it is to be there for someone in need. We can't do everything, but—when an opportunity comes our way—we can do something. We can be people others know they can count on.

For us, joy still bubbles up each year when we find ourselves collecting for our Christmas appeal, knowing that what we do really can make a difference in someone's life.

The Christmas Ornaments

Nonfiction

Grace Wulff

"I love crafting," my friend Helen told me, "and I'd love it if you could give these away!" She held out a bag of beautifully decorated Christmas ball ornaments she'd covered with colourful fabrics, crochet work, and beads. Each one was a work of art.

Helen loves to craft beautiful things. She looks for ways to use her creations and has given much of her work away to women's groups and to a local shelter. Now she hoped I could use them at the hospital to bring cheer to some of the patients.

As I took the bag, I wondered how best to use them. I serve as a hospital chaplain, and I know that Christmas can be one of the most difficult times of the year. It would be nice to have a small gift to offer those in the hospital.

We already had hundreds of little Christmas stockings, both sides cut from old Christmas cards, and the stocking's edges joined with yarn stitches. Each stocking held a handmade bookmark and a candy cane. Many volunteers help with this project every year.

But the ornaments were beautiful, and I knew they'd bring extra cheer to those who might need encouragement.

In early December, I started taking the bag of ornaments with me as I walked into hospital rooms. Our hospital has close to 200 beds, so I knew I couldn't give one to each patient. But, as I often do, I prayed that God would lead me to those who needed them the most.

"Where should I hang this?" I asked one elderly gentleman whose room was devoid of any decoration.

I decided that his IV pole looked like the best place. And the smile on his face when he looked up made me so glad my friend had given me the ornaments.

On I went, creating Christmas trees out of IV poles. For some patients, it was their only Christmas ornament, their only decoration, their only gift.

One lady, who had been thrilled to receive the Christmas ball, sent me a picture of it still hanging on the IV pole a few days later. I was delighted, and I sent the photo to Helen. All three of us shared in the joy this gift had brought!

Christmas was close, but I still had a few ornaments left.

One morning, I was chatting with one of our hospital volunteers. She was telling me about the grief she felt because this was her first Christmas without her sister, who had died suddenly earlier in the year.

I remembered my own grief-filled years after the death of my husband and, shortly after that, the death of my grandmother. The first Christmas afterward, someone gave me an ornament for each one, to hang in their memory. They brought me comfort, year after year, as I hung them on the tree.

After I shared these memories, I reached into my bag and said, "Would you like a Christmas ornament?"

The lovely gift took on a new meaning as I gave it to the volunteer—it was a way to honour her sister.

By Christmas Day, I had only one ornament left in my bag. I wondered who might need this one.

Earlier in the fall, I'd spent many sacred moments with a woman who became a dear friend as she battled cancer. We talked about faith and life…and about death. She told me proudly about her family and her grandchild and another one to come. And then, one day, she died. I missed her and felt deeply for her husband and family, who would be without her for the first time this Christmas.

It's hard to believe, but I discovered that my friend's daughter-in-law was in the hospital, in labour. Yes, my friend's grandchild would be born on Christmas Day.

And what gift did I have to bring to this new child?

A Christmas ornament. It was waiting right there in my bag, a lovely gift to hang on an IV pole, and then later on a tree. A gift to remember both a very special grandma and the birth of her grandchild.

Helen was touched and delighted that I was able to use her gifts, and I was moved to be a channel through whom she could share her creations with others.

The simplest of gifts—lovingly made, freely given—and I had them just at the right time. Gifts of comfort and cheer when people, including me, needed them most!

Christmas Song for the Broken

Nonfiction

Evangeline Inman

In May of 2011, my daughter and I went on a mission trip to Moldova, a republic between Romania and Ukraine in Eastern Europe. While there, we worked with the girls at Stella's House, a home where orphaned girls are kept safe from sex-traffickers. I've heard it said that one of Moldova's biggest exports is beautiful European girls who are sold into slavery.

One of the things we learned while we were there was that the United States and Canada aren't immune to sex-trafficking. Even in our countries, young girls, and boys, too, are being sold and used in the sex-trade industry.

After our experience in Moldova, I felt passionate about ministering to more of these vulnerable girls, but I also felt inadequate. I wanted to help bring healing to them, but I wasn't sure what I could do.

Months passed. Then, one morning close to Christmas, I woke up with the words, "Come to Me, all who are weary and heavy-laden, and I will give you rest,"[1] going over and over in my mind. As I crawled out of bed, the words stayed in my head. I kept hearing, "Come to Me, all who are weary! Come to Me, all who are weary! Come to Me, all who are weary!"

I was busy getting ready to fly to California for the holidays, and, while the words were beautiful, they didn't particularly speak to anything I was facing that day. But throughout the morning, that verse continued pounding in my heart.

Finally I went online and found the reference for the Scripture. It was Matthew 11:28, part of a passage where Jesus was teaching. I really felt God was speaking to me, but I didn't know why or what He was trying to tell me.

I read the verse in several different translations, but nothing struck me. However, I'm a songwriter. Because the words were so persistent, I sat down at the piano and began the process of writing a song based on them.

At first I sang the words exactly the way they were written in Scripture. Eventually a melody emerged. Once the music was flowing, I continued to tweak the lyrics until they rhymed and fit the melodic phrasing and the rhythmic patterns of the song. Then I worked on a chorus and added a second verse. When the song was finished, I felt a sense of relief and went on with my day.

As planned, I flew to California with my husband, Mark, and our daughter, Marquelle, to spend Christmas with my mom and siblings and their families.

A few days after Christmas, my sister-in-law Shurece asked me if I'd go with her to lead worship at a home for young girls who had been rescued from the sex-slave trade.

This was the first time since the trip to Moldova that I'd been offered an opportunity to minister to girls like this, and I quickly agreed. My heart was overwhelmed by the enormity of these girls' needs. Plus, because this was in North America—close to my home, in a sense—it broke my heart even more.

I felt honoured by the invitation to minister in such a setting, and I knew it would be rewarding, but I also knew it would be hard for me emotionally.

The day we were to go to the home for girls, my husband and I spent a long time near the ocean, walking along a beautiful beach in Carmel. It was very relaxing. But, unfortunately, spending so much time in the wind rolling off the ocean wasn't ideal for my voice, especially since I'd already developed a cold. By late afternoon, my throat was raw and I wasn't feeling great.

We went back into the city, and I took a couple of sinus tablets, hoping they would relieve my cold symptoms before we headed out.

The location of the house we were going to was kept a secret for the safety of the girls.

A woman named Sharon,[2] who had invited my sister-in-law to come, met us at a gas station, and we followed her in our car.

Before taking us inside, Sharon gave us some idea of the terrible abuse these girls had suffered. Her eyes grew moist as she

  Christmas with Hot Apple Cider

spoke, as did ours. She said they still lived in fear of the men who had handled them and thought of them as property to be sold and used.

On the outside, the house looked like a normal upscale family home outside of the city limits. It was surrounded by manicured lawns, and it had a large fenced-off area for horses they used in therapy.

The peaceful-looking location didn't prepare me for the pain I felt in the air the moment I stepped through the front door.

Nine girls were waiting in the living room. As we were introduced, I was surprised by how young some of them were. One of them was only 12.

Not all of the girls who lived in the house attended, and a couple of them wandered in and out as we were singing. The ones who remained sat huddled together on a dark brown, leather sectional couch. My heart was overwhelmed with compassion as I looked at these girls who had experienced such hurt in their short lives.

As we settled in for a time of worship, I realized that this was going to be a totally different experience from anything I'd known. I've led worship for years. I've sung in churches, prisons, and in third-world countries, but this was a whole new level of hurting. Pain and depression were thick in the room. A heaviness seemed to have settled over all of us.

After Shurece led some songs, it was my turn. I sat at the piano, wondering what to sing. I'd made a list of possible songs, but nothing felt right. After a moment, I began singing about being in the hands of Jesus and finding healing. I thought, *This will be perfect, and will really touch their hearts.*

I wasn't in the best shape to sing. The cold medicine hadn't helped at all, and I felt miserable. Plus, my range was limited and I couldn't reach all of the notes. To make it worse, I kept coughing. I knew I should have cancelled, but I'd really wanted to be a part of ministering in this setting.

As I was singing, I realized that the song I'd chosen didn't seem to be clicking with the girls. I was only a few feet from them, and I could read their expressions pretty clearly. I tried a few other songs, but I knew I wasn't hitting the target. Finally, I remembered the song I'd written that morning when I'd awakened with the Scripture verse on my heart. I'd never sung it in front of anyone. But I was desperate. I started to sing the chorus:

> Come to Me all who are weary,
> Come to Me with your heavy load,
> I can carry your burdens,
> Come to Me, you'll be made whole.

I immediately sensed a change in the atmosphere. It was as if the heavens had opened, and healing was spreading through the air. The Holy Spirit was moving, and I could visibly see the song speaking to the girls.

Amazed and thankful that God was working through it, I sang the entire song. Then I moved into another song I'd written called, "Rest and Be at Peace."

As I finished singing, one of the leaders began a time of prayer. I played the piano softly in the background as the girls started to pray for each other. One by one, each girl prayed basically the same request, "God, please help each of us to be able to sleep through the night."

I was stunned by their prayers. They were asking God to give them rest and help them have an undisturbed night without bad memories waking them up in a sweat. I'd never thought they'd have so much trouble sleeping at night. Tears came to my eyes. How horrible that these precious girls were being tortured by nightmares from their past.

I prayed that God would grant their requests, just as He had answered my prayer that He would use me.

I sat on the piano bench deeply humbled. I'm not trained in how to deal with issues of sexual abuse and the sex-slave trade. I had no idea what the girls were facing. But God used me anyway. Right in the middle of the busy Christmas season, God had stopped me that morning because He wanted to send a message of love and comfort to that small roomful of girls.

Although they were far away from their families during that Christmas, their Heavenly Father was thinking of them. He knew exactly which words needed to be sung over the girls that night, and I am so thankful that I was obedient when I sat down and wrote out the song God had placed within my spirit.

That night was a great confirmation for me that God is leading me and giving me words that He can speak through me. I may not understand when I feel the gentle nudging of the Holy Spirit. I may not know who the song is for. But if God can give me the words of a verse for a group of wounded girls in central California while I'm thousands of miles away in Fredericton, New Brunswick, then I can trust Him to use me for more things than I can imagine or dream.

I can honestly say that the best Christmas present I received that year was the opportunity to sing the song God gave me to those beautiful young girls.

1. Matthew 11:28, New American Standard Bible

2. Name changed for privacy.

Affliction

Fiction

Kevin J. Dautremont

Charlie was hurting. He was hurting real bad. He was tired; he was hungry; he was cold; but most of all, he was hurting. He knew he had to get some stuff soon or the hurt would get worse.

Maybe Bennie would just give him some, you know, as a loan. *Nah, no way.* Not after Charlie had stiffed him the last time.

Maybe Karla would give him some of her methadone. It wouldn't be the same but it would hold off the hurt for a while. Charlie shook his head. That wouldn't work. Karla had told him her doc had gotten all bent out of shape over something, cut off her carries. Now she had to drink the whole dose in front of the pharmacist every day. They made sure she did it.

They were all like that. Big shots looking down on everyone else. Yes, sir. No, sir. What do you want now, sir? Expecting everyone to bow down. But not him. Not Charlie Westerman. No way.

Charlie shivered and swayed. A swirl of snow danced around his legs and sneaked into a hole in his shoe. He stamped his feet in a futile attempt to shake off the cold. He should have gone west. Big Joe had wanted him to. Told him to come to Vancouver, or even Victoria, but he had stayed. *What an idiot. Stuck in Saskatoon in December!* But nobody told him what to do.

Something else did, though. The hurt. It was telling him to move, to get something fast or he would hurt a lot more than he already did. It coiled in his gut and laughed at him. Charlie had to admit that he really wasn't in charge anymore. The hurt was.

Maybe—just maybe, he could try Edgar.

"You want what?"

Charlie grimaced and sucked air in through his teeth as Edgar pushed him hard against the wall of the alley. He didn't like Edgar.

He didn't like how he looked, how he acted, or even his name. It was never Eddie or Ed, always Edgar. But Charlie was desperate. "C'mon, man," he said, "I just need a little bit of cash."

"You want money? From me?" Edgar jabbed his finger in Charlie's ribs. "Sure thing. No problem." His smile was hard and cold. "All you gotta do is go into the store around the corner and bring me back some stuff. Sunglasses, Blu-rays, watches, whatever."

"Man, I can't do that." Charlie sniffed and wiped his nose on his sleeve. "I can't. I'm on probation. I can't go back inside."

Edgar pushed him back against the wall. "Then go crawl in a hole somewhere." He turned away. "Or maybe go beg for it. You're good at begging."

It should have been easier. Being this close to Christmas should have put people in more of a giving mood. Charlie had even managed to make a cardboard sign to plead his case.

OUT OF WORK
NEED MONEY TO
GET HOME FOR XMAS

It wasn't helping much. For starters, he wasn't at the main entrance but off at one of the side doors. Oh, he'd tried to grab one of the prime spots, but after a couple of whispered threats from the regular panhandlers, he'd shuffled away.

Plus, the cold was fighting against him. Everyone rushed into the mall as quick as they could, head down and hands in pockets.

"Hey, thanks, man. It all helps," he said as a business man dropped some coins in his hand before hurrying toward the mall doorway. Charlie glanced down and grimaced. *Fifty cents? You gotta be kidding.* He felt an urge to throw the cash at the man's feet but instead shoved it into his pocket. *Cheap bastard.* The rest of Charlie's opinion was swept away by a blast of chilling wind.

An old woman smiled at him as she passed but didn't stop. Maybe he didn't look pathetic enough. If it got any colder or if the hurt got any worse he sure would.

He could see through the glass doors into the mall, and he watched with growing anticipation as the old woman stopped at the ATM just inside. Maybe there was hope after all. But the woman just disappeared deeper into the mall.

He grunted and shook his head.

"Hey, man, you need a place to stay?"

Charlie turned and stared at the young man who'd spoken. His clothes were old and worn but clean. His skin was marred by acne scars, but his eyes were clear. His long black hair shone bright and clean as it coiled in a neat braid over his shoulder.

The young man smiled as he held a card out to Charlie.

Charlie did a double-take as he glanced at the outstretched hand and grimaced in recognition of the blackish green tattoos at the base of the thumb and forefinger. He leaned back, hands lifted in a defensive pose. "Look, I ain't no gangbanger. I don't want no trouble."

The young man's smile broadened as he lifted his hand higher. "What? These? They're from a different life. I'm with the Mission House now. Look, there's a hot meal and a bed there for you if you're interested." He held the card out again.

Charlie hesitated, then took the card. He'd heard about this place. Some real food and a warm place to sleep sounded mighty good. He'd have to put up with some preaching but it might be worth it.

Something twisted in his gut and shot a wave up his spine that burned through the base of his brain. He knew they wouldn't let him in if he was high, and the hurt was only going to get worse if he wasn't. With a grunt, he shoved the card in his pocket and shook his head. *No.*

"Just think about it, okay?" The young man reached out to touch his arm, but Charlie shook him off and turned his back, waiting, staring at nothing, until he heard the young man walk away.

Another do-gooder. Trying to save the world. Charlie didn't need saving. He just needed to stop hurting.

Charlie resumed his quiet harassment of the people passing on the sidewalk. A few coins here, a handful there. Not much. Never enough.

He spied the old woman he had seen earlier. She was coming out of the mall doors, carrying a bulging paper bag emblazoned with a fast food logo in one hand and a tall coffee cup in the other. She was headed straight for Charlie.

"Sir? Excuse me, sir?" Her voice was soft, barely a whisper. "You look so cold and hungry I had to do something." She held out the food and drink.

Charlie's eyes widened. The burn in the base of his brain crackled and spit. *Burgers? Coffee?* That wasn't what he wanted. It wouldn't stop him from hurting. And it wouldn't help him buy what he needed. Something snapped.

Quicker than thought, his hand flashed out and slapped the coffee cup from her hand. As she staggered from the blow, he snatched the purse from her arm and began to run. Her cries echoed through the night.

"No! Please! No!"

Charlie wasn't sure how long he'd run or even in what direction he'd gone until at last he found himself crouching behind a dumpster in an alleyway. A single street lamp cast just enough of its sickly glow to allow him to see. He pulled open the purse. *She went to an ATM. Where's the money? What did she do with it all?* A small paper bag from a pharmacy looked promising but held only a couple of bottles of heart pills. The purse held little else, a handful of coins, a phone bill, an old yellowed sheet of paper, the old woman's bank card, and a receipt. Nothing.

In desperation now, he searched through the purse again. The ATM receipt showed she had taken out 40 dollars leaving a balance of less than ten. The pharmacy bill was for just over 20. Charlie's head jerked upward. She had spent the rest, almost all of her money, on food and coffee for him.

He sank further down against the pavement. Why would she do that?

Charlie pulled out the yellowed paper and slowly unfolded it. It was a single sheet of paper—a letter, and it had a newspaper clipping stapled to it. An obituary. The photo in it was that of a young woman. *Looks about my age.* He lifted the clipping and stared at the letter.

> *Mom, I'm really sorry. I know that I've hurt you time and time again. I know that I was wrong. I should have stayed. I wish I had.*
>
> *It's been hard but I'm better now. I was found by some good people. They helped me a lot. I've been clean for almost two months now, and I don't ever want to go back. I won't go back.*
>
> *Mom, can I come home? I just want to see you again. By the time you get this I should be on my way. I'll be home for Christmas. If you let me. Please, Mom.*
>
> *I love you.*
>
> *Rachel*

Charlie looked at the date on the clipping, then lowered it. The young woman had died on December 24, five years ago that day. She never made it home for Christmas.

Gently he refolded the letter and placed it back in the purse. At that moment, the street lamp flickered and died. From the darkness, Charlie looked up. The clouds had dispersed and he could see the stars. They seemed to shine brighter than he had ever seen them before.

The old woman sat in her kitchen, staring at her hands. Her eyes were dry—there were no tears left. *Why, Lord? Why even this? Haven't I lost enough already? My husband, my daughter, and now my letter? Why?* She looked around her house. There wasn't much to indicate it was Christmas. Just a tiny tree on an end table—a toy really—but Rachel had loved it. All the old woman had left of her daughter were the toy tree and her last letter. And now the letter was gone.

She dropped her head, the familiar words of Psalm 42 running through her mind. *Why, my soul, are you downcast? Why so*

disturbed within me? Put your hope in God, for I will yet praise him.
The tears came again, but softly, like a cleansing rain.

The doorbell's sharp tones pulled her from her thoughts. Who could that be?

She shuffled to the door and opened it a crack. "Who is it? Who's there?" Something caught her eye and she glanced down at the landing. Her purse!

Falling to her knees she wrenched it open and peered inside. It was there! Rachel's letter was there! Pulling herself upright she stepped out through the door. "Are you there? Can you hear me?"

The low moan of the wind was her only answer.

The old woman called again. "Thank you. Thank you so much."

The young man with the long braid stood at the doorway of the Mission House and watched the street. Behind him, the long tables were filling with the homeless, the addicts, the poor, and the lost. Waiting. Waiting for their Christmas feast. Waiting for the promise that Christmas would bring.

He thought of the guy panhandling at the mall. Would he respond to the invitation on the card he'd been given? The young man had been praying that he would. Praying that God would reach out and call him to the feast.

He smiled and continued to stare out into the darkness. There was room for one more. There was always room.

Not This Christmas

Brian C. Austin

Clang of bars.
>Great gates of steel.
>>Metallic crunch of massive locks.

The movies play it well
>but . . .

Different . . . the sounds fall on the ears
>from the inside—
>>the wrong side
>when the keys
>>by other hands are guarded.

Different . . . the eyes search
>old, heavy steel,
>>pitted and painted,
>>cruel and cold.
>Steel that forms the cell
>>or outer block,
>>>still barred.

Different . . . the nose tastes stale air,
>hatred breathed,
>>innocence damned,
>the curse more natural than breathing.

Clang of bars.
>Great gates of steel.
>>Metallic crunch of massive locks.

Still, somewhere Christmas is celebrated.
>Somewhere . . .

Somewhere . . . children stare at a tree,
        floor covered
                with gaily-coloured packages.

"Wait for Daddy,"
        the older has three years,
                told the younger.
                        But not this Christmas.

Clang of bars.
        Great gates of steel.
                Metallic crunch of massive locks.

Alone, Daddy sits,
        stares,
                bars shadows sharp across his face.
        Grieves for children
                whose Daddy won't be home.
                        Not this Christmas.

Grieves for Daddy,
        who won't hold his son,
                or hear his daughter laugh.
                        Not this Christmas.

Grieves for Mommy
        who strives, alone,
                to fill an empty place
        in children's hearts;
                in her own heart
                        and arms
                                and bed.

Aches over promises broken.
        Cries in the awful aloneness.
                Prays for courage to even believe in God,
        to trust,
                to surrender.

Hard and cold, the bars remain
      but a man who knows he is loved
            may find courage.

Home?
      Not this Christmas.
            But other Christmases *will* come.

Clang of bars.
      Great gates of steel.
            Metallic crunch of massive locks.

The Christmas Lesson

Fiction

N. J. Lindquist

"I hate Christmas!" Antonia Valdez proclaimed as she stepped into the empty kitchen in her church's basement. "Hate it! Hate it! Hate it!"

"And why is that?" a male voice called out.

Startled, Antonia whirled, then stepped back into the hallway, muscles tense. It was eight o'clock on Monday night and she'd assumed she was alone in the church.

A tall man with ebony skin stood beside the door of one of the classrooms they used for Sunday school. The kindergarten classroom, to be specific.

Antonia relaxed a little. "Sorry, I didn't know anyone else was here. The back door was locked."

"I locked it after I came in," the man said. "Habit, I guess. You're—?"

"Antonia. I'm the Christian education director."

"Oh, yeah." He nodded. "When I saw you before, you were wearing church clothes. I guess you know I'm Rafe." Like Antonia, Rafe was wearing jeans and a T-shirt.

"I know." Rafe Montgomery—no, Pastor Rafe Montgomery—had been hired recently by the board of Antonia's church, the small church where she served as the volunteer CE director. They'd met twice before, briefly, and she'd been opposed to the board's hiring him as the new pastor, but here he was. Although today was the day he'd been slated to start, she'd never dreamed he'd be in the building this late.

"But I'm still curious. Why do you hate Christmas?"

"Because it's so fake."

"Fake?"

"You know. Everything. Not only Santa Claus, but spending money you don't have trying to come up with expensive gifts, the decorations and Christmas movies and food and the whole politically correct thing, and—just everything! Most of that stuff has nothing whatsoever to do with the real meaning of Christmas! How do you convince the kids it's about Jesus' birthday when they're deluged with everything else?"

Pastor Montgomery nodded. "Yeah, I get what you mean. So, do you have kids?"

"No, but I work with the Sunday school teachers and the youth group leaders, and I talk to the kids. It's not that big a church. Plus I'm neither blind nor deaf."

"Ri-ght."

He drew the word out, the way the teens might. Not that he was old. She'd read his resume. He was 31. Two years older than she was. And he wasn't married either.

"Well, I have things to do." She turned to go back into the kitchen.

"What are you working on?"

Antonia's temper flared. It was none of his business what she was doing. But she bit her tongue. Not good to start off on the wrong foot. Not if she planned to stay in the church. "The Christmas nativity pageant," she said.

He looked puzzled. "It's only September."

"We have to start planning and organizing for our Christmas programs now."

"In the kitchen?"

She fought to hold her tongue. "There's a storage cupboard at the back of the room where we keep the decorations for special Sundays. Christmas, Easter, etcetera."

"Need some help?"

She started to say, "Of course not," but managed to stop herself in time and substitute a lame, "If you're sure you have time."

He shrugged. "Just familiarizing myself with things. Sounds like this cupboard would be good for me to know about."

She let him pull out the boxes and set them on the counter, then thanked him. As if she couldn't have pulled the boxes out herself. She assured him she could manage from there.

He nodded. "I'll leave you to your work then."

Two days later, Antonia got a phone call during her lunch hour. She saw the name and waited until after the third ring before answering. "Can I help you?" she asked.

"It's Rafe," he said. "Pastor Montgomery, if you prefer."

"I know. Call display."

"Of course. I have a few questions about the church and I figured you'd be a good person to ask. Could we get together and talk? Maybe over dinner?"

Antonia screwed up her face. Good this wasn't a video chat. She'd be happy if she never had to talk to him, but that wish was neither practical nor feasible. "Do you mean tonight?" she asked.

"If you're free. Or tomorrow. I know this is short notice."

"Tonight is okay."

"Could we meet at Mandrigo? At 6:30?"

"Where is that? I've never heard of it."

"It's not far from where you work. I'll text you the address."

"Okay." She hung up, then realized she'd never told him where she worked or given him her cell number. Presumably one of the board members had. Likely discussed her with him, too. Given him pointers on how to get on her good side.

If Antonia had been inclined to swear, she would have. She'd grown up in the small church in a residential area of Toronto, and she loved it there. These people were her family. She loved listening to the stories from the older folk and working with the leaders as part of a team. She loved the teenagers and the children. And she wanted things to stay the same. So what if there were only a hundred or so people, including babies? It was big enough for her.

Pastor Grayson had been there since she was ten, and he'd been like an uncle to her. But last spring he'd decided to retire, so they'd had to find a new pastor.

The search committee had narrowed it down to two men, and she'd have been very happy with the other one, who'd reminded her of Pastor Grayson. But Rafe Montgomery was nothing like their former pastor, and she knew that he was going to change everything. And not for the better.

She stayed late at work, then took the subway to the restaurant. When she reached it, she stood outside staring at a sign that said this restaurant was owned and operated as a charity and staffed by former convicts who were on probation. She hesitated.

"Glad you were able to find it okay," Rafe said from behind her.

"It—it looks interesting."

"They have great food," he said as he stepped forward and opened the door. She had no choice but to go inside, with him behind her.

"Hey, Delight!" Rafe greeted the young cinnamon-skinned woman who came toward them holding menus. She smiled, greeted him by name, and led them to a table for two at the back.

"You come here often?" Antonia asked as she sat down.

"Yes."

"You're sure the food's okay?"

"It's great. Honest."

"Okay." She didn't want to ask her real question: Is it *safe*?

Judging by Rafe's body language, he felt safe. He was sitting back in his chair, one leg stretched out, one arm at his side while his other hand held the menu.

As soon as they'd ordered, Antonia crossed her arms and leaned back. "You said you had some questions?"

"You've been CE director for quite a while? As a volunteer?"

A cold wave flashed over her. Here it came. Either he'd want her to do things his way, or, if she didn't cooperate, he'd try to get her to resign. "About—about six years, I guess."

"How many hours a week would you say it takes on average?"

"Do you mean prep or actually doing things?"

"Everything."

"Maybe 20 to 25 hours, on average. Some weeks I work more, some less."

"But you have a job?"

"That's right."

"A full-time job?"

"I work for a construction company. Nine-to-five, no weekends."

"What do you do?"

"I hold down the office—arrange things, order, invoice, track hours, and so on."

"So you have time and energy to do all the church stuff?"

"Yes. My job involves mundane things like scheduling appointments and paying bills. I want to do more than that. I enjoy working with people and doing creative things."

"Like CE?"

"Yes." If he thought she was going to do things his way without a fight, he was wrong.

Their food had arrived, so they ate in relative silence.

When they'd finished, Antonia said, "So, do you have any other questions?"

"A couple."

"Okay." She waited, her arms crossed.

"Why do you dislike me so much?"

An electric shock went through her, paralyzing her brain. Like a small child, she said the only thing she could think of: "I don't dislike you."

"Is it because I'm Black?"

"Of course not."

He raised his eyebrows. "There's no 'of course' about it."

"I'm not racist. Or prejudiced. Good grief, my father is from Guatemala."

"So? He's not Black."

"I have friends who are Black."

He smiled. "Isn't that what they all say?"

"In my case, it's true."

"There aren't many Black or Hispanic people in the church."

"I know. I wish there were more." She made a face. "It was my mother's church. If we're being honest, although my dad is happy enough here, I think he's always felt a bit like an odd duck." She looked into his eyes. "Maybe with you here…"

"Maybe. So if it's not that I'm Black, what is it? My age? The fact that I'm single? That I came from the school of hard knocks? In case you weren't aware, my father was the one who came up with the idea for this restaurant."

She thought about what that meant.

"Yeah, he was in jail. That's where he found God. When I was 13. It took me a while to realize he had something I wanted."

"I—I—didn't know that. But, no, that isn't it."

"No? So you just don't like me?"

"It's not *you* I dislike."

It was his turn to make a face. "I don't get it. You dislike me, but it's not *me*?"

Antonia used both hands to push her long hair back. "It's what you want to *do*," she whispered.

He frowned. "What I want to *do*?"

"I like our church the way it is. I don't want it to change."

After a moment of silence, he frowned. "Okay, I get that. You like the familiar. You know all the people. It's working for you."

Crossing her arms in front of her chest, Antonia said, "I grew up in this church. It's part of who I am."

"Right." He thought for a moment. "Let me ask you this. Why do you think the board hired me instead of the other candidate, who was older and, from what I've heard, a lot like the former pastor?"

"Because this church isn't growing."

He nodded.

"But numbers aren't the whole story," she said. "If you look at conferences, the speakers are always from mega-churches. And Christians are always talking church growth—as if a church can't be any good if it's small. But all too often, people are there to be entertained; they aren't part of a church family, at all."

"Being part of a church family is important to you."

"Yes."

"What's the best part?"

After a moment's thought, she said, "Acts 2. They were all together, sharing, eating, and caring for one another."

"So that's what you want?"

"That's what I've *known*, growing up in this church. Most people—even most Christians—don't have that."

"You mentioned your father. I think someone told me that your mother died?"

She nodded. "Cancer. When I was 11."

"And the people in the church helped your family out during that time?"

"Not just then. Always. We're like an extended family."

He nodded again. "And you want to keep it that way—comfortable and safe."

She just looked at him, her arms still crossed.

"Okay, I think I understand a little anyway. But now, tell me again why you hate Christmas?"

"I told you the other day. Because it's all *wrong*. All the Santa garbage and the emphasis on presents, and treating the story of Jesus' birth as if it's a cute Disney story instead of a time of violence and hatred, and—" Antonia stopped speaking and put all her efforts into holding back the tears that were fighting to come.

Rafe leaned in. "If we could come up with a way to emphasize the birth of Christ and the joy it brings while de-emphasizing all the other hoopla—would you be interested?"

"I always try to do that."

"Including the pageant with the kids as the main service?"

She looked down. "It's what everyone expects."

"What if we tried something different?"

"Like what?"

"No idea. We'll have to brainstorm. Maybe we could both read Acts 2:44–47 on our own and then get together for a couple of hours to talk about new ideas for things we could do at Christmas this year?"

"Acts 2 isn't the Christmas story."

"No, but you mentioned it earlier. And although Christmas is about Jesus' birth, Acts 2 is the story of the birth of the church."

The moment she got home after leaving the restaurant, Antonia pulled out her Bible. Rafe—she really should call him Pastor Rafe—had something up his sleeve, and the sooner she figured out what it was the better.

Antonia loved Acts 2. True, she hadn't sat down to read it in a while, but she loved it.

An hour later she was still sitting in her favourite chair, mulling over the meaning of the last paragraph.

> All the believers were together and had everything
> in common. They sold property and possessions to
> give to anyone who had need. Every day they con-
> tinued to meet together in the temple courts. They
> broke bread in their homes and ate together with
> glad and sincere hearts, praising God and enjoying
> the favour of all the people. And the Lord added
> to their number daily those who were being saved.

This was the model of community she'd given to Rafe. What she'd always felt her small church was. Okay, not to an extreme. Not like a commune. But they helped each other out in many ways—financial loans, babysitting, providing meals during times of illness or loss, and much more. And they ate together a lot. Had fun together. Worshipped God together.

But what about the last verse? *And the Lord added to their number daily those who were being saved.*

God wasn't adding to their numbers. Not really. Yes, new families moved into the area, but that was balanced by other families moving away. At best, the church was holding its own.

She felt sad and confused. She'd been so sure she was right. A part of her still believed that. But—could she have been wrong all along? Thinking only about herself and what she wanted?

She put her head down on her arms and began to sob.

Shortly after five on Friday, Antonia was leaving work when she spotted Rafe Montgomery propped against the fence outside the front doors. Her first instinct was to run back inside and try to sneak out the back way. But she knew she'd have to face him at some point. Might as well be now.

She walked toward him. "Did you want something?" she asked. "I'm in a bit of a hurry."

"What do you think you're doing?"

"Going home."

"Why did you send the church board a letter of resignation?"

"I decided it was time to move on."

"Speaking of moving on, this isn't a good place to talk. Let me give you a ride home."

"I take transit." She started to walk away.

He caught up and grabbed her arm. "I just want to know why."

She stopped. "All right. There's a coffee shop across the street."

Once seated, she said, "I read the verses in Acts, and I understand what you want to do."

"Which is?"

"To have a large church."

"Where did it say that?"

"'And the Lord added to their number daily those who were being saved.'"

"How does that mean a large church?"

"It's obvious."

He bent forward, elbows on the table, head resting on his clasped hands, his eyes mere inches from hers. "Not to me, it isn't."

She looked down. "I don't blame you. Like I said, it's what everyone wants these days—the bigger, the better."

"That's *not* what I want."

She raised her eyes to meet his.

He looked up at the ceiling, as if hoping a message would be written there. Finally, he settled back in his chair, hands on his hips. "Okay, let's try this. When Jesus was born, aside from his parents, Zechariah, and Elizabeth, who did God tell about the baby?"

"Well, the angels told the shepherds."

"Right. Why not tell the rulers?"

"Herod would have had him killed. He tried to, later on."

"Why didn't God tell the religious leaders? The Pharisees and Sadducees?"

"They wouldn't have believed it."

"Why tell anybody, then?"

"Well, otherwise, no one would know."

"So why shepherds?"

"I don't know. Maybe because they were simple, ordinary people who'd be mesmerized by the angels and would want to believe?"

"What did the shepherds do afterward?"

Antonia picked up her cell phone, found her Bible app, and went to Luke, Chapter 2. She read, "'When they had seen him, they spread the word concerning what had been told them about this child, and all who heard it were amazed at what the shepherds said to them.'"

"Don't you see how similar that is to the passage in Acts?"

"Maybe."

"Maybe?"

"You're saying we have to tell people."

"No. We have to *show* people."

She set down her phone. "I don't see how. I mean, I get that we want to reach out to people, but most of the things we've tried in the past haven't worked."

"What have you tried?"

"Inviting people to come to the church. Having daily vacation Bible school for the kids, special services at Easter, Thanksgiving, and Christmas. Kids' programs. Women's programs. Men's programs."

"What people have you invited?"

"Families who live in our community."

"And who came?"

"Mostly people from the church. And sometimes a new family. Some people send their kids but they never come."

"Who did God send the angels to again?"

"The shepherds."

"Right. So where do we find shepherds today?"

There was a long silence. Then she said, "Maybe people who are struggling in some way. Ones who have low-paying jobs. Those who are homeless. People in hospitals. People who are or have been in prison."

"In other words, people in need."

She nodded.

"So what should our job be?"

"To be like the angels. Go where God sends us and point people to Him."

"Do we reach out to them because we want a bigger church?"

"No," she whispered. "Because they need God in their lives."

"That's what I want to do." He stood up. "Pray about it, please. Call me when you're ready to talk some more." He started to walk away, then turned back and said, "By the way, I'll resign before I'll let you leave."

As she watched him go, she felt as if the ground underneath her had shifted and she'd been moved to another place of existence.

She went home and told her father what had happened. They prayed that she'd know what to do.

She didn't go to the church the next day or on Sunday, choosing instead to drive north and stay in a small bed and breakfast. She needed time alone to think and listen to God.

Monday morning, she phoned Rafe and asked him to meet her for dinner at Mandrigo.

He was already seated when she came in. As usual, he wore jeans and a T-shirt. So totally unlike their former pastor.

When they'd given their orders, she said, "I withdrew my resignation. After that, the chair of the board suggested I talk to you."

"I'm glad to hear that. Okay, let's get to it. Since my focus is more toward reaching out and empowering, and yours is nurturing and teaching, I think we'd make a great team. I'd like us to be co-pastors."

She looked at him as if he'd lost his mind. "But…"

"I'll get a part-time job, and you'll need to see if you can work fewer hours. I'll split my pay with you, or maybe we'll get a slight increase since it's going to be both of us."

"But—"

"You'll be responsible for organizing the care-giving, and I'll organize the reaching out. What do you say?"

"The board—"

"They've given me their blessing. After getting your letter of resignation, they suddenly realized that you're the one who's been responsible for holding the church together for the last five or six years, and they plan to apologize to you for not recognizing how much you were contributing."

"They realized that?"

He grinned. "Well, I might have helped them see it."

"I don't know what to say."

"How about 'Yes'?"

"Are you sure?"

"Positive. What does your heart tell you?"

As her eyes teared up, she whispered, "Yes."

Rafe pushed the back door open with his foot and muscled inside, his arms loaded down with boxes and bags.

Antonia was in the kitchen, working at the counter. When she saw him, she moved some things to clear a spot for him to deposit his burden.

"This is only a small part of it," he said. "The van's full."

"I'll check it off the Christmas list."

The list was on a large whiteboard in the back of the sanctuary. Everyone in the congregation aged three to 96 had spent one Sunday having breakfast together, followed by a time of praying and brainstorming. Then they'd spent a week in prayer—as individuals and families. Following that, they'd spent a Sunday morning and afternoon divided into small groups, first by age, then by interests, creating a gigantic list of the things they could do to reach out with love.

The list included a wide variety of things, as diverse as collecting food for the local food pantry, going to a First Nations community to build a new school, and hosting a party for children who lived in group homes in the area.

A week later, after more prayer and discussion, they narrowed the list down to things they felt their small congregation could accomplish this year. The list was still quite long, but throughout October and November, checkmarks had gradually appeared on many of the items.

Yes, a few people had decided the new direction wasn't for them, and had left the church. But other people had quickly taken their place. And while a few people had come to check out the new pastor, Antonia's fear that Rafe and his sermons would become the

  Christmas with Hot Apple Cider

focus had melted away. The truth was, he gave very few sermons, allowing more time for discussion and conversation than for instruction. And he'd challenged Antonia and a few other members of the church to speak, too.

This week's goal was to collect new and used-but-in-good-condition toys and sports equipment. Everything would be wrapped and labelled and given to the parents of children living in a nearby low-income area a week before Christmas. One of the church members had a brother who was lending them his truck for the deliveries.

Next week, Antonia would be helping a couple of the seniors from the church lead a discussion on "Grieving at Christmas" at the local library.

The following week, the youth group would be helping at a shelter for homeless people while the junior high group hosted a party for all the children ages two to eight who lived in foster homes in the area.

Several families had been making the rounds of the local nursing homes for the past couple of weeks. The musical people played instruments and sang while the others distributed handmade cards and small, useful gifts to the seniors.

On Christmas Eve, everyone involved would gather together to pray and to talk about how they felt about their list and the results.

On Christmas Day, there was a sunrise prayer and worship time when the church members gathered together.

After that, people scattered. Some travelled to be with their families; some invited people who had no family in the area to spend the day with them; one group was busy hosting an online party with live videos, prizes, and discussions; several families were helping out at a shelter for women and children from abusive homes; and one group of singles and couples without children had chosen to go out in pairs, wandering the streets in their area and talking to people, looking for anyone who seemed despondent or alone, and inviting them for a common meal that a group who enjoyed cooking were preparing.

Antonia stood near the door of the Mandrigo restaurant watching her dad play guitar while several members of the church sang a variety of songs, including "White Christmas," "Jingle Bells," "Jesus Loves the Little Children," and "I Heard the Bells on Christmas Day." Delight, the waitress who'd served them that first day back in September, led the singing with her beautiful alto voice while Antonia greeted people and showed them to tables.

Rafe was there, too, seated at a table in the back, where he could participate in the online group event and text comments and answers to questions. He motioned, and Antonia made her way over to his table.

"Do you need something?" she asked.

"Nope."

"How's the virtual party doing?"

"Good. Got a lot of interaction. Some good questions. Some prayer."

"Great."

"So, how are you doing, partner? Having a good Christmas?"

She smiled. "Only the best Christmas ever. Beyond my wildest dreams."

Rafe grinned. "Most people want to do something for others and for the Kingdom, but just don't know what to do."

"And they need a team to work with."

"Exactly."

Before moving away to greet a new customer, Antonia winked at Rafe. "I can't wait to start planning for Easter!"

   Christmas with Hot Apple Cider

The Best Christmas Present

Nonfiction

Rob Harshman

The cold north wind chilled my whole body as eddies of snow swirled around me and the snow crunched under my boots. Nevertheless, I trudged down the driveway, my arms loaded with extension cords, Christmas lights, and a couple of electric timers. With only two days left before I headed out on a three-week trip to Nigeria, I had little time to complete my annual task of stringing coloured lights through our trees and bushes for the month of December.

Looking down the street, I could see that most of our neighbours had already put up their decorations. Every home glowed with the multicoloured lights of the season. I knew that one guy a few doors down from us had spent $1,500 on his Christmas décor. It included a motorized, lighted reindeer whose head rotated 180 degrees. Next to his front door, he had a snowman that changed colour every 15 seconds.

Wearily, I strung our lights through trees and bushes and then escaped back into the warmth of the house.

Inside, we had two Christmas trees surrounded with stacks of presents we'd bought for family and friends. Each gift was carefully wrapped with matching ribbons and cards. Among the presents were a camera and a coffee maker, plus gift cards for Starbucks.

One of my favourite areas of the house was the main staircase. We'd decorated it with evergreen boughs, lights, and gold ribbon. At night, it glowed magically and set the mood for the whole house.

As our family prepared for Christmas, I kept thinking about my upcoming trip to Nigeria. I knew it was going to be different from Canada, but I wasn't prepared for how different it would be or for what I would learn.

Three days later, I arrived in Nigeria. A week after that, I was in a van bouncing over a heavily rutted dirt road on the outskirts of Jos, the capital of Plateau state. The sky was clear, but it was the Harmattan dry season. The Harmattan winds blow from the Sahara desert, bringing with them a haze of dust that hangs over the city like grey gauze. We could taste that dust in the van, so we kept the windows shut even though the temperature inside had risen to well over 40°C (104°F). I remembered the frigid air I'd left at home, and a shiver went down my back.

We had only a kilometre more to go to reach a boys' home— an orphanage for boys who had been abandoned on the streets or whose parents had died. Having taught high school geography for many years, I was really looking forward to meeting the boys and hearing their stories. In the back of the van, we had several cartons of T-shirts, clothes, and toiletries. We even had a couple of soccer balls.

Suddenly, we made a sharp left turn and found ourselves in a driveway leading up to a closed steel gate set in a high concrete wall. As we approached the gate, it opened and we entered the main courtyard of the boys' home.

The walls of the one-storey buildings were washed light yellow, and their corrugated steel roofs glistened like silver in the sunlight. A couple of tall palm trees swayed in the breeze on the far side of the compound while slender green lizards skittered across the walls in search of insects for dinner. The grounds were dry and dusty, so different from home, where everything was covered in snow. Not unexpectedly, there wasn't a single Christmas decoration to be seen. Even before we stopped, our vans were surrounded by dozens of boys who were anxious to see us. Visitors to this compound were few.

After greeting the boys and the "parents" of the home, we toured the dormitories, each one housing 16 boys in bunk beds. Four single light bulbs hung from the ceiling of each dorm to provide light when electricity actually flowed, which was not often. Individual mosquito nets that hung over the beds were the boys' only defence against malaria. I thought of my daughters' rooms, each of which was larger than any one of the dorms.

  Christmas with Hot Apple Cider

John, one of the "parents," said, "Most of the boys were abandoned on the streets of Jos or some nearby city." John was a young guy from Pennsylvania with short brown hair, green eyes, and an easygoing manner. "Mostly, we don't know who their parents are and probably never will, but the boys are happy to be here because they have a roof over their heads, food to eat, and a school to attend."

After the tour, we returned to the central courtyard to hand out T-shirts, toothbrushes, toiletries, and hats. The boys eagerly accepted the gifts and slipped the donated T-shirts on over the shirts they were wearing.

We took photos of their new outfits and they sang a few songs for us, including a couple of Christmas carols.

When the photos and songs were over, one of the older boys began walking my way. Unlike the rest of the boys, he hadn't put on his T-shirt. I approached him and we began to talk.

He was tall and slim, with intense brown eyes. I learned his name was Joseph.

"What do you do in Canada?" he asked in his strongly accented and formal English.

"I'm a teacher."

"What are the students like?"

"Similar to you in some ways. Some even like to play soccer—like you."

Joseph smiled.

"Tell me about yourself."

"I'm eighteen. And I have lived here for five years."

"Where did you live before you came here?"

"I had no place to live. I slept anywhere I could. It was very dangerous. That is why I am so glad to be here. This is a great place."

I looked at the T-shirt he was still holding. "How come you haven't put your new shirt on like all the other guys?"

He looked at me strangely, and then he explained. "I am saving it for Christmas. I have never had a Christmas present before."

As I looked at this young man with a big smile on his face, I couldn't speak. My mouth opened, but no words came out. I suddenly felt very selfish and very spoiled.

My mind went back to the Christmas preparations that were taking place back in Canada. When contrasted with an 18-year-old boy who had never received a Christmas gift, the lavish decorations, the lights, and the gifts suddenly seemed extravagant.

Meanwhile, Joseph stood in front of me with a quizzical look on his face. He displayed no sign of self-pity at all. In fact, he was genuinely happy and grateful for what little we had given him.

"That's okay." I said weakly. "You'll have a good Christmas."

Joseph smiled and shook my hand.

As I stood in the dust under a hot African sun I had realized something. The most valuable gift I would give this Christmas wasn't among the elaborately wrapped presents under our Canadian Christmas tree. Rather, it was a T-shirt with a company logo that Joseph would wear on Christmas morning.

  Christmas with Hot Apple Cider

The Call for Help

Nonfiction

Susan Stewart

"This is Daisy. I was wondering if you could send some warm clothes?"

Daisy Munroe was calling from Missabay Community School in remote northwestern Ontario, where she works as a social counsellor.

"It's pretty cold up here right now, and a lot of the kids are coming to school with no mitts. Their hands are freezing. It's –27°C (–17°F) today."

Daisy's call for help to a mutual friend came a few weeks before Christmas, and the need was quickly posted on Facebook.

"Hello, friends. We just had a phone call from the school in Mishkeegogamang, the First Nations community with which we have a long relationship. They're in desperate need of warm mittens as some children have none. It's way below freezing there today..."

As soon as my friend Holly read this, she texted me to discuss what we could do. I'd also read it, and immediately, if a bit recklessly, we decided that we had to help.

Children have a way of losing their mitts, but for parents who live that far north, getting replacements can be an impossibility. Local prices are exorbitant. The nearest stores with affordable goods are many hours away. Besides which, with limited employment opportunities, it can be a struggle for families just to put basic food on the table, let alone replace lost mittens.

Holly and I were sure we could help, but we'd need a lot of mittens of varying sizes to respond well to Daisy's call.

After talking it over, we decided we'd love to be the ones to deliver the mittens.

Missabay Community School serves the Mishkeegogamang Ojibway Nation, a community six hours northwest of Thunder Bay. The school is perched on a long, sloping bank overlooking the Albany River. It has approximately 160 students from Junior Kindergarten to Grade 8.

Holly and I had been there together a few months earlier with a group from our church. We'd helped provide support to the community through a short-term summer activity program for the children. It had been my fourth trip, spread over a dozen years, and Holly's first. Like me, Holly was smitten with the children she'd met there, and now she jumped at another opportunity to help the community and stay connected.

We'd not only worked with many of the people there in the summer, but we'd also maintained contact with several of them throughout the year, mainly through Facebook.

It didn't seem a hard thing at all for us to answer Daisy's call and head north.

Of course, Holly and I weren't the only ones to see the post on Facebook.

"I have a few I can donate," was the first response, from a young mom.

That comment was quickly followed by more from willing hearts. Plus, the post was shared and reshared.

To our amazement, within hours, dozens of offers of mittens, gloves, and more clothing items had poured in.

The project quickly assumed the name "Mittens for Mish" and seemed to take on a life of its own. It was as if, caught up in the spirit of Christmas, people couldn't give enough.

A score of individuals responding to the Facebook call began scouring local thrift stores, Canadian Tire, and shopping malls. People networked with other churches and made phone calls to local businesses asking if they would like to help. The Salvation Army offered us several huge bags of brand new mittens, gloves, hats, scarves, and warm socks left over from their Christmas-giving program and toy drive.

Right up to the day we were leaving, we were still getting phone calls with offers of warm winter clothing, boots, blankets, and more. One man, who had lost his beloved wife to cancer just the previous summer, dropped off carefully packed boxes containing her winter clothing, which must have been a difficult and tender transfer for him. We picked up the last two boxes of donations at a friend's house along the way.

When Holly and I had volunteered to make the trip together to deliver the items to Mishkeegogamang, we were thinking that my largish SUV would be quite full but manageable. It wasn't long into our preparations for the trip before we realized that even if we folded down the seats, stuffed every corner, nook, and cranny, and added an enclosed roof rack, we wouldn't have enough room for all the items that had been gathered. We started to think about renting a trailer.

And that's why, a few days after Christmas, two middle-aged women in an SUV filled with gloves and mittens left our homes in southern Ontario to drive northwest along the Trans-Canada Highway into the deepest, most brittle cold we had ever felt. Behind us was a U-Haul stuffed to the gills with all manner of warm winter clothing, blankets, and footwear. We'd barely been able to close the door on the U-Haul and there was literally no room for anything more in my vehicle except our small overnight bags and some food to keep us going.

The windshield wipers slapped away the snow that started falling just as we were leaving mid-afternoon and continued deep into the night. We took turns driving over roads turning whiter and whiter from fresh-fallen, then wheel-packed snow.

Our plan had been to take turns sleeping, but instead we found an endless list of things to talk about. We laughed at the idea that if we'd driven south instead of northwest, we could have ended up on a beach in the Florida Keys in the same amount of time.

After a long 24 hours of driving, we rolled into the town of Pickle Lake, trailer still in tow, and pulled up at the motel. We were too excited to stop and waste time sleeping. We wanted to deliver our precious and miraculous load as soon as we possibly could. We needed to know that a plan was in place before we could allow ourselves to indulge in a few hours of sleep.

Knowing that Daisy would be anticipating our arrival, the first phone call we made was to her. We arranged to meet at the community centre the next morning at 9:30. We wanted her to have the first opportunity to go through the donations and take what was needed for the school children. The leftover items would be offered to the rest of the community after that.

Arrangements made, at long last we slept, woke up to have dinner from food we had brought from home, and then slept again.

The morning dawned crisp, clear, and bitterly cold. Holly and I were still a little groggy from our sleep-deprived drive the day before, and we slept later than we'd intended. We rushed out of the motel room door at 9:15 a.m., breakfasted on some of the munchies we'd stowed in the car, and headed to the community centre to meet Daisy, empty the trailer, and get set up. We'd arranged through Facebook for some young friends we'd met the previous summer to help us unload.

In our sleepy fog, we were confused as to which time zone we were in and actually pulled up to the door of the community centre at 8:30 their time (9:30 ours). But Daisy was already there, so eager to make sure the children of the community were taken care of that she had arrived with a friend and helper a full hour ahead of time, and was waiting for us at the door.

Though she's a grandmother several times over, Daisy is spry and lean. It would be hard for me to guess how old she is if her daughter, Harriet, a teacher and also a friend of mine, hadn't mentioned her age on Facebook a few weeks earlier. Harriet described hearing noises above her bedroom early one morning. She'd gone outside to find her 70-year-old mother, Daisy, on the roof of their home, shovelling off the heavy snow.

We had barely parked and exchanged a few quick hellos before Daisy, with her signature black beret pulled down to cover her forehead, was attacking the thick ice that had coated the lock on the back door of the trailer.

Along with her friend, I rushed to help. When the stubborn lock finally succumbed to our efforts, my hands felt frozen and were aching to the bone in the –30 degree weather. But I had no time to rest and recuperate. When we finally raised the door, Daisy dove in, grasping at boxes and bags and hauling them into the community centre's gymnasium, where Holly and our young

Christmas with Hot Apple Cider

friends were busy setting up tables. With aching fingers, I followed Daisy's unspoken lead.

It took longer than we'd hoped to empty the trailer and SUV, even with help. But instead of resting for a minute, Daisy began darting around the gym opening boxes, untying bags, and sorting through the mountains of donations like a squirrel after seeds in an orchard. As it dawned on her how much stuff we'd actually brought and how big the job was, she pulled her cell phone from a pocket and quietly texted several of her friends and coworkers to come help. Holly and I did our best to help, too.

As we unpacked, we would draw Daisy's attention to items we thought would be suitable.

She was definitive in her decisions. Tiny mittens were matter-of-factly rejected with quiet, firm pronouncements of "too small." Suitable offerings were either taken out of our hands and placed quickly into her rapidly growing pile or approved with a quick nod of her head that told us what to do with them.

Her helpers managed to find some things for their own families as they helped to set things aside for the school, but Daisy's focus was singular. She was there for "her" kids, and she wouldn't rest until she had every last pair of suitable mittens in that gym safely put away.

Finally, after a full three hours of bending, lifting, sorting, and carrying—all the while gently but firmly directing her helpers—Daisy let us know that she would be heading over to the school now with her cache. Holly and I offered to help, but her friends chimed in, saying they would go along and help her put everything inside the school. They all seemed well-satisfied with their haul.

Daisy was gone for an hour or so, during which time Holly and I visited with members of the community who had come to sort through the leftovers.

Shortly after noon, Daisy returned. She began to sift through the piles again, just to be sure she hadn't missed anything. Only when she was positive children at the school were taken care of did she allow herself the luxury of pulling out a few things for herself.

I saw her eyeing a pair of black gloves with ruffles at the wrist and encouraged her to take them. Her deep brown eyes sparkled with humour as she said, "Oh, yes, I will need these when I am at my *func-tions*." She drew out the last word in two distinct syllables, with just a hint of a chuckle escaping.

I went closer and again encouraged her to take them. "You'll need those when you're on stage in front of your thousands of fans," I said, a ring of truth in my teasing words.

She laughed—clearly at herself, but a little in wonder at what she'd experienced in the weeks leading up to Christmas.

Daisy, with other members of her family, had travelled the province of Ontario at the invitation of their new friend, Gord Downie, the lead singer of the signature Canadian rock band, The Tragically Hip.

In the few months leading up to her sorting through mittens with us in Mishkeegogamang, she had accompanied her sisters while they were interviewed on television and radio, and as they stood on stage before thousands of people. She'd even sat next to and spoken with Justin Trudeau, the Prime Minister of Canada, in a front row seat at an event in Ottawa.

As with her age, if I hadn't been aware of the facts surrounding her sudden rise to fame, I never would have guessed. In spite of all the flurry of attention and activity, her feet remain firmly planted on the ground.

In October of 2016, Gord Downie had released *The Secret Path*,[1] a project he created after becoming aware of the death of a young aboriginal boy, Chanie Wenjack. Gord first read about Chanie in a magazine article that told the true story of the 12-year-old boy who was so miserable at the residential school where he'd been placed in the late 1960s that he ran away from the institution and attempted to walk the 600 kilometres from Kenora back to his home and family on a reserve in Northern Ontario. Ill-equipped and under-dressed for the impossibly long journey, Chanie died of hunger and cold on the way. His body was found beside the railway tracks that he had hoped would lead him home.

Chanie was the only boy in the family. He left behind his parents and several sisters who dearly loved him.

One of those sisters was named Daisy. *Our* Daisy. The Daisy who couldn't stand the thought of children coming to the school where she works with their bare fingers exposed to winter's bitter and unforgiving cold. Maybe she was thinking about her beloved brother, or maybe her thoughts of him were buried deep in the recesses of her heart that December morning, but she was moved to make the call for help. And because she did, a school full of children in the north came back from their Christmas break with warmly clad hands and feet.

Holly and I drove back south very much aware of the many small contributions that had added up to make a significant difference in one small community. We'd had the fun and adventure (and hard work!) of making the delivery, but many people had contributed in a variety of ways to make the trip possible.

Some gave actual mittens. Others shared and reshared the message on Facebook. Financial gifts came in to cover the cost of gas and motels for the trip. Phone calls were made to arrange pickups.

Sometimes people hesitate to do something toward reconciliation with First Nations because they feel like their contribution might be too small to make a difference. Well, they say it takes a village—a village making many small individual contributions—to raise a child. And it took a village to answer that call.

1. Gord Downie began an album, *Secret Path*, as 10 poems incited by the story of Chanie Wenjack, a 12-year-old boy who died 50 years ago on October 22, 1966. Charlie had left the Cecilia Jeffrey Indian Residential School near Kenora, Ontario, and was walking home to the family he'd been taken from, which was over 600 kilometres away. Gord was introduced to Chanie Wenjack (miscalled "Charlie" by his teachers) by Mike Downie, Gord's brother, who had read Ian Adams' *Maclean* story from February 6, 1967, "The Lonely Death of Charlie Wenjack."

The Secret Path is an animated film adaptation of Gord Downie's album and Jeff Lemire's graphic novel of the same name. Working with Downie's poetry and music, Lemire has created a powerful visual representation of the life of Chanie Wenjack. The film is divided into 10 sections, each a song from Downie's musical retelling of Chanie's story—from his escape from the residential school to his subsequent and heartbreaking death from hunger and exposure to the harsh weather. The final product is a uniquely immersive emotional experience—an insight into the life of a little boy who, as Gord said, he never knew "but will always love."

Proceeds from the sale of *The Secret Path* (secretpath.ca) will be donated to the Gord Downie Secret Path Fund for Truth and Reconciliation via The National Centre for Truth and Reconciliation (NCTR) at the University of Manitoba. The NCTR is dedicated to preserving the history of residential schools in Canada, making this history known, and moving our country forward on the path of reconciliation. These funds are dedicated to finding missing children.

A Carol Sing to Remember

Nonfiction[1]

Cori Mordaunt

"You'd better knock, Dad," my teenage son said as we walked through the nursing home to my mother's room. "Last time, you barged right in. Scared her half to death."

"I remember," I said. Duly chastened, I knocked, and then barged in. "Merry Christmas, Mom." I planted a kiss on her forehead. "Time to get your teeth in, company's coming."

"Company?"

"Yep," I said. "The gang's going to be here."

My sisters and my wife got Mom looking pretty good in her best dress, with a fresh hairdo, and said dentures in place. Sometimes she fought the attention, but not today.

We're a fairly large family, so we'd booked the visitors' lounge for what we all realized would probably be Mom's last Christmas. Alzheimer's had deteriorated her once active and quick mind. Her wit and delight in the absurd were a memory to all of us—except her, that is. And now her health was failing.

Ready to greet her guests—if you can call family guests—we began the slow shift, wheeling Mom along the corridor, past warm smiles, empty stares, and gnarled hands grasping, into the relative cool of the visitors' lounge.

A keyboard was perched in the far corner. It had a mound of music books and sheets piled on its cover. Chairs and couches were scattered around facing every direction, although my kids and their cousins were already rearranging them. We would have plenty of space to visit here.

"Where's the entertainment?" Mom asked as we crossed the threshold.

"What entertainment?" I asked.

"They're always late," she snapped. "And here all these good people are left waiting." She looked around at us as if we were strangers at a matinee instead of on a family visit. "It's a shame. Sometimes, they don't even show up."

If it's entertainment she's looking for, let's give it to her, I thought. None of us played the piano, but we could sing. I dug through the music, found some Christmas carol booklets, and passed them around. "Do you have a favourite, Mom?" I asked, knowing full well what the answer would be.

"That one about joy," she said. "What is it again?"

"'Joy to The World,'" I offered. And she led us right into verse one. As soon as we started singing, she switched to alto. Harmony. That's how she'd governed her life: taking the dissonance thrown her way, turning it into melody, and over time and much prayer, adding harmony. Pleasing to the ear. Pleasing to life. Pleasing to Jesus, whom she'd sought to honour by living a joy-filled life even in the midst of difficult circumstances.

"IS THERE A PROGRAM THIS AFTERNOON?" shouted a slight man, cocking his face up at us as he stood in the doorway, bent over his walker. "NO ONE SAID ANYTHING ABOUT A PROGRAM. THEY SHOULD TELL US IF THERE'S GOING TO BE A PROGRAM."

He shuffled inside and took a seat. Someone handed him a booklet, and after a quick glance, he hollered, "'SILENT NIGHT!'"

As we sang, more people edged into the lounge. Some I knew from previous visits; most I didn't.

"Oh, good. Entertainment. Why didn't anybody tell us?"

"Anyone playing spoons? Nothing like a good spoons player."

"Haven't found anyone to match Charlie and Marg's singing. They were the best. Never missed a show."

"I play the piano," said a man who appeared to be a visitor. "Would you like me to help out?"

"We'd love it," I said. And did he ever play the piano! He pulled up to the keyboard as though it was the most comfortable seat in the house, and, without reading a note of music, his fingers whirled over the keys. At this point, I asked my sister to take over leading, which gave me a chance to peek into the corridor.

A traffic snarl-up of walkers, sometimes two abreast, was heading toward the lounge. Looked like our last Christmas with

Mom would be a party—a Christmas carol-sing party—just like the ones she'd hosted every December when we were growing up.

My sisters guided anyone who needed help to a chair, folding up their walkers, like butterfly wings, to sit beside them.

We sang more Christmas songs.

Every time the elevator door opened, the occupants getting off on Mom's floor would peer into the lounge then join our group. Before long, they lined the walls.

"This is the third time they've requested 'Silent Night,'" moaned my son.

"Did you notice they're singing all the words?" I said.

"But three times in an hour?"

"It's not over yet," I said. "Keep counting."

He shook his head and sighed.

"Take a look at Grandma," I suggested. "What do you see?"

"A happy face," he said. "Grandma's beaming, Dad. Glad Mom put her teeth in for her."

"Me, too," I said. My mother had never gone out in public without making sure she looked her best, and she was looking the best I'd seen her in a long time.

We sang until the streetlights came on and staff arrived to escort the residents who needed help to the dining hall for dinner. A gaggle of grandchildren wheeled Mom off to eat while the rest of us sat in the visitors' lounge awaiting her return.

No one wanted to leave. No one wanted to be the first to rend the joy of the afternoon, to assign it to memory. This experience needed to be savoured, replayed, discussed, shared.

When Mom finally returned to her room, my sisters helped her into bed. We said our goodbyes then drifted into the hallway.

As we waited for the elevator, my son said, "Dad, that was the best. Just the best."

I had to agree.

1. Thanks to Craig McCallum for sharing this story about his mother, Marjory McCallum.

The Search

Dramatic Fiction

Glynis Belec

In the latter days of 2017, three women stare skyward only metres away from the main entrance of a busy department store and look a little puzzled.

Melody, the oldest, wears a brown corduroy coat and matching toque with an oversized pompom. She clutches an open leather journal.

Belle wears glasses and a fuzzy grey coat with a red scarf.

Grace, the youngest of the three, is bundled up in a pink-and-white jacket with matching snow pants.

Melody: I'm telling you, Grace, we took a wrong turn in Elmira. The stars aren't looking like they should.

Grace: I think you're right, Melody. Belle, what do you think?

Belle: Hmmm…

Melody: C'mon, Belle. You're the one with the PhD in astronomy! What do you see?

Belle: Streetlights. Mall lights. Neon Lights. Car lights. Lots of twinkling Christmas lights. It's tough being a stargazer in the city, y'know.

Grace: What about stars? Do you see any stars?

Belle: If I squint, I can see a few. Maybe.

Melody: Are they saying anything?

Belle: Not much. I can tell you one thing, though.

Grace: What's that?

Belle: I think we're lost!

Melody: Okay, ladies. Since we're here, let's try this place.

Grace: W-E-L-C-O-M-E to Stuffmart? You really think we'll find Him in there?

Melody: It's worth a try, isn't it?

The other two women shrug and follow Melody into the store where a young woman is standing at the Returns desk near the entrance. As the three of them come in, she speaks over the PA system.

Clerk: Good evening shoppers, and welcome to Stuffmart, where all your Christmas dreams will come true! We have everything you could possibly be looking for this wonderfully busy time of the year. Our daily specials will surprise you, and our helpful staff are here to serve. Happy holidays and, more importantly, happy shopping! And thank you for coming to Stuffmart.

Grace: Wow! Look how busy it is. Look at all the people shopping.

Belle: *Pointing at the Christmas decorations.* I see lots of stars in here, but I don't think they're the ones we're looking for.

Clerk: Ladies, may I help you?

Melody: Uh…We seem to be lost.

Clerk: Well, you've come to the right place. I'm the lost-and-found department plus the returns department, the complaints department, and the general information department. Just give me a minute. There must be guidelines here for what to do when an older person is lost. *She laughs nervously.* Usually it's the children who are lost, though.

Grace: Where are we?

Belle: Stuffmart, remember?

Clerk: That's right. Stuffmart, where holiday buying is beyond all your wildest imaginings. Gifts galore! Whatever makes you happy, we have it. Are you ladies from around here?

Melody: Actually, no. We've travelled for many days. We're not sure what to make of it, but we have a sneaking suspicion that we'll find the King somewhere around here.

Clerk: The king?

Belle: Yes. The King. We're astronomers. We study the stars. And right now, the stars are aligned perfectly.

Clerk: What sort of king?

Grace: The Christmas King.

Clerk: The Christmas king? Do you mean—uh—Santa? He's right over there. *Waves to Santa, then whispers to the women.* He's actually the security guard, moonlighting.

Melody: No. Our King represents love and compassion, kindness and sacrifice.

Belle: He's the Everlasting Father and the Prince of Peace.

Clerk: Prince of Peace? You—you mean— *She whispers,* Jesus? *She looks around.*

Grace: Jesus. Yes!

Clerk: Shhh. Uh…sorry. We're encouraged not to say that name here in the store.

Melody: What? Why can't you say the name of Jesus here?

Clerk: Our new store owner's policy. He says because it's been more than two thousand years since Jes—since *He* was born, He doesn't have much to do with Christmas any more. Plus, he says that we have to be politically correct. That times have changed and this is just another busy holiday. Nothing more. And it's true. Just look around. For most people, Christmas is about giving and getting gifts.

Grace: I see what you mean. *Turns to do a quick look over the store.* Just look at all the stuff here! And all the frantic shoppers! Why are people walking around with such long faces? Some of them look really stressed.

Belle: Gifts aren't what Christmas is all about! If people don't believe that Jesus was born in a stable on that first Christmas morning, then why are they celebrating at all? What are they celebrating?

Melody: *Peering closely at the clerk.* Do *you* believe that Christmas is about Jesus?

Clerk: Well, yes, of course I do, but I—we can't talk about it here. Which reminds me. I'm supposed to be putting on the holiday tunes. *She plays "Jingle Bells" and rocks with the beat.*

Belle: The stars, when we left home, were in perfect alignment. According to my records, they were in exactly the same position they were in more than two thousand years ago, when Jesus was born in a stable in Bethlehem.

Grace: Isn't that just so exciting?

Melody: We don't really understand it. Belle is the greatest astronomer, but this even baffles her.

Clerk: So, what are you saying?

Belle: We're convinced that we'll see Jesus today.

Clerk: Impossible. How can that be?

Melody: I know it sounds crazy, but we've analyzed, deliberated, and after much discussion, prayer, and debate, we've agreed. We feel in our hearts that we will see Him soon. If not today, then tomorrow.

Suddenly a commotion is heard. A young girl comes near. She's crying and appears distraught.

Child: I can't find my mommy. Where's my mom? I want my mom!

Clerk: Uh, oh. It seems I'm needed.

The rock music has faded. "White Christmas" begins to play.

The three women observe as the clerk gives the lost child a drink. After soothing her and speaking with her for a moment, the clerk picks up the phone to call security. Then she takes the child to Santa, who is on the far side of her desk.

The mother comes running up, and the clerk and mother speak for a little while. The child is happy, and the mother appears grateful. They both wave goodbye to the smiling clerk.

The clerk sees the women still watching.

Clerk: Poor little thing. I'm glad she found her mother. That was pretty scary for them both.

Grace: You have a tender heart. It was very kind of you to help that little girl.

Clerk: Oh, it was nothing—just doing my job. Now, where were we?

Melody: Analyzing and deliberating.

Clerk: Oh, yes. So you think you will find—um—Him? Here?

Belle: The stars *did* seem to be pointing in this direction. But I don't know. A department store doesn't seem a likely place to see Jesus. It's not exactly the little town of Bethlehem, if you know what I mean.

Outside the glass doors, a homeless man, who has been lying on a bench just outside the store, stirs and slowly gets up.

Clerk: You know, all this talk about Jesus is making me a little nervous. And I have work to do. *She gets out some paperwork.*

Melody: It would help if we knew what Jesus looks like. *She pulls out a small iPhone and googles "appearance of Jesus."*

The homeless man enters the store and comes toward the desk.

Melody beckons the other two women to look at a Scripture verse she's found. They look interested and whisper to one another.

Homeless Man: *To the clerk.* Hey, do you know where I can get a cup of coffee? It's pretty cold out there.

As "White Christmas" fades, "Santa Baby" starts to play.

The clerk smiles at the homeless man. She offers him a seat behind her desk and gives him a blanket that she had tucked behind the counter. Then she pours him a cup of coffee from her thermos.

The man eagerly sips the coffee. The clerk chats with the man, gives him a cookie from her lunch bag, and points to the phone. She makes a call, looking at the man as she talks. After the phone call, they continue to chat.

A few minutes later, a policeman enters and talks to the clerk. The officer shakes the hand of the man and they begin to leave together.

The clerk stops them, opens her purse, and hands the man some money.

At the doorway, the man turns and nods his thanks to the clerk. She waves—weakly—mouthing, "Merry Christmas."

The wise women have been watching from a distance. Now they gather around the clerk.

Clerk: That poor man. Imagine being homeless, but especially at Christmas. Sad. Very sad. That nice policeman is taking him to a shelter so he can get a good meal and have a warm place to sleep.

Belle: What's your name?

Clerk: Jenny. Why?

Belle: Jenny, you have a way with people. Do you know that?

Clerk: Oh, it's just my job.

Grace: You could have kicked him out of your department store.

Clerk: Why would I do that? Anyway, sorry about the interruption. What were we talking about?

Melody: Jesus.

Clerk: Right, Jesus. Oh, look at that. Somehow His name is getting easier to say in here every minute. It must be your influence.

Belle: I don't think we can take credit for that.

Melody: Jenny, there's something we want to tell you.

Grace: We've realized we aren't lost after all.

Clerk: *Warily.* Uh—what do you mean? You—you've found Jesus? She looks incredulously at Santa.

Belle: *Laughing.* Yes, Jenny, we've found Jesus. But don't worry, it's not Santa.

Clerk: Well that's a relief.

At that moment, a young girl about 10 or 12 passes them, leaving the store. Santa jumps up and the girl runs, pursued by Santa.

Santa: Wait! Stop! Security! Get back here, young lady!

Santa comes back in with the girl, who is crying.

Girl: I'm sorry. I didn't mean to—I don't have any money and I wanted to get a Christmas gift for my mom. I'm sorry.

"Santa Baby" fades and "Jingle Bell Rock" starts to play.

The clerk motions to Santa to bring the distraught girl to her desk. Santa and the clerk whisper. The clerk indicates she'll look after this.

Santa goes back to his chair.

The clerk sits and talks to the girl, who wipes away tears. She gives her phone number to the clerk. The clerk makes a call, then hangs up after a few moments. The clerk chats again with the girl, who gives her the things she had taken. The clerk walks the girl to the front door. As the girl leaves, the clerk waves and mouths, "Merry Christmas."

The girl turns to say thanks, then wipes her face and walks away.

The clerk goes to a cashier and pays for the things the girl had been trying to steal. She puts the bag they're in behind her desk.

The wise women have been watching the whole scene.

Clerk: My, what a lot of excitement we're having this evening. That poor girl. I know her situation. I've spoken to her mother before. She's ill and can't work. They don't have any money for Christmas. The dear young thing… All she wanted to do was get her mom a gift.

Grace: But she was wrong to steal.

Clerk: Of course she was. And she knows it, too. I had a good talk with her. It turns out they don't even have a Christmas tree this year, let alone a turkey. Times have been tough for them.

Melody: Let me guess. *Smiling.* You're having them over to your place for Christmas?

Clerk: How—How did you know?

Melody: Let's just say it was in the stars.

Clerk: I couldn't bear to think that someone might be alone at Christmas. And they don't live too far away from me. It'll be fun.

Belle: Jenny, you've done it.

Clerk: Oh, my. What have I done now?

Melody: *You've* allowed us to see Jesus, Jenny.

Clerk: Jesus? *I* have? How?

Melody: "For I was hungry and you gave me something to eat."[1]

Belle: "I was thirsty and you gave me something to drink."

Grace: "I was a stranger and you invited me in."

Belle: "I needed clothes and you clothed me."

Melody: "Whatever you did for the least of these brothers and sisters of mine, you did for me."[2]

Clerk: I just do what's in my heart.

Belle: Obviously.

Melody: *That's* where we saw Jesus, Jenny. In your heart.

Clerk: Um... Wow! I'll have to do a lot of thinking—maybe even some praying—about that. Look, it's just about closing time. What are you three doing on Christmas Day? I've got a huge turkey that needs eating and I was thinking about having a party for the Christmas King.

Grace, Melody & Belle: For who, Jenny?

Clerk: Jesus, of course! *She's shocked at herself.* What's happening to me? Oh, my. I'm feeling a little light-headed.

Belle: "The Word became flesh and made his dwelling among us. We have seen his glory, the glory of the one and only who came from the Father full of grace and truth."[3]

Clerk: *A little flustered; makes PA announcement.* Excuse me, shoppers. This is a reminder that we will be closing in thirty minutes. Please take your purchases to the nearest checkout. Thank you for choosing our department store for your Christmas shopping experience this evening, but more importantly, we wish you a blessed Christmas and may the name of Jesus be proclaimed loudly in all our celebrations. God bless you all. Oh, and thank you for shopping at Stuffmart!

"Joy to the World" plays loudly as the lights dim.

1. Matthew 25:35–36a

2. Matthew 25:40

3. John 1:14

Author's Note:

  For permission to produce this play, and a pdf of the script, please contact the author at writer@glynisbelec.com.

No Room?

Fiction

Robert White

The innkeeper? What do I know about the innkeeper?

I clicked on "end call" as I thought over the short conversation I'd just had with the church's worship director. The call was an unexpected follow-up to a project begun four years earlier.

Back then, he'd told me they wanted to add a dramatic reading component to the Christmas Eve service. "Each year, we'll focus on one of the characters in the nativity story," he'd said.

At the time, I was between assignments and my latest book was at the publishers being edited. I figured I had the time and said I was interested.

At first, my sole task was to write the monologue. But on the day before Christmas Eve, the person who was to "be" Joseph came down with strep throat and laryngitis. Since I already knew the content, they begged me to read the narrative.

The pastor was so pleased with how things went that a new Christmas tradition of writing and reading had begun. Having covered Joseph, we moved on to Mary and then a nameless shepherd. We found a woman to read Mary's narrative, but I did the shepherd's.

This year, I'd expected to be asked to write about one of the magi—despite the historical inaccuracy that places them at the manger far too early. In fact, I'd already started the research and played around with a few ideas.

However, with two weeks left before Christmas Eve, I still hadn't been called with this year's assignment.

I admit I'd felt somewhat disappointed, and a little frustrated. I figured the pastor and worship director must have decided against including the narrative this year but had neglected to tell me.

Until today's call, which started with an apology. It seemed the recent funeral of one of the church's founding elders, along with a

Christmas with Hot Apple Cider

wicked intestinal virus that was going through the church staff, had delayed most of the planning for Christmas. The worship director apologized for the short notice, but asked if I could please still put a new reading together.

I agreed to do it.

And then he said, "We'd like it to be about the innkeeper."

Having already agreed, I couldn't very well argue. So I said I would.

Other than Caesar Augustus, who made the holy family take the long trek from Nazareth to Bethlehem in the first place, and maybe King Herod, who tried to kill the baby, the innkeeper is probably the most reviled character in the Christmas story. What was there to know about him except his fateful words to Joseph and Mary that there was no room in the inn?

With that thought, I felt I'd hit on a beginning to the narrative, so I wrote:

> "There's no more room," I shouted to my wife as mothers scolded their children behind me. "Send them away."

I sat staring at the blinking cursor for the next 10 minutes. Then I did what every writer in my writing circle does when stuck: I googled "innkeeper, Israel, New Testament era." Discovered there were 71,900 results. Began wading through links until inspiration struck.

Struck out.

Looked at the clock. Realized I needed to eat something before my blood sugar took a nosedive. Shaking my head, I started downstairs toward the kitchen.

When I was halfway down, I turned and plodded back up to my office to hit "save" on the only sentence I'd written.

The next day, I began with more research. I had to find something to use as a storyline!

By noon I was wading through the notes I'd copied from various websites into a file titled "Innkeeper-background."

I read that in New Testament times most inns were actually homes that had two rooms: a main living area for the family, which was frequently used to house livestock at night, and a second room that was turned into a "guest room" for visitors, who were crammed in. The more people crammed in, the more money the innkeeper could earn. During warmer periods, people would even be housed on the flat roof. And, of course, charged for the privilege.

But what had I learned that was useful? Not much. I knew most of it from sitting through or taking part in decades of Christmas pageants and Christmas Eve services. Basically, Bethlehem was full of people who'd been forced to travel there because Caesar Augustus, back in Rome, decided he needed a census. He'd ordered everyone to go back to the town in which their ancestors had first settled, where they would be counted. Since Joseph's ancestors were from Bethlehem, that's where he had to go.

So I had a crowd of people and a frustrated innkeeper who had no more room. But how was I going to find a moving story about the innkeeper in all of this?

I spent some time thinking about the other Christmas Eve narratives I'd written. What I'd discovered was that people were the most moved by a sympathetic character. They felt for teenaged Mary who, in the face of public shaming or worse, held on to her unswerving belief that she carried God's Son. They related to Joseph, a man caught up in circumstances he never expected but who, again, relied on his faith to carry him through. They even felt sympathy for the outcast shepherds who were the first to hear the angel announce the Saviour's birth.

But how was I going to make the innkeeper sympathetic?

The thing is, it's really hard for a writer to make a character sympathetic unless he feels some sympathy for the character himself. And I didn't.

I jogged downstairs, grabbed a can of diet cola and an already open bag of chips, and headed back to the office. Maybe if I tried to put myself in the innkeeper's sandals, I'd be able to dredge up some sympathy for him.

I began writing again.

The inn had never been this full. As guest areas spilled over with frail old men, young children, and those women who were unable to join their husbands, brothers, and sons who had gathered for prayer or were off looking to find temporary work, I recalled how I got here.

This inn was originally owned by the father of my best friend. Well, we were best friends until a business deal between his father and mine went sour. My father ended up being blamed and our family was not only forced out of business but out of Bethlehem…

My wife called me with a question. This was no time to dwell on the past. I had too much to do. By nightfall, even my roof would be packed.

"Curse Caesar Augustus," I hissed. "I'd been happy when I first heard about his decree, but he obviously gave no thought whatsoever to what his census might mean to the ordinary person—never mind the towns that would be overflowing with families."

Seriously, every cubit of space I had was occupied, often by more than one body.

As much as I relished the thought of the extra denarii, because of the crowd, I was fatigued and frustrated as I tried to figure out where to squeeze in the new arrivals.

Collecting taxes had been easier than turning people away!

Oh, that's good. There's a possible backstory! Maybe there's hope for the innkeeper after all.

After we'd left Bethlehem, our family had moved from place to place until we landed in Caesarea. It was there that, as a young man, I'd been told tax collecting was the way to get rich. All I had to do was collect and submit whatever sum the Romans wanted. Any denarii or shekels I was able to add to the bills were mine to keep. But no one warned me that I'd be shunned. Treated as a leper. Even by my own family.

Wait! What was I writing? That wasn't going to make him sympathetic. Everyone knows what kind of parasites most tax collectors were. Only in Zacchaeus[1] and Matthew[2] do we find stories of redeemed tax collectors.

Usually I let my characters lead me as I write, but I knew I needed to turn a corner on this particular trail. I couldn't let him become too hated. So where did I go from here?

> While in Caesarea, I began plotting my revenge. I saved all the money that wasn't needed for the bare necessities of life. My plan was to return to Bethlehem with enough money to buy respectability.

Plotting revenge? That certainly isn't sympathetic! How do I get this story on track? Time to jot down a few more paragraphs before a snack and some tea.

> My wife's quiet pleading snapped me out of my thoughts and back to the present. "We can't turn this couple away. Have you seen the woman? It's almost her time."
>
> Yes, I'd seen the couple. I'd even noticed the young woman's condition.
>
> I mentally counted the paying guests. Even if I moved one of the younger families to the already-crowded roof, there still wouldn't be room for someone who might give birth at any minute.
>
> "We have to do something."
>
> "I—"
>
> My objection echoed off my wife's back as she strode outside and asked the couple to sit on the bench by the door.
>
> They thanked her as she ladled water into wooden goblets for them.

Hmm. Writing that line reminded me I was thirsty. And hungry, too.

  Christmas with Hot Apple Cider

My break ended up taking longer than I expected. I was just about to head upstairs with my cup of Earl Grey, hot with cream and sweetener, when…

"Dad, where are you? I really need to talk to you," my daughter yelled from the front door.

For the next three days, crisis piled on crisis. There were the seemingly endless conversations trying to comfort my daughter, who was distressed about being unfriended by someone she thought was a BFF. Then the stomach flu that had incapacitated the church staff hit me like a snowplow. Next, the battery in the van died at an awkward time. I tried to look after it, but believe me when I say I have no mechanical abilities.

Each crisis was eventually resolved. My daughter found out that her friend's brother had hacked her social media account and unfriended everyone. My churning stomach kept me in the bathroom instead of in front of the computer until adequate amounts of rest, ginger ale, and vanilla ice cream banished the bug. And the auto club replaced the battery.

With my deadline looming, I finally made my way back to the computer with only five days left. While I had convalesced, parts of the story had been rolling around in my head. I re-read the last few paragraphs I'd written and began typing, the words flying from my fingers. My plan was to transform the innkeeper from the old curmudgeon found in most depictions of him into a man who was doing the best he could under difficult circumstances.

> I felt helpless. The same way my childhood friend must have felt when I finally obtained my revenge. It had taken a while after I'd moved back to Bethlehem, where I temporarily took over from the local tax collector who had become ill. After saving even more shekels, denarii, and drachma, I was ready to drive my friend, whose father was long dead, out of business. I just needed the right opportunity.

In the end, a tragic accident involving one of their guests placed my friend in a position where his family was forced to sell the inn. When I bought it from them, I showed the same pity my friend's father had shown mine: none. My friend and his family ended up living in a hovel, and he became a shepherd.

Wait a minute. Wasn't I supposed to be making the innkeeper more sympathetic?

I'm always amazed at the way words flow from brain to fingers to computer screen, especially when I'm facing a time crunch. The characters seem to take over.

Sometimes, my own words even evoke the same emotion in me that I intended for the character. When that happens, I know I've hit the mark as a writer.

Unfortunately, that wasn't happening with this piece. Just the opposite. I didn't like this guy at all.

At least this was only the first draft.

But if I wanted emotion, I'd have to quit woolgathering and keep writing. I forced myself to keep adding words.

"This is where you've run off to," said my wife.

I looked around and realized I'd walked to our stockyard where our guests put their animals. It's out at the edge of town. At the back, there's a small hill with a cave we use as a stable.

"Have you forgotten you have guests to take care of?"

Her accusation hung in the air.

As I filtered my thoughts to find the most appropriate response, I noticed the feeding trough. "What about here?" I said.

She didn't speak. But her darting eyes spoke volumes.

"It could work," I said. "We can put blankets in the cave. They can use the feed trough for the child when it comes."

We spent an hour preparing and cleaning.

Later, over a stew of lamb and vegetables, I told the young couple about the arrangements.

"I'm sure it will be fine," said the man, who I guessed was at least 10 summers older than his very pregnant wife.

It was dark when we got back to the inn and settled down for the night. The day had worn me out, so I slept the sleep of the prophets. Until my wife jabbed me in the ribs.

"Wake up," she urged. "Something's happening!"

I dressed and stepped outside. An unnatural light came from the direction of the cave at the stockyard.

It's still difficult to describe what happened next. When my wife and I arrived at the cave, an unearthly brilliance lit the area.

Shepherds and sheep were crowded around the feeding trough, where a newborn child lay swaddled in a blanket.

One of the shepherds moved aside so we could get closer.

I'd seen many newborns. But as I gazed into the face of this one, I saw something unusual. A glow.

I looked around to see if the light came from the stars or from oil lamps. But even the stars seemed dim as his face radiated a glory the rabbis would have compared to the shekinah[3] of the Holy One. When the child turned toward me, I was transfixed by a pair of dark eyes that pierced deep into my soul.

As I re-read that last line, I shuddered. Eureka! I'd found the sympathetic innkeeper at last! If I was affected by that line, I knew it would definitely send chills down the spines of the people at the Christmas Eve service.

I printed off the finished first draft. I wanted my wife to read it before I began editing. She's always been my sounding board and I've rued the few times I've ignored her advice.

The next morning, I stared at the sheets on my desk, my wife's words still ringing in my ears.

"I don't know," she'd said. "It doesn't seem finished. What about the friend?"

The friend?

"The childhood friend who became a shepherd. What happened to him?"

I didn't have room to fit that into this story, did I?

I re-read the last few paragraphs. Began typing. Hit backspace. Played some Scrabble. Started typing again. Stared at the blinking cursor.

I knew my wife was right; the ending did seem somewhat rushed. But no matter how hard I tried, the words for a more effective ending weren't coming.

I began working on another project, hoping inspiration would strike.

It didn't. Every day for the few days left before the Christmas Eve service, I sat writing, deleting, and rewriting, but to no avail.

The day before the service, I decided to leave the piece as it stood and began rehearsing the delivery with the faint hope that I'd still be able to come up with something.

Christmas Eve came and I was in the choir room in my inn-keeper costume (a worn-out terrycloth bathrobe, a towel head-dress, and an apron borrowed from a chef friend). I was going over what I'd written for the last time and visualizing my delivery. Then, as unexpected as the angel's appearance before the shepherds, the words to a new ending started rolling around in my mind.

I scrambled around the room, looking for my canvas shoulder bag among the pile of choir members' coats and scarves.

I gave up and ripped the pen, string still attached, from the cork board where notes were posted, and began scribbling on the bottom of my typed script. As my name was announced from the pulpit, I dotted the last "i" and crossed the last "t."

My heart racing, I stepped into the spotlight and began to read. As I reached the original end of the story, I paused for dramatic effect, then began to read what I'd furiously scribbled.

> Just then, the shepherd who'd made way for us laid a hand on my shoulder. When I turned, I found myself looking into the face of my childhood friend.
>
> Our eyes locked. But instead of the anger I'd felt toward him and his family, I felt intense sorrow. Sorrow for what our parents had done. Sorrow for what I'd done.
>
> At that moment, he asked me to forgive him and his father.
>
> I said I was the one who needed to ask for his forgiveness.
>
> I still don't know what happened, but in that brief moment it seemed as if all our animosities melted away. As we embraced, I felt, for the first time in years, a peace I had longed for but never found.
>
> After the embrace, I looked back at the Babe. I could swear he smiled.

When I got back to the choir room after the applause, I looked at the tear-stained manuscript in my hand and realized that in this story, God had given me a gift. He'd waited until just the right moment to give me the words I needed to bring the story of the innkeeper to life. And, like the innkeeper, I felt an overwhelming sense of the presence of the Babe of Bethlehem.

I knelt beside one of the chairs in that choir room and whispered, "Thank You, Lord."

1. Luke 19:1–10

2. Matthew 9:9–13

3. In Jewish and Christian theology, *shekinah* is a word used to denote the glory of the divine presence, often represented as fire or light. For examples, see Exodus 3 or 2 Chronicles 7:1–3.

Dialogue Between Shepherds

Vilma Blenman

"Safer to stay with the sheep, I say.
What good could come of taking off,
hurrying down dark hillsides, lion lying in wait,
two shepherds showing up in town, stinking.
Town folks staring while we babble 'bout a baby.
Segub, I say we stay with the sheep."

"And I say we leave the bleating sheep,
stench and all.
All my life, Gershon, all my life, I've counted sheep;
awake or asleep,
smelt sheep, sheared sheep, summoned sheep.
But never, till this night, have I heard a symphony,
never seen an angel parade."

"Well, Segub, the parade's gone, sheep still be here,
dawn's soon to come, cool morning light
might show this night's dream untrue.
Sit with your sheep, go back to sleep—
I'll keep watch.
Tending sheep is what you know.
Why risk them for a wish?
I say we stay."

"I suppose I could stay, Gershon,
could wait to see what may be.
But the songs!
The songs still swirl about my brain,
rising, ringing notes that won't let me be
until I go and see this infant king."

"We have a hundred sheep!
That's no small matter, Segub.
If we leave, who's to watch them at this hour?

Bandits or beggars?
Both count sheep by starlight.
And even if no predator appears,
you can't trust the lambs to stay put
or the new ewes to wait for a late morning call.
Think, think aright, Segub,
stay the night.
Tomorrow, maybe we'll hear more."

"Gershon, I would stay—you know I would—
if I were not
seared by a vision,
commissioned by a choir,
a commoner called to court.
I must see with my own eyes
if the angels spoke true.
So I say, keep my sixty sheep, Gershon,
keep 'em for all you've done for me,
saving me when I slipped over that cliff
listening to my ramblings through many a night,
staying awake while I slept on my watch.
I fear I'm not the same, will never be sane again
until I know what I was meant to be—
until I see something more
than sleeping sheep."

"Are you just going to walk away, Segub?
That anxious to find that baby the angels talked about?
What could a baby do for us?
What difference could a baby make?
Look at the moon, Segub, look!
Moonlight shining on sleeping sheep.
Listen. All quiet and calm again,
west wind warm and—"

"Gershon, I'm off.
Are you sure you won't come?"

Light of the World 2.0: Alternative History

Fiction

Rose Seiler Scott

I pour myself a cup of coffee and sit down to drink it. But just as I lift the cup to my mouth, the phone rings. I hope it's good news, because as a reporter in the city of Surrey, I've had enough of the other kind.

"It's Carl." As usual, his voice has a hard edge. A no-nonsense, don't-say-no-to-the-boss kind of edge. "Just got an anonymous tip. The guy insisted there's something important going down at an old barn on the Number 7 Highway near Clover Valley. We've had good tips from this guy before, so it's probably legit. Could be a big story. You need to get on it. Just keep your wits about you in case it's some kind of criminal set up."

Clover Valley? Is he kidding me? Ever since the highway got rerouted, people have avoided the charming, false-fronted downtown. The only reason businesses survive there at all is because occasionally the old main street is used as a movie set.

The immediate area is surrounded by agricultural land, mostly blueberry fields and greenhouses, and a few vacant, run-down properties. Surrounded by housing developments on all sides, Clover Valley is a sleepy place that time has forgotten. But I can't say no to Carl; I have three kids and a wife to support.

Freezing rain is pelting down like wet ball bearings as I drive across town. Magnified by the rain, lights twinkle on the houses, the malls, and the temples of Surrey. This festival of lights, Diwali, celebrated by the South Asians in the area, symbolizes light and hope over darkness and despair.

The South Asians aren't the only ethnic group, though; there are large populations of Chinese, Filipinos, and Hispanics. As you can imagine, racial tensions often run high, and my job is to report those goings on in addition to the regular occurrences of home-lessness, gang shootings, and drug overdoses. The strings of lights are cheerful, but I often wish there was some real help and hope for the people of this city.

I get out of my car and slog across a mucky yard to a ram-shackle barn that reminds me of a photo calendar picture. I have a sense that this is the one Carl was talking about. The roof is caving in, and vines have grown up around it. The closer I get, the more I smell the ripe stench of animals. Sure enough, in the light of a lantern hanging from the rafters, I can make out a couple of mangy cows and an old horse with her ribs showing. One of the cows moos softly. Maybe I'm here to report on an SPCA raid.

As my eyes adjust, I notice a few hay bales in the corner, and on top of them what appears to be a pile of rags and old blankets.

I'm a seasoned reporter. I've seen it all. But I don't see how this dim old barn is the scoop my boss was making it out to be. There's no sign of anyone or anything. If it's the SPCA I'm waiting for, they haven't shown up yet. Why would they, on a night like tonight?

Just then, a young man steps out of one of the stalls and into the light. "What are you hoping to find here?" he asks.

An odd question. It's almost like he's been expecting someone to come by. Maybe it's a code phrase for a drug exchange? But if he's homeless, he has an aura of respectability. His plaid shirt is faded and his workboots are worn, but he's clean and shaven.

I shouldn't judge, I guess. They aren't *all* drug addicts. With the price of housing, even in this lower-priced area, some working poor can't afford even part of a room.

Now that I've assessed the situation, I put on my professional voice. "Hello, I'm from *Surrey News*, here to report—" I look down at my notebook and realize I have no idea what I'm supposed to be reporting on. "Sorry," I say. "I must have the wrong address." Obviously, this guy is just holed up here for shelter.

"Come in." He gestures to the hay bales. "This is my wife Mar-issa." The pile of blankets moves as a young woman turns toward me and smiles. A barn cat is nestled at her feet and a tiny hand reaches out from the bundle of rags next to her. "This is our baby," she adds.

"So, you're a proud new dad?" I ask the man, mostly for something to say. I still can't figure out why I was sent here. *I suppose now we're going to stand around and smoke cigars. Don't they have any friends or family to celebrate with?*

"Actually, I'm not the father," he says calmly. Apparently he's at peace with what he just said, but the thin band of gold adorning his left ring finger has a brand new sheen.

I scratch my head. "Looks like you're just married," I say, puzzling this over in my mind. I wasn't born yesterday.

"That's right. Our wedding was a couple of months ago," he says. He goes over and puts his arm on his wife's shoulder. "We got engaged when we found out Marissa was expecting."

Wait a minute! Who gets engaged to a girl knocked up with someone else's baby? But, hey, you never know nowadays.

I just look at him, no idea what to say.

He says, "By the way, I'm Joe."

I'd forgotten to ask. Not good if I was going to report on this. Assuming there was even a story.

I realize I haven't given my name either. "Lucas." We shake hands.

"So, Joe… Who *is* the father?" *Awkward, but as a reporter, I'm supposed to ask questions, and I still have no idea what the story is here.*

"That would be God."

"God?" I don't even bother writing this down. Why on earth did my boss send me to this part of town on the wettest night of the year? So I could talk to crazy people?

Joe blinks. "Yes, the God of Abraham, Isaac, and Jacob."

So he's Jewish. That's odd. I'd passed a mosque and a Sikh temple on my way here, but the few synagogues I know of are in Vancouver, not on this side of the river. I've heard they're guarded 24/7 against terrorist attacks. Honestly, I don't even know how the Jews still exist. They've been persecuted and driven out of everywhere they've ever lived.

"He promised He would send His Son," Joe continues. "The prophet Isaiah said, 'The virgin will conceive and give birth to a son, and will call his name Immanuel.'[1] That means 'God with us.'"

  Christmas with Hot Apple Cider

I feel like I've entered the twilight zone. *Is this couple really so naïve they don't know how babies are made? For crying out loud!* I look at my watch. I'd really like to be home right now in my own family room, drinking eggnog. With a lot of rum.

But I get paid to write stories, so I have to follow through and see if there's anything here.

Joe smiles proudly and picks up the baby. Droopy rags have been pinned around him in lieu of a diaper, and he wears an over-sized blue T-shirt with a big silver heart emblazoned on it. The lettering states, "I LOVE," but the rest of the words appear to have worn off. Looks like it came from a thrift store.

"We're going to call him Joshua," Joe says. He grins proudly, as if this tiny boy was his own flesh and blood.

Well, at least the poor kid's name isn't weird, even if his parents seem to be. "Joe, do you mind if I talk to Marissa?"

"Yeah, sure." He walks over to touch her shoulder gently.

Marissa sits up, pulling the blankets around her shoulders. She smiles at me.

At most, she's in her late teens. But she's looking beyond me; her face lit up in some kind of eerie postpartum glow. She whispers, "He is 'God with us.' Our salvation."

I don't know who she's talking to. *Is she having a breakdown? High on something?* I wonder if she's capable of taking care of a child. Maybe I should call Social Services. But I'd hate to do that. They'd probably take the baby and put him in one of their horrible foster homes, where the kids are put to work almost as soon as they're out of diapers.

But I'm worried about Marissa. She looks kind of strung out. Or euphoric. I can't decide. "Do you need medical attention?" I ask. I pull my cell phone out of my pocket. "I can call an ambulance."

"I'm fine." She says this softly, dreamily. "God has blessed me. I just want to praise Him."

Yes, you're blessed all right.

I don't have anything coherent to say to her, so I change the subject. "Why didn't you have the baby in a hospital?" Then I think, *How stupid can you get? They're probably hiding from Social Services. Or perhaps, being Jewish, they've experienced intimidation.*

"We were on our way to mail the census form when the pains started," Marissa says.

"When we got back to our basement suite, there was an eviction notice on the door." Joe hangs his head. "We're behind on the rent."

"There just wasn't time," Marissa adds.

"I work in construction," Joe says. "Not much work lately, so we can't afford a car. And even if we'd made it to a hospital in time, we've heard how crowded they can be."

Well, he had that right. The big news stories last week were about all the people being treated in the hallways at Regional Hospital, and the crowds sitting outside because the waiting rooms were full.

But that's not the story here.

I'm no closer to finding something to write about when I hear the rumble of a motor outside. Slivers of light illuminate Marissa's makeshift bed of hay. *Now what? More reporters?* If so, they'll be sorely disappointed. Aside from a bit of religious weirdness, there's no story here as far as I can tell.

Stepping to the doorway, I watch an old pick-up come to a stop next to the barn. From underneath a worn canvas tarp, a group of men climb out and jump off the back of the truck box. They're holding flashlights and blankets. One of them is carrying what appears to be a lamb.

"Who are you?" I ask. By now, I've decided that although Joe and Marissa are a bit loopy, they're not criminals. In fact, they might be in need of protection, and I feel an odd compulsion to make sure they aren't harmed. I step forward. "What do you want?"

In the glow of the headlights, the men shake their heads and step back, as if afraid. "*No policia, por favor,*" says an older man.

I reassure them. "It's okay, I'm just a reporter." Perhaps they're illegal immigrants or migrant workers. "Why you are here?"

"We working at farm up hill, and we see—" he shrugs.

"Maybe explosion from a movie?" states a younger man with a better command of English.

A man wearing a turban steps forward. "More lights than Diwali," he says, his eyes widening.

"Yes, big light," the older Hispanic man continues. "We see very big people." He holds his arms wide apart and searches for the word, "Like, like…*ángeles*."

"You mean…angels?" I supply the most obvious word. This is getting stranger all the time.

The men nod in excitement, speaking in different languages.

"*Si.*"

"*Aaho.*"

"Yes, angels."

I sigh. *What did I ever do to deserve this job?* I'd even be willing to watch *City of Ember* with my wife and kids for the umpteenth time. But something is clicking in my mind.

With a deep breath, I'm back in reporter mode. "And what did these—beings—say to you?" This time, I really do want to know.

The older man answers, as slowly and clearly as he can pronounce the words. "They say 'Peace, to everyone. A baby born to save all people.'"

The younger Hispanic man pipes in again. "Even *our* people. We get taken advantage of, you know." He points his finger at me.

"Shh, we want no trouble, Juan," says the man holding the lamb.

I realize I need to step back to allow the men space to see what they came to see.

The older man moves toward the child and its mother and raises his hands in the air. "*Gloria a Dios.*" His voice is a reverent whisper and his wrinkled face, behind the bearded stubble, shines with an otherworldly joy.

I leave the barn and look up. *It's remarkable.* The monsoon has stopped completely, and the temperature has dropped to below freezing. In a nearly cloudless sky, the stars are glittering and an extra bright star that I've never noticed before pierces the blackness.

In the dystopian *City of Ember*, while the lights were going off in the underground city, the people were waiting for the builders to lead them out of darkness, even though the answer was right in front of them. For me, light is beginning to dawn. Could it be that this baby, little Joshua, here in this run-down barn, is the way out of the darkness of our world?

What will I do with this story? God. God with us. Gloria a Dios. Young Marissa's words and the old shepherd's praise echo in my mind. *It's too strange not to be true,* I think. But will anyone believe it?

I'll have to think on this, and then I'll write—something, perhaps about hope and light. This world could use some of each.

1. Isaiah 7:14

Home for Christmas

Nonfiction

Nikki Rosen

I grew up Jewish. Not just in name, but in practice.

One day as I sat beside my mother and sister and gazed around the temple, my eyes rested on the Torah displayed on the front platform behind the rabbi. The velvet curtains, which are usually kept closed, had been opened to reveal the Holy Scriptures for all to see. Since looking at the Torah was considered a sin unless done in specific ways and at certain times, the mood that morning in the temple felt sacred, holy.

After the service, since it was forbidden to drive on the Sabbath, we walked home. Before we entered our house we kissed the mezuzah, a small decorative case that held Scriptures from the book of Deuteronomy. My parents had attached these to every door in our home in compliance with the teaching to write God's commandments on the doorposts of our house.

I had learned from a young age that, in order to please God and earn His favour, I needed to adhere to a myriad of rules and obligations. For example, we weren't allowed to drive the car, answer the phone or doorbell, watch television, listen to the radio, or turn the lights on during the Sabbath or on certain holidays.

An endless list of do's and don'ts centred around food and eating. We kept two sets of dishes, pots, pans, and cutlery—one for meat products, one for milk. The two food groups could not come into contact with each other. All meats had to be blessed by a rabbi and deemed "kosher," or clean, before we could consume them. And certain foods, such as pork and shell fish, were strictly forbidden.

I knew little of Christmas and its meaning, except the stories I heard from friends from school about reindeer with red noses, a fat, jolly Santa Claus who came down chimneys while everyone slept, sleighs packed by elves with toys to be given only to good children, and Christmas trees adorned with ornaments and glitter. Some mentioned a baby born in a stable, but I had no understanding of the significance of that.

However, as a young Jewish girl attending a Protestant school, I loved when we sang the song "O Little Town of Bethlehem" during the Christmas/Hanukkah season. I found the melody soothing. The words played in my head and created images of what they actually meant. I had never heard of Jesus, salvation, or God's grace. I knew only the Torah and the multitude of laws God required His people to keep in order to attain His favour.

From the outside, our family seemed perfect, but behind closed doors I lived in constant fear of my parents. They beat and bullied both me and my older sister.

For many years I ached with what I can only describe as a profound sense of homesickness. I'd often scream silently to myself, *I want to go home. I just want to go home!* The term "home" signified much to me. It conveyed what I had seen and experienced in friend's homes—warmth, affection, care, belonging, and support—all the things I didn't feel in my own house.

As a young child, I yearned with a deep longing for a place such as that to run to, a comforting shelter where I could hide from the storms of life. Unfortunately, the conflicts and battles I endured mostly existed within the confines of the house in which I lived, and with those responsible for looking after me. Joy, peace, and faith were foreign concepts in our family.

During the holidays I'd wander outside in the cold winter chill, looking in the windows of other people's houses. I marvelled at the bright, coloured lights and yearned to sit in front of the fireplaces that burned their warm flames. And I ached to be part of the families I saw laughing and embracing each other.

I climbed atop snow banks to watch the happiness of others, wishing desperately that I could be part of their festivities and warmth.

Eventually, though, I had to descend the snowy hills and trudge "home." I'd open the door to greetings yelled in harsh tones:

"Where have you been?" "Go to your room!" "I don't want to have to look at your stupid face!" Sometimes a hard slap on the head accompanied the cruel greeting and emphasized my worthlessness.

I'd retreat to my small room and crouch in a far corner, letting the tears fall down my cheeks. I'd close my eyes and imagine the homes I'd seen moments earlier. My young mind would pretend that those families had welcomed me into their loving world and drawn me into the warmth and joy of their festive celebrations.

Home to me meant criticisms, beatings, terror, shame, and hiding. There were no brightly burning lights, no warm crackling fireplace, no meals that smelled inviting, and no loving happy family to hold close and share stories with.

My mother lay in her bed in the upstairs bedroom, dying. My father, full of rage and venom, was someone I tried hard to avoid.

Relatives bustled about caring for my ailing mother and maintaining the upkeep of our house. They cared little for me and my older sister. To them, we were nothing more than annoyances. They pushed us downstairs to the basement, out of sight, hidden away, until one of them needed a scapegoat to lash their irritations on. Only then did we become the object of their focus.

Too many losses and trauma from age nine throughout my teen years eventually caused me to seek solace through a serious drug addiction and other self-destructive behaviours. But one winter morning, I turned on the radio and heard, "Yet in the dark streets shineth the everlasting light."[1] My heart leapt within me. I listened to the sweet voices singing that Christmas carol, and deep within my spirit I yearned to know more about "the Everlasting Light."

I remember strolling through the malls during the Christmas season, when the music piping throughout the shops declared the glory of the risen Lord and proclaimed the peace of knowing God's wonderful Gift to the world. As I listened, I wanted to open the door of my heart to the One those songs spoke of. The words "Fall on your knees, O hear the angel voices,"[2] made me want to drop down right there, amidst all the harried shoppers, and ask this Jesus to help me. But I didn't want to look foolish, so I kept walking.

In my mid-twenties, I finally did accept Christ into my life, and after all those years of longing to go home, He made it possible. In Him, I found true peace, incredible joy, warm friendships, and a love that went beyond anything I'd imagined.

Sometimes I think of the songwriters who penned the beautiful carols. I wonder what they experienced that led them to write hymns with such deep conviction and understanding of the power and majesty of God and the hope of the gift that was given.

As a Jew who now serves the Holy Child of Bethlehem, I am grateful to them. For me, the powerful Christmas carols are songs of truth that can be sung any day of the year. They're a testament of God's ultimate love for the people He created. Like those who chose to compose carols with a strong message of hope, I pray that my life will create a similar message to all who hunger for peace and hope.

My own children have never known the emptiness and pain of not belonging or the awfulness of not celebrating the joys of God's love. As a new mother, I decided that my children would never experience the wretchedness of not being a part of something wonderful, and I chose to do everything in my power to make our home similar to the homes I had peeked into as a young, lonely child.

Perhaps because of my own childhood memories, "home for Christmas" now also means going beyond our family get-togethers and reaching out to others who are broken, lost, and in desperate need of our Saviour's presence. As His hands, His feet, and His smile, I strive to touch the lives of others who are hurting and yearning for a safe haven that will provide them with the peace and comfort they so desperately seek.

God gave the wonderful gift of Jesus to the world to provide hope, salvation, and peace. All who accept His glorious offering will undoubtedly experience the true meaning of "home for Christmas."

1. "O Little Town of Bethlehem," Phillips Brooks (Public Domain)

2. "O Holy Night," John S. Dwight, English translation (Public Domain)

  Christmas with Hot Apple Cider

Christmas Revelation

Nonfiction

Ruth Smith Meyer

There I was, just before Christmas, entering the grandeur of Massey Hall in downtown Toronto with my parents, my 16-year-old brother, and my 13-year-old sister. Among the elegantly dressed concertgoers, our plain black garb stood out in sharp contrast.

What had caused my father—an Old Order Mennonite minister—to order tickets so his family could hear Handel's *Messiah*? Was it his quest for knowledge and understanding? We had no radio or TV—not even a record player—so he had never heard anything like it. Whatever it was that motivated him, that year, when I was in my late teens, Dad stepped far outside his (and our family's) comfort zone.

After finding our way to the most affordable seats on the second balcony, we sat gazing in awe at the splendour around us. The intricate architecture and heavy red velvet drapery were impressive. Our Mennonite churches were small, with plain white interiors and unfinished wooden benches—quite a contrast to the opulence of our present surroundings.

After a while, the members of the orchestra found their seats. I was fascinated by the cacophony as they all tuned their instruments at the same time. Since we sang a cappella exclusively—whether at home or at church—the instruments were unfamiliar to me. I could name only a few of them.

At last, a hush came over the audience as the huge Mendelssohn Choir entered, followed by the evening's soloists. Finally, everyone clapped as Sir Ernest MacMillan, the director, took his place. I only knew who he was from having read the program, but it didn't take me long to admire the way he controlled both the choir and the orchestra.

From that moment on, the entire evening was almost overwhelming. It certainly was out of our usual realm.

Four-part, whole-congregation hymn singing was our norm. Occasionally, at our young people's meetings, a men's quartet or a ladies trio would sing a special piece, but no one would have presumed to sing alone—that would have signified pride in one's own voice. As for the musical instruments, to be honest, because I was so unused to them, they were a bit of a distraction.

We came away from that first encounter with the *Messiah* hardly knowing what to think. It was all so new that it was hard to absorb the enormity of what we'd experienced, and we didn't talk about it a great deal.

Although Dad was impressed by the way the music told the familiar Scripture story, I think he was content having heard it once. I, on the other hand, was captivated and wanted to hear it again.

The following year, I went back to Massey Hall to see Handel's *Messiah* with my fiancé, who was curious about my experience and quite willing to try it out. I found myself able to appreciate, a little more, the different parts of that great oratorio that second time. My fiancé, too, was passionate about the presentation, and we determined to make it an annual tradition.

On our fourth year, we deemed it worth the money to get seats on the main floor. I settled into my seat with great anticipation, which wasn't in vain. The words to the various parts were printed in the program, so I was able to follow along. From the first strains of the overture, followed by "Comfort Ye My People," then "Every Valley," my heart was moved. As "And the Glory of the Lord Shall Be Revealed" was sung by the full choir, I was drawn further into the realization of the splendour of God's plan.

Lois Marshall was the soprano that year, and although I've forgotten the names of the other soloists, I know the bass had a booming, rich voice and the alto was sung by a male. The soloists all sang as though they were experiencing the richness of the message in their own hearts. I'll never forget how the bass bellowed the part of the "Refiner's Fire," nor Lois Marshall's sweet rendition of "There Were Shepherds Abiding" and "Come Unto Me."

The choir, too, presented their significant parts with great expression. Both the choir and the orchestra swelled and hushed in tune with the words of the text and the skillful conducting of Sir Ernest. His competence and exuberance alone were fascinating, and it seemed that, like me, he was caught up in the meaning and importance of this great piece of Handel's music.

My mind and heart absorbed the meaning of the words—from the Old Testament proclamation of the coming Messiah, to Christ's birth and death, to the end of the New Testament and a glimpse of what is yet to come. The composition heralded the eternal message of God's love.

Understanding blossomed in my heart that God so loved the world He gave us His Son. I realized that life with God can begin now with our own little part of history. If we open our heart to Him, our knowing will come into full fruition as we, with believers from all ages, sing our "Hallelujahs" and our great "Amens" to "Him who sitteth upon the throne."

Suddenly, it all came together in my heart and mind: the reality of how the music so vividly portrayed the meaning of the words; the glory of the full choir aided at times by the auxiliary choir in the side balconies; the trumpet player's appearance in a small balcony above the choir, like an angel in the sky; Sir Ernest's wonderful conducting—it all combined into one magnificent entirety.

As we stood for the "Hallelujah Chorus," it seemed that we were already part of the heavenly choir.

Afterward, I sat in my padded chair mesmerized while the final chords of "Worthy is the Lamb" died down and were followed by the "Amen" with its joyous repetition of worship honouring the Lamb who is worthy. I was filled with exhilaration and a sense of wonderment and worship.

Amid the splendour of this beautiful edifice, with the glory of God's eternal love so vivid, I felt all-consuming awe that made me want to stay there forever.

I'd caught a vision of what heaven could hold, and I was loathe to return to my mundane everyday life.

Gradually, it dawned on me that I could carry that revelation into my daily life, letting it colour my perception in each moment. It was only then that I rose to accompany my husband down the aisle.

The Messiah did become a part of our family tradition. We weren't always able to hear a live presentation, but the record played throughout each December and we listened to it on the radio each Christmas Eve.

It was my husband's request to hear it on the last night of his life, and the "Hallelujah Chorus" was played at the end of his memorial service.

In my 75th year, as a special treat, my family got tickets so we could again attend a live presentation.

My dad had no idea what he started when he took us to Massey Hall!

  Christmas with Hot Apple Cider

The Greatest Gift of All

Fiction

Robin Livingston

It was still dark when Peter Walen threw back several layers of heavy woollen blankets and levered himself to his feet. He tugged the knitted cap he'd slept in more snugly over his ears and shoved his stockinged feet into the felt boot liners that he wore in the cabin.

He shivered a bit in his long johns and blew an experimental breath. He wasn't surprised to see a ghostly vapour hang in the air in front of his face. It was going to be another cold one. He'd get the fire built up before he thought about getting dressed.

He pulled one of the blankets over his shoulders and grasped the flashlight he kept by his bed to light his way to the wood box. He wished he had something other than poplar to burn. No matter how he packed the stove, the fire never seemed to last the whole night, and by morning there would barely be enough coals to get it started again. "Never mind, Pete, old boy," he said into the silence. "You can find some nice maple to cut for next year."

In the meantime, he meant to use up the wood he'd cut back in the spring when he was clearing this spot to build his cabin on.

He struck a match to light one of his oil lamps and turned off the flashlight to save the battery. It didn't take him long to get the fire going. He was becoming an expert.

Pete stood still for a moment, listening to the cheery crackle and hiss of the flames that licked the kindling, and breathing in the tangy scent of the wood smoke. The heat from a wood stove always seemed friendlier to him than the electric heat he'd depended on when he lived in the city. You certainly never took wood heat for granted. "Gotta cut more kindling this morning," he muttered.

He glanced at the thermometer on the table and saw that it was only about 5°C (41°F). It was probably closer to –30°C (–22°F) outside, not unusual for this part of Northern Ontario. After all, it must be getting close to Christmas.

He turned to the calendar hanging beside the door and frowned as he counted out the days since his last visit to town. He was a little shocked to see that it was Friday already. That meant it was actually the day before Christmas. He'd been so caught up in the work it took to live out here that he'd completely lost track of the days!

He shrugged. What difference did it make anyway? When you got right down to it, Christmas was just another day, especially when there was no one to celebrate it with.

Pete held his hands out to the warmth beginning to radiate from the cast iron wood stove that dominated the space in his tiny living room. It would take a couple of hours to get the cabin feeling comfortable. In the meantime, he put the kettle on to boil for his first coffee of the day.

It hadn't been a hard decision to come here after his retirement from the furniture factory. He'd done a lot over the course of his life, from operating a forklift to crewing on a fishing boat. He'd just never done any of it long enough to build up any savings. His small pension wasn't enough to get by with down south, and besides, he'd always dreamed of doing this very thing, living off the grid in a cabin built with his own hands.

There was nothing tying him to the city anyway. He had no family to speak of. He'd had a wife once, but that was long ago. After his one attempt at marriage went sour he'd never had any desire to repeat the experiment.

He stared into his coffee cup, his thoughts far away. "Face it, Pete. You're a loner, and better off that way," he told himself.

He thought back to the day a few years ago when he'd somehow been drawn into a conversation with a couple of guys in the lunchroom at work. He'd ended up sharing his idea of heading north and finding a spot to build himself a place to live off the grid after retirement. That was when Charlie had mentioned he'd inherited this piece of property up north from an uncle.

"There's a rough camp set up by the lake, and some good fishing, but not much else. Why don't you come up with me and take a look?" Charlie had invited. "I'm not looking to sell it, mind you, but I wouldn't mind renting a piece of it out."

They'd come up together that first time and done a lot of talking on that trip.

"You could build a place up here, you know," Charlie had suggested. "If you don't mind putting it back in the bush a ways. There's 50 acres to choose from and the old logging road takes you right to the back of the place. 'Course, you wouldn't be able to get your truck back there in the winter. Come to think of it, you'd have to be a little crazy to want to live up here full time. Too lonely for me. I didn't picture you as some kind of modern day Jeremiah Johnson, so maybe it's not what you had in mind."

Pete had just smiled. It was perfect.

In the end, he and Charlie had worked out a deal and even had it all written up by a lawyer so it would be legal. The rent he paid Charlie for his little patch of heaven wasn't much, but it was enough to cover the taxes Charlie paid on the whole property, and Pete was able to get by on what was left of his pension every month. It worked for both of them. He had his dream, and Charlie was happy, too.

He smiled in remembrance and ran his fingers through the tangled strands of the beard he now wore. It was shot through with grey and tended to stick out in every direction, but it helped keep his face warm and he liked not having to bother with shaving. He wondered what the folks back in the city would think of him now.

He set his empty cup in the sink. It was a nice sink even if it had no taps and drained into a bucket under the counter. It was just one of the little touches that made his cabin feel like a home. He'd put his heart and soul into the building of it, and even now he spent a lot of time making little improvements.

That reminded him, he'd have to do another round of the thrift stores on his next visit to town. Maybe he'd be able to find one of those big copper kettles that he could keep on top of the wood stove. Hot water on demand would be the height of luxury. Next summer he would dig a well, but for now he had to haul water from the lake, and that could be an all-day job when you had to cut through the ice. He supposed he'd better get at it.

His gaze flicked again to the calendar on the wall. Christmas, his first one out here in the bush.

He shrugged. It was what it was. Not as if he'd ever been into all the decorations and stuff.

He leaned close to the glass to peer out the second-hand window he'd put in above the sink. The sky was beginning to lighten to a silvery grey and he could just see the outline of the outhouse he'd built out back. It was still full dark under the trees, but a new fall of powdery snow blanketed everything in a ghostly white. Nothing was moving.

Inside, it was quiet. Really quiet. The ticking of the clock on the wall sounded loud in the stillness. Okay, maybe it was a bit too quiet. He shrugged into his warmest clothes and put another chunk of wood into the stove before sitting at his little table to pull on his boots. He looked across at the empty chair opposite him. Why on earth had he bought two chairs? The likelihood of anyone coming to visit him was pretty slim. He sat for a moment staring at nothing and then shook himself, as if that could rid him of the deep melancholy that was beginning to settle over him like a suffocating shroud.

Maybe he should forget about chopping ice and trek out to the road to dig his truck out. He could drive the 40 kilometres into town for breakfast. It might do him some good to see a few people, and he could stock up on some things, stop at the laundromat, maybe even go to the YMCA to have a shower. At least he'd be clean for Christmas even if it was just another day.

He could stop at the post office and check his mailbox, too. Maybe he'd even discover that someone had sent him a card. Did people still do that? He supposed it was possible, though he wouldn't hold his breath.

He pulled on his mitts and stepped out into the frosty morning to start his day.

Many hours later, he locked up the truck and piled the last of his assorted purchases on his toboggan for the long hike back to the cabin. Straightening from his task, he reflected with some disgust that going to town on the day before Christmas hadn't been the brightest idea he'd ever had. The library and the YMCA were closed till after Boxing Day, and he hadn't been able to find a parking place at the grocery store.

The whole town was bedlam! Tinsel and coloured lights and Christmas trees and gaudy inflated Santas everywhere you looked. It was exhausting in a way that hauling water and chopping wood had never been.

He clipped the tow rope for the toboggan to the belt he wore wrapped around the waist of his parka and strapped on his snowshoes. He shook his head. No sense dwelling on the negative. At least he now felt a greater appreciation for the peace and quiet of his cabin in the woods. And, wonder of wonders, his mailbox hadn't been empty!

He thought of the envelope he carried tucked in the inside pocket of his coat. He hadn't opened it yet, but it felt like a card. The address was his old one but someone in the post office had slashed through the original scrawled handwriting with a bold black line and slapped on a change of address label. There was no return address on it, so it was a mystery—one that he was in no hurry to solve. He was saving it for later.

He hefted his walking stick in one hand, thinking of the wolf tracks he'd spotted on his way out to the truck that morning. He wasn't too worried about the wolves, but the heavy stick did make him feel a little less defenceless.

"Walk softly and carry a big stick," he said into the silence, his breath clouding the air. His cheeks stung with the cold, but he'd warm up once he got moving. He gave the rope a jerk to get the toboggan started and set off for home.

By the time he got to the cabin, chopped some fresh kindling, and got the fire burning to his satisfaction, most of the day was gone. It didn't take long to get his few purchases stowed away and attend to the other chores he'd put off by going to town that morning. He dumped a last armload of wood in the box and slapped at the bits of bark clinging to his sleeves while his eyes strayed to the envelope propped on the table by the door.

On an impulse, Pete went back out into the fading daylight and circled around behind his neatly stacked cords of firewood. There were balsam trees on that side of the clearing, and he gave their branches a quick shake to dislodge the accumulated layers of snow. He twisted off a few sprigs of the greenery and carried them back inside where he held them up to his face and inhaled deeply to take in the aromatic scent of wintergreen. He smiled to himself and arranged them along the edge of the table next to the wall. *Better than some old Christmas tree,* he thought.

He ate his supper of canned stew without really tasting it, the unopened envelope propped on the table across from him his only company. He tried not to look at the empty chair. Finally, he pushed his bowl aside and reached for the card or letter or whatever it was. He turned it over and over in his work-roughened hands before carefully slitting open the edge with his pocket knife and pulling out the contents.

It was a card. The front of it showed an embossed silhouette of a stable with the Christ Child lying in a manger and Mary and Joseph bending close to gaze down at the infant Jesus. There was a star all done up in golden glitter adorning the sky above the stable.

Pete sat staring at it for a long time before he opened the card to see if there was a message inside. The beautifully handwritten words jumped out at him.

The Greatest Gift of All

Emmanuel, God with Us

"You've got to be kidding," he whispered in astonishment. It was from Mrs. Bleacher, his old Sunday school teacher and a friend of his mother's. He'd had no idea she was still alive. He hadn't seen her in 50 years.

"She's got to be at least ninety years old! Why would she send me a card?" He shook his head, puzzled. Nevertheless, he set the card up to stand in the midst of his gathered greenery and stared at it for a few minutes longer.

With a newfound sense of purpose, he cleared away his supper dishes and reached up to the shelf above his couch that held his collection of books. He pulled down the worn copy of the Holy Bible his mother had given him when he first left home and held it in his hands. He'd carried that book from place to place for most of

  Christmas with Hot Apple Cider

his life because it reminded him of her, but when was the last time he'd opened it?

"She meant it to be more than a souvenir, you big idiot," he growled.

He dredged up the memories of Christmases long past, the candlelight services and Advent wreathes of his childhood. They hadn't held much meaning back then. He had to admit he'd spent most of his time living inside his own head. The life he imagined had always seemed better and more interesting than the real world. Well, he was a lot older now and he liked to think he might be a bit wiser than that boy had been. The real world was all you had. Maybe it was time to revisit some of those old traditions.

Pete fumbled in a box and pulled out the remains of four candles. They were almost burned to the end, but he'd kept them just in case. He placed them in a row in front of his little Christmas display. He couldn't remember if there should be four candles or five, and he didn't have a wreath, but what did that matter?

He sat in the chair and opened the Bible to the passage in Luke about the birth of Jesus. It was full dark outside by now and the soft yellow glow of the oil lamps wasn't quite enough to read by. He put on his headlamp so he could see the words more clearly and began to read out loud even though there was no one to hear.

"Do not be afraid, Mary; you have found favour with God. You will conceive and give birth to a son, and you are to call him Jesus. He will be great and will be called the Son of the Most High."[1]

He paused. What a promise! But then, she was right to trust it. It wasn't an empty promise. It turned out to be true.

Other words came swimming up out of his past, words like, "I will never leave you nor forsake you."[2] God had made a lot of promises.

He nodded to himself and lit the first candle. He would call it the Candle of Hope.

Pete picked up the book again and continued through Mary and Joseph's journey to Bethlehem and their search for a place for their baby to be born.

"She wrapped him in cloths and placed him in a manger, because there was no guest room available for them."[3]

He paused to look at the picture of the stable on the card in front of him. In spite of everything, it had the look of a refuge. He glanced around at his cozy home and smiled.

He lit the second candle and called it the Candle of Peace.

He read till he got to the part about the angels appearing to the shepherds. "'I bring you good news that will cause great joy for all the people. Today in the town of David a Savior has been born to you; he is the Messiah, the Lord. This will be a sign to you: You will find a baby wrapped in cloths and lying in a manger.' Suddenly a great company of the heavenly host appeared with the angel, praising God and saying, 'Glory to God in the highest heaven, and on earth peace to those on whom his favour rests.'"[4]

Pete imagined he could almost hear them singing for joy and he wished he could have been there.

He lit the third candle and called it the Candle of Joy.

He stared at the card one more time, thinking of the words written inside.

The Greatest Gift of All
Emmanuel, God with Us

The promise and also its fulfilment. He lit the last candle, the Jesus Candle, and gently closed the book. Christmas wasn't the tinsel and the hectic craziness he'd experienced in town that morning, but it wasn't just another day either. It was a day for remembering. Remembering the promise fulfilled.

He thrust his feet into his heavy boots and pulled on his parka and mitts. When he stepped out into the snowy night he felt his skin pucker in the frigid air.

In the silence he could hear the distant creaking of tree limbs rubbing together in the forest.

He looked up. The night sky stretched above him like a lofty cathedral adorned with millions upon millions of shimmering stars. The Milky Way was splashed across the heavens, and every constellation stood out in sharp relief.

Pete's breath caught in his throat as ribbons of green and blue rippled across the glorious expanse.

Aurora Borealis, the Northern Lights. They were so beautiful he wanted to weep.

"Emmanuel, God with me," he whispered, and he knew in his heart that it was true. He could feel it. He wasn't alone after all.

He threw his head back and spread his arms wide, his rich baritone ringing out with the strains of "Angels We Have Heard on High." When he got to the chorus and sang out the Glo-o-o-o-o-o-ria, he could have sworn there were angels singing with him.

1. Luke 1:30–32a

2. Based on Hebrews 13:5

3. Luke 2:7

4. Luke 2:10b–14

Christmas Choir

Ron Wyse

Line after line we sing, trying
Desperately to intonate well and
Convey all that the authors, old and new,
Envisioned as they composed.

Turning the page, such a
Staggering of lines and words! 'Til
Finally, happily, there emerges
An island of striking togetherness;

All parts finally sing together,
Just two brief words—"si-lent prayer,"
But I catch my breath; for a moment
I feel it—I'm part of a living whole.

Such my isolation, begun so long ago.
Although many came for many occasions,
Aloneness endured, untouched by
All kindly words to the contrary.

This brief taste, a sampling
Of what the blanketed crib
Came to bring together
(Although we see too little, as yet).

The moment passed. But the seed sown,
The dizzying thought, the ancient dream,
Spreads deeper, I feel it still; *Peace*
On earth, to all of good will.

What's Next?

1. Visit our website and we'll give you a special gift.

hotappleciderbooks.com

2. While there, sign up for our reader updates to get:

- Special offers
- Information about author signings
- News about upcoming books
- Reviews and endorsements
- Information on how to get bulk copies of these books at a discount

3. Did you enjoy this book? Let our writers know:

- Post a comment on our website (hotappleciderbooks.com).
- Like our Facebook page (facebook.com/hotappleciderbooks).
- Write a short review and post it on Amazon, Barnes & Noble, Kobo, Goodreads, your blog, or any other place you frequent.
- Tell people about the book. Better yet, buy copies to give as gifts to friends and family who would enjoy them.
- Buy the writers' other books. Or get them from your library.
- Connect with the writers whose work you like by signing up for their newsletters and/or following them on Facebook, Twitter, or other social media.

  Christmas with Hot Apple Cider

ℰⅆⅈⅆℴⱳ and Writers

Photo by Stephen Gurie Woo

N. J. Lindquist

www.njlindquist.com

N. J. Lindquist is a full-time writer, speaker, and teacher. Her published work includes more than 20 books, one play, and numerous columns, articles, and short stories. A number of her books, columns, articles, blog posts, and stories have won awards.

She also speaks to adults and teens on various topics, including creativity, making disciples, trusting God, and leadership. She's currently using the blog on her website to talk about things that interest her, from living with curly hair to meeting her birth mother at the age of 50.

N. J. has taught workshops for writers in every province of Canada except Newfoundland (one of these days!) as well as in the United States. She continues to post advice for writers at www.writewithexcellence.com.

N. J. is passionate about empowering writers from the Canadian Christian faith community. In 2001, she co-founded The Word Guild and she served as its executive director until January of 2008. She also directed the Write! Canada conference for 11 years. In the fall of 2007, N. J. realized that an anthology of true stories, fiction, and poetry would be the perfect way to showcase the work of Canadian writers who are Christian. That led to the publication of the first of the Hot Apple Cider Books—*Hot Apple Cider: Stories to Stir the Heart and Warm the Soul*, early in 2008.

Born in Saskatchewan and raised in Manitoba, N. J., together with her husband and business partner Les, lives in Markham, Ontario, close to their sons.

More Than a Friend (That's Life! Communications)

The Misadventures & Tribulations of Princess Persnickety & Stefan the Stable-boy – as Alana Menzies (That's Life! Communications)

Jeannette Altwegg

Jeannette loves words. She enjoys writing plays and inspirational reflections for worship services as well as regaling her writers' group friends with fantastical stories. While usually more at ease writing fiction, she surprised herself by placing third in the Wellington County Historical Society's annual Jean Hutchinson Essay Contest in 2016. When not writing, Jeanette either reads or buys books for her church library.

Jessica Lynn Photography

Brian C. Austin

Brian C. Austin is a writer and speaker. His work includes print and audio poetry, nonfiction articles, historical fiction, and dramatic monologue. Brian is a contributing author to the best-selling Canadian anthologies *Hot Apple Cider*, *A Second Cup of Hot Apple Cider*, and *Hot Apple Cider with Cinnamon*. His subjects include aging, suicide intervention, homelessness, grief, grandparenting, and humour.

Brian's first published novel, *Muninn's Keep*, a finalist in The Word Awards, is historical fiction set in northern England in 892 AD. Brian lives with his wife, Carolyn, in Walkerton, Ontario, and loves his title of "Fish Tank Grandpa."

Muninn's Keep (Word Alive Press)
Laughter & Tears (Word Alive Press)

Tandy Balson

www.timewithtandy.com

Tandy Balson is a wife, mother, grandmother, friend, volunteer, and observer of life. Her mission is to inspire by bringing a fresh perspective to everyday life. She does this through her books, speaking engagements, blog, and weekly program on Hope Stream Radio. Tandy makes her home in the outskirts of Calgary, Alberta.

Sarah Grace Photography

Inspirations from the Everyday (Friesen Press)
Dragonflies, Snowdrifts & Spice Cake (Friesen Press)

Christmas with Hot Apple Cider

Glynis Belec

www.glynismbelec.com

Glynis Belec, an award-winning children's author, freelance writer, and custom publisher, faces each day with hope and thanksgiving. Her publishing company, Angel Hope Publishing, keeps her busy. If she's not helping someone else realize their publishing dream, she's catching up on some of her own projects. Glynis lives in a small southern Ontario town with nearly two thousand mostly happy people!

T&J Studios Photography

Jesus Loves Me When I Dance (Angel Hope Publishing)
Good Grief People (Angel Hope Publishing)

Vilma Blenman

writerteacher.wordpress.com

Vilma Blenman is a registered psychotherapist practising at LifeCare Centres. She recently retired as a teacher-counsellor with the Toronto District School Board. Vilma has pieces in *A Second Cup of Hot Apple Cider, A Taste of Hot Apple Cider,* and *Hot Apple Cider with Cinnamon.* In 2013, Vilma published *First Flight,* an eclectic collection of poetry. She also tied for first place in the Writers' Commun-

ity of Durham Region summer slam competition, performing her poem, "Fat Girl Feelings." She co-edited *S.I.S.T.A. Soul Food: Delightful Recipes & Recollections.* Vilma lives with her family in Pickering, Ontario.

Bill Bonikowsky

www.facebook.com/bill.bonikowsky

Bill Bonikowsky's love for writing found expression when he served as editor of Youth for Christ's *Report to the People* newsletter and as editor of the *Alpha News* for Alpha Ministries Canada. He was a contributing writer for the *NIV Life Application Bible,* and had stories published in *A Second Cup of Hot Apple Cider* and *Hot Apple Cider With Cinnamon.* Bill shared intimately on Facebook his experience of losing his wife of 45 years to cancer. Recently re-married, Bill lives with his wife, Shirley, in Nanaimo, British Columbia.

Donna Bonnett Tanchez

Donna has loved reading and writing for as long as she can remember. In elementary school, she wrote her own plays, which her friends performed for the class. She also entered various local writing contests. As an adult, she invented stories to entertain her children. The poem included in this book was inspired by her memories of worshiping as a child during a Christmas Eve service and acting in the Christmas pageant. This is her first attempt at having her writing published. Donna lives in Milton, Ontario, with her husband, daughter, and son.

Ann Brent

writerbrent.wordpress.com

Ann Brent is passionate about getting God's Word and His message of salvation through Jesus to as many people as possible. In her 25-plus years working in Christian missions, Ann has written countless articles to inform, inspire, and encourage people with how God is at work around the world today. She is determined to face life's challenges and changes through the filters of faith, laughter, and optimism. Ann lives in southwestern Ontario.

"My Mother's Gift" in *A Second Cup of Hot Apple Cider*
"Visual Gymnastics" in *A Second Cup of Hot Apple Cider*

Lynne Collier

lynnecollier.com

lunariaphotography.com

Lynne Collier, founder of White Rose Writers—The Business of Being An Author, is a contributor to four anthologies and the author of one autobiography and six as-yet-unpublished speculative fiction novels. She lives in southern Ontario with her husband, Stephen.

Raising Benjamin Frog: A Mother's Journey with her Autistic Son (Amazon CreateSpace)
The Novel Author's Workbook (Etsy)

  Christmas with Hot Apple Cider

Photo by Stephen Gurie Woo

Janis Cox

www.janiscox.com

In 2008, Janis started blogging as a way to express her faith. Today, she is the award-winning author/illustrator of the children's picture books *Tadeo Turtle* and *The Kingdom of Thrim*. Janis also podcasts on Hope Stream Radio. Her talk "Growing Through God's Word" can be heard each Tuesday. Janis is a member of The Word Guild, InScribe Christian Writers' Fellowship, and American Christian Fiction Writers. A grandmother of seven, she lives in Haliburton, Ontario, with her husband and her dog, Snowball.

Marguerite Cummings

margueritec.wordpress.com

Marguerite Cummings has a distinctively international background. Born in Belgium into a French-speaking family with roots in Austria, Belgium, Poland, and Romania, she moved to England in her late teens, then to Toronto, Ontario, in 1998. Marguerite is thrilled to have been part of two previous Hot Apple Cider anthologies. She also designed Reader's Guides and co-edited Discussion Guides for the series. In addition, Marguerite contributed several poems to *As the Ink Flows: Devotions to Inspire Christian Writers & Speakers* (Judson Press), which was a finalist in the 2017 The Word Awards.

Kevin J. Dautremont

thestethoscopeandpen.com

Photo by Dawnelle Brown
brown-eyedgirlphotography.ca

Kevin J. Dautremont, MD, is a family physician in Moose Jaw, Saskatchewan, and an associate clinical professor with the University of Saskatchewan College of Medicine. His writing focuses on mysteries and historical fiction. In 2008, Kevin won the Best New Canadian Christian Author Award for *The Golden Conquest*. This alternative history novel is set during the Spanish Conquest of Mexico. His story "Dazed" is in *A Second Cup of Hot Apple Cider*.

The Golden Conquest (Castle Quay Books)

Beverly DeWit

www.bevdewit.weebly.com

Beverly DeWit is a freelance writer and artist. Beverly's devotions have appeared in *Journey Devotional Magazine* by Lifeway. While she has self-published some of her stories, others have appeared in *Hot Apple Cider with Cinnamon*, church publications, medical journals, medical newsletters, and on blogs and websites. She is also a women's ministry leader who enjoys speaking to women and assisting her husband, a senior pastor. Beverly enjoys researching family history to produce works of historical fiction.

Patricia Anne Elford

stillwatersanddancingwings.blogspot.ca

Patricia Anne Elford, OCT, BA, M Div, is a professional member of The Word Guild and InScribe Christian Writers' Fellowship, educator, clergyperson, poet, enthusiastic freelance book and article editor, and award-winning writer. She has been published in literary journals, newspapers, periodicals, anthologies, worship publications, and online. With four book manuscripts under development, Patricia—wife, mother, grandmother, and cat's domestic servant—leads a full, God-nourished life in the Ottawa Valley.

Grandmothers' Necklace (Epic Press)

Sharon Espeseth

Sharon Espeseth says, "There is life after teaching!" While her days still seem full, they do include keeping in touch with loved ones. Although her husband, adult children, and grandchildren are super important to her, she is happy to squeeze writing and church music into the mix. Her published work includes nonfiction and poetry scattered about in periodicals and anthologies. You can find her monthly blogs posted on inscribewritersonline.blogspot.ca.

Angelina Fast

www.facebook.com/angelinafast5

Angelina Fast is a 20-year cancer survivor who begins each day with thanksgiving. Her writing includes nonfiction books, articles, and poetry. She has won three first-place awards for writing. Widowed twice, she walked with her second husband through a decade-long struggle with dementia. In her upcoming book, she hopes to encourage other caregivers. She makes her home in St. Catharines, Ontario.

Seven Angels for Seven Days (Castle Quay Books)
The Valley of Cancer (Word Alive Press)

Doris Fleming

www.facebook.com/doris.fleming.3152

Encouraging others in their God-given calling carries day-to-day enjoyment for this author and life coach. Doris writes and journals daily for the sheer pleasure of it. Baking also provides delight. Raised on a dairy farm in Alberta's beautiful wild rose country, she presently resides in Wallace, Idaho, serving alongside her pastor/chaplain husband.

Seeds in the Wind (Lighthouse Publishing)

Carol Ford

carolfordassociates.wordpress.com

Carol Ford is a speaker, career coach, and writer. One of her interests is in sharing her adoption reunion story with women's and seniors' groups. As a contributor on Hope Stream Radio, she gives advice on work life. From Newmarket, Ontario, Carol, who volunteers with The Word Guild, also leads a local writers' group. Together, this group penned a devotional book for writers, *As the Ink Flows*, which was a finalist in the 2017 The Word Awards.

As the Ink Flows: Devotions to Inspire Christian Writers & Speakers (Judson Press)

Ramona Furst

www.ramonafurst.com

Ramona Furst is a writer and artist who lives in North Bay, Ontario. A wife, mother, and grandmother, Ramona also has a heart for missions and has volunteered with Medical Missions International Canada, travelling to Ghana (Accru), Bolivia, Ethiopia, and India (Nagaland). She is a member of The Word Guild, InScribe Christian Writers Fellowship, and CANSCAIP. Ramona was a contributing author to *Hot Apple Cider with Cinnamon* and the illustrator of the award-winning book *When the Bough Breaks* by Bobbi Junior.

Valentina Gal

valentinawrites.ca

Valentina Gal was raised in Hamilton, where many displaced persons of World War II settled. While studying at McMaster University, she discovered that her area of the city was diverse in culture and peopled by interesting characters. Many of Valentina's stories are based on her own experiences, and explore the challenges and victories of a partially-blind daughter of Ukrainian immigrants as she negotiates her way through life. Her writing has been recognized by Diaspora Dialogues in Toronto, The Writers' Union of Canada, and the Ontario Arts Council, which gave her a grant for a book she's writing.

Theresa Goldrick

Theresa Goldrick is a Support Services Attendant for March of Dimes Canada and lives in Drayton, Ontario. She is married to her wonderful husband, Brad, and they have three grown children and seven adorable granddaughters. After a few hard knocks and many life lessons, including her challenging but rewarding work with people with disabilities, Theresa feels she has learned a lot and has many more stories just waiting to be told. Theresa is thrilled to be part of *Christmas with Hot Apple Cider*.

Laureen F. Guenther

Laureen F. Guenther is a freelance writer and elementary school teacher who lives near Calgary, Alberta. She has written Sunday school curriculum, ministry training guides, and hundreds of newspaper stories. Her story "Not the Love I Was Looking For" was published in *Hot Apple Cider with Cinnamon*. When Laureen looks back on the year she wrote about in *Christmas with Hot Apple Cider*, she celebrates the reminder that the God who watched over her then is still watching over her today.

Pamela Photography

Rob Harshman

Rob Harshman is a retired high school teacher. He travels widely and also enjoys gardening and photography. With his wife, he lives in Mississauga, Ontario, where he also has two married daughters and three grandchildren. Rob has been a contributor to *Hot Apple Cider with Cinnamon* and the Chicken Soup for the Soul series. He plans to continue writing short stories.

Pat Hennan

A former teacher who had the privilege of working with young offenders for close to a quarter century, Pat is semi-retired. He is currently running a painting business with his daughter, doing home renovations, and, along with his wife of 37 years, enjoying his three daughters, one son, and 10 grandchildren. Pat has previously edited two books for prison ministries and enjoys unplanned creative writing. This is his first published story. In the not-too-distant future, he hopes to write a book about his life before and after Christ, and the amazing adventures he has had along the way.

Evangeline Inman

www.evangelineinman.com

Evangeline Inman feels compelled to speak, sing, and write in response to the Great Commission to share the Father's heart around the world. As a communicator of the gospel of Jesus Christ, she has written several books and more than 1,000 songs. She's also produced multiple award-winning albums, a weekly television broadcast, *Women Who Worship* conferences, and radio devotionals. Evangeline is the lead pastor at Cornerstone Worship Centre in Fredericton, NB. She is married to Dr. Mark Inman.

The Divine Heart Mender (Amazon CreateSpace)
Ancient Secrets of Success (Amazon CreateSpace)

Maureen E. Kowal

Maureen E. Kowal is an Early Childhood Education teacher and a poet who writes for *Glad Tidings*, a Presbyterian Missionary Magazine. She has also written poetry for *Alive Now* and *Eternal Ink*, an online magazine. Maureen is a children's author whose two Grade 1 vowel books, *The Candy Map* and *The Loud Chime*, were published in 2014 by The Perfection Learning Company. She is a member of The Word Guild and CANSCAIP. Maureen lives with her family in Bolton, Ontario.

Marcia Lee Laycock

marcialeelaycock.com

Marcia enjoys life across from a pond in central Alberta, along with her pastor husband. She has five published novels and four devotional books, all sold on Amazon. Marcia's column, "The Spur," is widely distributed, and she blogs regularly for novel-rocket.com. Marcia has been a frequent winner at The Word Awards and InScribe conferences.

One Smooth Stone (Castle Quay Books)
Christmas (Small Pond Press)

  Christmas with Hot Apple Cider

Robin (R. K.) Livingston

www.rklivingston.com

Robin grew up in the mining communities of Northern Ontario. She remembers family gatherings as having two constants: music and the lively recounting of stories. In fact, she comes from a long line of storytellers and has always believed that a good story is the best way to teach. It can also be rollicking good fun. One of her greatest joys is capturing story on paper, and so, she writes.

Eyes Wide Open: When life happens you want to see it coming (CreateSpace)
Elijah's Boy (CreateSpace)

Sally Meadows

sallymeadows.com

Sally Meadows is a six-time national/international award-nominated author, singer/songwriter, and speaker. Sally writes in a wide variety of genres, from inspirational fiction and true-life short stories to children's books, magazine articles, and songs. She joyfully embraces the doors the Lord opens and passionately follows wherever He leads from her Saskatchewan home.

Erin Crooks Photography

Red & White (Christmas CD)
Beneath That Star (Word Alive Press)

Cori Mordaunt

corinnemordauntflickr

Cori is an award-winning writer with works published in *Nature Friend Magazine* and the anthology *Grandmothers' Necklace*. Recently retired from the Toronto Public Library, Cori plans to continue pursuing writing, music, and photography. Cori and Gene live in Toronto, Ontario. They have two happily married sons and six amazing grandchildren.

Shelley Norman

Shelley Norman draws inspiration for her writing not only from the One who gave her the gift but also from the family farm she operates with her husband, their animals, and the children who attend her home childcare. Shelley's short stories have been published in various magazines, literary journals, and anthologies in Canada and the United States. She also has one published children's book.

Bruce County Counts (The Brucedale Press)

Kimberley Payne

www.kimberleypayne.com

Kimberley Payne is a motivational speaker and author. Her writings revolve around a variety of topics: raising a family, pursuing a healthy lifestyle, everyday experiences, and building a relationship with God. Through her work, Kimberley hopes to inspire people to live their lives to glorify God.

Fit for Faith: 7 weeks to improved spiritual and physical health (Kimberley Payne)

Women of Strength: A devotional to improve spiritual and physical health (CreateSpacee)

Niki Allday Photography

Judi Peers

judipeers.wordpress.com

Judi Peers is an author, speaker, and engaging Bible study leader. She has written several children's books and Bible studies, as well as contributed stories to award-winning anthologies. When Judi is not working with words, she can be found weeding her garden, travelling with her husband, Dave, or enjoying family and friends on the shore of the Otonabee River in Peterborough, Ontario.

Playing Second Fiddle: God's Heart for Harmony Regarding Women and the Church (Word Alive Press)

Margo Prentice

Margo Prentice writes from the heart in New Westminster, British Columbia. A member of the writing group Waves, Margo has had short stories published in *Canadian Magazine, Vancouver Sun,* and *Royal City Literary Arts* online magazine. Her poems have been published in different anthologies locally and in Ontario. She has also written four plays. Performing as a stand-up comic, Margo enjoys writing her own material. She is in the process of editing and organizing her writing for publication.

Gloria Raynor

www.facebook.com/heartingheartsministries

Gloria Raynor was born in the beautiful island of Jamaica and emigrated to Canada in 1976. She is a motivational speaker, poet, and writer. When she isn't writing, she's busy caring for people who are oppressed and depressed physically from the emotional cares of this life. Gloria is currently working on the publication of a book entitled *Bad Girls and Boys of the Bible.*

Esther Rennick

unashamedwomen.com

Esther is an adventurer, administrator, musician, writer, and songwriter. She toured North America with The Sky Family, a Celtic musical family from Prince Edward Island, sharing the gospel. Esther's writing is inspired by the God-adventures she has encountered. She worked in the financial industry for 30 years before setting out on a new adventure of sharing the gospel. She lives in Fredericton, New Brunswick, and has one adult son, James.

Nikki Rosen

www.write2empower.webs.com

Nikki Rosen uses her writing to empower others to reach for their best. Nikki is the author of I*n the Eye of Deception: A True Story*, winner of the 2010 The Word Award for life stories, and *Dancing Softly*, which was shortlisted for the same award in 2014. Nikki has won a number of short story contests and has been published in various anthologies and magazines across North America. She lives in Burlington, Ontario.

In the Eye of Deception: A True Story (Gentle Recovery)
Dancing Softly (Gentle Recovery)

Rose Seiler Scott

roseseilerscott.com

Rose believes that fiction can be a vehicle for telling the truth. She's wanted to be a writer since fifth grade, but she took a few career detours, including bookkeeping, piano teaching, and being the mother of four. Eventually, family history drew her back to writing and resulted in her first novel, *Threaten to Undo Us*, which won The Word Award for historical fiction in 2016. Rose lives in Surrey with her husband, Andy, and their two youngest children.

Threaten to Undo Us (Promontory Press)

Carrie Seavers

clsfergy.blogspot.ca

After several careers, including real estate and children's ministry, Carrie Seavers is now a stay-at-home mom and grandmother who enjoys a good cup of coffee and the new treat of extra time to spend on her writing goals. She grew up as an MK (missionary kid) and a PK (pastor's kid). Carrie resides in Medicine Hat, Alberta, but also calls "all of Saskatchewan" her home. Her prayer is to encourage and bring joy to every life, in every season of life. She shares her thoughts and often humorous life lessons on her blog.

Jayne E. Self

www.jayneself.com

Jayne E. Self is an award-winning author whose Sea Glass Mysteries, *Murder in Hum Harbour* and *Death of a Highland Heavyweight*, both won The Word Awards. She is also a former director of Write Canada. A pastor's wife, mom, and grandma, Jayne now resides in Strathroy, Ontario, with her husband. Visit her website, "Where Faith and Mystery Converge."

Murder in Hum Harbour (Pelican Book Group)
Death of a Highland Heavyweight (Pelican Book Group)

Marian Shehata

Marian is an educator who is passionate about social justice, spiritual formation, and the empowerment of young women. She enjoys writing in several spheres, particularly human rights curriculum and devotional writing. She was the visionary and lead author of a small group Lenten curriculum used in her church and beyond. Marian is especially proud of her work as co-editor of *S.I.S.T.A. Soul Food: Delightful Recipes & Recollections*—an anthology of recipes and women's stories. Based in Toronto, Ontario, Marian is a foodie who is always up for an adventure, locally and globally.

Darcie Sutherland Photography

Eleanor Shepherd

Eleanor Shepherd, from Pointe Claire, Quebec, has more than 100 articles published in Canada, France, the United States, Belgium, Switzerland, and New Zealand. Thirty years with The Salvation Army in Canada and France, including ministry in Africa, Europe, Haiti and the Caribbean, furnished material for her award-winning book, *More Questions than Answers: Sharing Faith by Listening*. Eleanor recently retired from being a pastor in Montreal with The Salvation Army.

More Questions than Answers (Wipf and Stock, Resource Publications)
Why Families? with Glen Shepherd (The Salvation Army)

Martin Smith

Martin Smith has worked in the book and music distribution world for more than 30 years. He is active in community theatre in Brantford and Paris, Ontario, as an actor, director, and writer. Martin has written several plays, including *The Strong Hand of Love*, *The Other Noise*, *Baked Muffins with Dates*, and *Where Dust Settles*. He is also the stage manager for the Brantford Symphony Orchestra and President of ICHTHYS Theatre in Brantford.

Ruth Smith Meyer

Ruth Smith Meyer enjoys discovering words to communicate inspiration, both written and spoken. She has written two novels, a children's book, and her autobiography, as well as contributions for six anthologies. She also is a regular contributor to *REJOICE!*, a daily devotional magazine, and she has had poetry published in several publications. Ruth speaks to varied groups and is thrilled to meet people and make connections. Widowed twice, Ruth now lives in Ailsa Craig, Ontario, when she's

not on the road promoting books or visiting her large combined family.

Out of the Ordinary (Word Alive Press)
Good Grief People (Angel Hope Press)

L. June Stevenson

www.facebook.com/junestevenson

L. June Stevenson has been writing most of her life. She would say she was born with a silver pen in her hand. Her best and most satisfying works are poetry and short reflections. She hopes that, through her words, people will find something they have been seeking, such as inspiration, hope, or courage. June believes her insights come from her unusual life experiences and her quirky thought process. She's received The Word Awards for her poetry and song lyrics. Her first poetry book, *Mark My Words*, was published in 2016.

Mark My Words (Essence Publishing)

Susan Stewart

Susan Stewart is the Executive Director of True North Aboriginal Partnership, a not-for-profit organization that fosters connection with First Nations peoples, building bridges of understanding and providing encouragement on the journey of true reconciliation. Susan takes any opportunity to further this cause through writing, speaking, and social media. She is retired from a secondary (15-year) career in developmental services. Susan lives with her husband near Alliston, ON.

Melony Teague

www.melonyteague.com

Melony is a freelance writer who believes everyone has a story to tell. As a ghostwriter and biographer, she is passionate about telling real-life stories. She handles communications for various non-profit organizations in the Toronto area, two of which are medical mission organizations. She also reviews Christian fiction. As one of the authors of *As the Ink Flows: Devotions to Inspire Christian Writers & Speakers* (Judson Press), she uses her words to www.merkphotography.com encourage and inspire others. This book was a finalist in the 2017 The Word Awards.

John Paul Tucker

johnpaultucker.com

John Paul lives in Cabbagetown, a Toronto downtown neighbourhood abounding in rare birds and odd bods. He writes children's novels, short stories, and poems, and contributes to www.thewriterslessonbook.com. Keep an eye out for *Shelter Island*, Book One of his children's fantasy series, The Song of Fridorfold (Brownridge Publishing). Drop by his website to watch a book trailer, read a poem, check for updates, or learn how to cook your Christmas turkey in a garbage can.

Tina Michele Weidelich

www.tinamichele.com

Tina Michele is a woman on a mission to make every day count, both for God and through Him. As a singer/songwriter/speaker/author, her desire is to write, sing, and share stories from her life that will inspire people to rejoice, reflect, and draw closer to God. She was the 2017 nonfiction runner-up in The Word Guild's In The Beginning contest. Tina Michele works as a senior marketing manager at Christian Blind Mission and lives in Richmond Hill with her husband and teenage daughter.

Robert White

artsconnection.ca/read

Robert White is an award-winning journalist with bylines in local, regional, and national publications. Robert's interests range from devotional (*Chasing the Wind: Finding Meaningful Answers from Ancient Wisdom*, winner of the 2010 Word Alive Press publishing contest), history (*The Mac: Edmonton's Historic Hotel Macdonald* with Sara Baxter, published by Tree Frog Press) and drama (*The Waiting Room*, produced by Audience of One Christian Theatre Company). An avid photographer, Robert lives in Guelph, Ontario, with his wife, Pam.

Madam Redrum Photography

Ray Wiseman

www.ray.wiseman.ca

Ray Wiseman of Fergus, Ontario, began writing seriously in the early 1980s, following careers in electronics and ministry in Canada and South Africa. Ray has written eight books, appeared in two anthologies, and penned over 1,000 editorials, newspaper features, and columns. In 2009, Ray received the Leslie K. Tarr Award. His wife and editor, Anna, received a special award as well.

When Cobras Laugh, with co-author Don Ranney, MD (OakTara Publishers)
Write! Better: A Writing Tip for Every Week of the Year (WordWise)

Grace Wulff

www.gracewulff.com

A chaplain, author, and artist, Grace loves to connect with people through words and art. Her work in the hospital brings her much joy as she shares God's love with patients and their families. Widowed at age 37, Grace has written extensively on the subject of grief and continues to support those who are on a journey involving grief. She shares her life with her second husband, Steve, and loves being a grandmother to eight little people. Grace lives in Vernon, British Columbia.

A Journey of Hope (Yellow Rose Publishing)
"Gifts for the Journey" (booklet available from her website)

Ron Wyse

www.ronrwyse.com

Love of learning, language, and letters has characterized Ron's life journey. This love has brought him four degrees, life on three continents, two amazing (now adult) kids, and one outstanding wife from half a world away. Although teaching and then tutoring used to be his occupations, he now does individual and relational counselling. Poetry, which can give snapshots of humanity across time and space, has long inspired him.

Beyond Survival: Marriage and the Quest for Paradise (VMI Publishers)

Melissa Yue Wallace

www.facebook.com/emuwallace

Melissa Yue Wallace was working as an editor at a news outlet in Toronto when she became disheartened by the many homeless people sleeping outside. She began working in communications at a Christian shelter and has since written for various Christian organizations and publications. Melissa is passionate about making Jesus known through the written word and raising awareness for God-centred organizations. She and her husband also enjoy spending time with their hilarious twin toddlers, who have their own stories to tell.

Acknowledgements

I'm delighted to have another opportunity to showcase work by Canadian writers, some of whom are being published for the first time.

Thanks to my husband and business partner, Les Lindquist, for encouraging (okay, *prodding*) me to create this book, for looking after everything to do with numbers, and for reading through the stories to help me make final, tough, decisions. Les also made sure that my judging was "blind;" even to the extent of changing titles and names so I wouldn't know whose work I was reading.

Thank you to Audrey Dorsch, who did a final copy edit and a proofread. She caught a number of things that we had missed.

Thanks to Krysten Lindquist for her help with the author photos.

Thank you to everyone who sent in submissions. There were many good stories and poems, and I wish there had been room for more of them. Thank you especially to the 55 writers whose work was chosen to be in this book for letting me mess with your carefully written words. It always surprises me when, instead of yelling at me, many of you thank me.

Thanks to the many contributors who checked not only their own work but also the rest of the book. Their comments were very helpful. In particular, many, many thanks to Marguerite Cummings for her enthusiasm and attention to detail. And to Laureen Guenther, Patricia Elford, Judi Peers, Kimberley Payne, Robin Livingston, and Melony Teague. Also to enthusiastic alpha readers Claire de Burbure and Armig Adourian.

Thanks to Grace Wulff for her suggestion for the dedication.

Thanks to Linda Hall, who, while busy with a number of personal projects, made time to write the foreword for this book.

Thanks to all who wrote endorsements.

And thanks most of all to our distributor and our readers who encouraged us to put together another book.

My hope is that each person who reads this book will benefit in some way from the words and ideas on these pages.

N. J. Lindquist

Hot Apple Cider

44 hope-filled stories from 30 writers

Trade paperback and digital

"A collection of short stories, poetry, and wisdom seeking to heal and mend the soul of the reader after difficult and stressful situations.... Highly recommended"
Midwest Book Review

"This is a book to sample, to savour, and to share."
Maxine Hancock, PhD, Professor Emeritus, Regent College; author

Winner, five The Word Awards

Church Library Association of Ontario One Book/One Conference

http://hotappleciderbooks.com

A Second Cup of Hot Apple Cider

51 encouraging stories from 37 writers

Trade paperback and digital

"Some books surprise you with their ability to take your breath away.... Be sure to buy more than one, for you will probably have the urge to share this gem of a collection with others."
Faith Today

Winner, 13 The Word Awards

Winner, Christian Small Publisher Gift Book of the Year Award

Winner, third place, The Book Club Network, Inc. Book of the Year Award

http://hotappleciderbooks.com

A Taste of Hot Apple Cider

16 heart-warming stories from 15 writers

Trade paperback and digital

"Through poems, fiction, and nonfiction alike, [the writers] remind readers that the struggles we face are common to everyone. Their honest descriptions of wrestling with cancer, caring for and losing aging parents, dealing with a spouse's dementia, moving beyond one's fear to tell neighbours about Jesus, and more, show us that hope is very much alive."
From the foreword by author **Grace Fox**

Discussion Questions Included!

http://hotappleciderbooks.com

Hot Apple Cider with Cinnamon

67 empowering stories from 60 writers

Trade paperback and digital

"In these pages you will find tales of love—love for a parent, for a friend, for a stranger—that span Canadian hockey rinks and African villages and Philippine homes. You will find people choosing hope in the midst of a panicky Alberta hospital room, choosing God in the midst of Alzheimer's, choosing peace in the midst of losing a child…. The stories in this book will help you choose love. Every time."
From the foreword by author **Sheila Wray Gregoire**

Winner, four The Word Awards

http://hotappleciderbooks.com

The Circle of Friends Series

Contemporary Christian Young Adult Romance

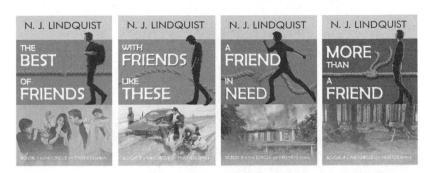

Trade paperback and digital

Easy-going Glen begins his last year of high school unaware that his tranquil life will be the first casualty of Charlie Thornton's arrival in town.

When the new doctor's family moves in across the street, Glen is happy to show the son, Charlie, around the small town. With his good looks, charisma, athletic ability, and sports car, Charlie soon has the whole town in his corner.

Except for Nicole, the prettiest girl in town (and the pastor's daughter), who has no intention of dating Charlie. No matter how many times he asks her. Or Luke, Glen's best friend since kindergarten, who dislikes Charlie on sight and longs to wipe that smile off his face!

As Glen sidesteps the hostility between Luke and Charlie and assists Charlie in his quest to date Nicole, he faces major problems—some life-threatening, others life-changing.

www.njlindquist.com/books/the-best-of-friends

In Time of Trouble

A Coming-of-age Novel about Second Chances

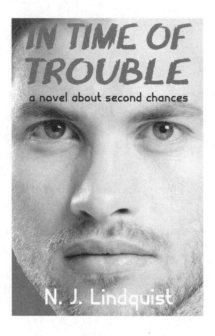

Trade paperback and digital

When the whole world seems to be against you, where do you go?

After getting fired from his part-time job and having his car confiscated for unpaid tickets, the last straw for Shane Donahue comes when his girlfriend, instead of showing sympathy, dumps him for one of his so-called friends. The fight is on.

But is winning her back worth the effort? For that matter, is staying alive worth the frustration and loneliness? Or is he missing something?

www.njlindquist.com/books/in-time-of-trouble

Realm of the Kingdoms, Book 1

A Middle Grade Fantasy

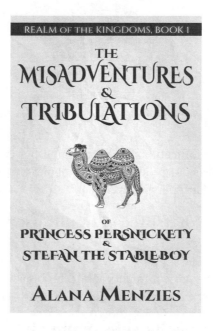

Trade paperback and digital

A stranger arrives at the castle of Practavia with a dire warning. The neighbouring kingdom has been taken over by a Sorcerer who is gathering an army to invade and conquer Practavia. The peace-loving Practavians begin to prepare for battle. But 14-year-old Princess Amber (known far and wide as Princess Persnickety) and her best friend Stefan discover that the camel the stranger was riding can speak. If that wasn't scary enough, the camel says the stranger is lying.

In the first book of this new series, the Princess and Stefan, aided by a talking camel, risk their lives to save the Kingdom of Practavia from certain destruction.

realmofthekingdoms.com

Publisher

That's Life! Communications

Books that integrate real faith with real life

That's Life! Communications is a niche publisher committed to finding innovative ways to produce quality books written by Canadians with a Christian faith perspective.

http://thatslifecommunications.com

We'd love to hear your comments about this book or any of our other books. Please post a comment on our website or write to us at:

comments@thatslifecommunications.com